Synthetic Membranes:

Volume II

Hyper- and Ultrafiltration Uses

Synthetic Membranes:

Volume II

Hyper- and Ultrafiltration Uses

Albin F. Turbak, EDITOR

ITT Rayonier Inc.

Based on the 20th Anniversary
Symposium honoring Drs. Loeb and
Sourirajan sponsored by the
Cellulose, Paper, and Textile
Division at the Second
Chemical Congress of the
North American Continent,
Las Vegas, Nevada,
August 25–29, 1980.

ACS SYMPOSIUM SERIES **154**

AMERICAN CHEMICAL SOCIETY
WASHINGTON, D. C.   1981

Library of Congress CIP Data

Synthetic membranes.
  (ACS symposium series, ISSN 0097-6156; 153-154)

  Includes bibliographies and index.

    Contents: v. 1. Desalination—v. 2. Hyper- and ultra-
filtration uses.
    1. Membranes (Technology)—Congresses. I. Loeb,
Sidney. II. Sourirajan, S. III. Turbak, Albin F.,
1929-   . IV. American Chemical Society. Cellulose,
Paper, and Textile Division. V. Series.

TP159.M4S95   660.2'8424   81-1259
ISBN 0-8412-0623-6 (v. 2)   AACR2
ISBN 0-8412-0625-2 (set) ACSMC8 154 1-474 1981

ACS Symposium Series

M. Joan Comstock, *Series Editor*

FOREWORD

The ACS SYMPOSIUM SERIES was founded in 1974 to provide a medium for publishing symposia quickly in book form. The format of the Series parallels that of the continuing ADVANCES IN CHEMISTRY SERIES except that in order to save time the papers are not typeset but are reproduced as they are submitted by the authors in camera-ready form. Papers are reviewed under the supervision of the Editors with the assistance of the Series Advisory Board and are selected to maintain the integrity of the symposia; however, verbatim reproductions of previously published papers are not accepted. Both reviews and reports of research are acceptable since symposia may embrace both types of presentation.

CONTENTS

PREFACE

This volume is the result of a symposium honoring Drs. Sidney Loeb and S. Sourirajan on the 20th anniversary of their discovery of the first functionally useful reverse osmosis membrane. During this four-day symposium membrane experts from 13 countries participated in paying tribute to Drs. Loeb and Sourirajan's pioneering efforts and 55 papers were presented covering most areas of membrane uses. These included the salt-rejecting dense membranes for reverse osmosis, which, as Dr. Sourirajan noted in his plenary lecture, is really a misnomer and might be described more accurately as hyperfiltration, and the more porous membranes for ultrafiltration.

The large number of papers necessitated publishing the symposium in two volumes. Volume I describes the desalination and salt-rejecting hyperfiltration membranes. Volume II covers hyper- and ultrafiltration membrane utilization in the following areas: food, medicine, pulp, paper, and textile industries, oily waste stream purification, and in the separation of gases, polymers, organic solutes, and biopolymers.

Many of these uses are very significant since they are described from the point of extensive commercial experience. This is particularly true of the food, medical, and waste treatment fields. For example, cheese whey solids that previously were pollution problems are recovered now at the rate of several hundred tons/day and sold as valuable food. Similarly the recent advances of hemofiltration over hemodialysis are improving the quality of life for thousands of patients who suffer from renal failure. Also pollution abatement by ultra- and hyperfiltration in the pulp, textile, and steel-processing industries is now a commercial reality for certain types of waste streams.

As the membrane field continues to expand, specific membranes will be available to perform an ever-widening series of important functions and much of the impetus for such expansion will be based on the original efforts of Drs. Loeb and Sourirajan.

The overwhelming number of papers originally submitted for consideration for this symposium coupled with the outstanding attendance at the symposium attest to the high esteem in which these two gentlemen are held by their peers. It was a distinct honor to take part in this 20th anniversary tribute. I would like to thank all of the participants for their wonderful cooperation in making this occasion such a great success.

I.T.T. Rayonier, Inc.   ALBIN F. TURBAK
Eastern Research Division
Whippany, NJ 07981   December 24, 1980.

S. Sourirajan, Albin Turbak, and Sidney Loeb

DEDICATION

Twenty years ago two researchers laboring diligently at the University of California at Los Angeles developed the first modified asymmetric membranes which seemed to have commercial potential for what was to become the exciting field that today is known as hyperfiltration or reverse osmosis. Since that time, these dedicated scientists have given freely of themselves and their talents not only to further contribute technically, but also to help guide, teach, and train others to grow in this frontier area.

It is little wonder then that so many contributors from so many countries throughout the world responded so enthusiastically to the initial announcement regarding the organization of a symposium to recognize, honor, and pay tribute to Drs. Sidney Loeb and S. Sourirajan on the 20th anniversary of their initial contribution.

From the beginning it was apparent that this four-day symposium covering a seeming myriad of membrane information and uses would be one of the major events of the Fall 1980 Las Vegas A.C.S. National Meeting. This symposium, highlighted by plenary lectures from Drs. Loeb and Sourirajan, had an outstanding attendance. Even on the fourth day there were still more people attending this symposium than normally are present for the initial phases of most other sessions. This in itself says more than anyone could say regarding the universal interest in membranes and the high esteem in which Sid Loeb and S. Sourirajan are held by their peers throughout the world.

Today their initial work on the preparation of suitable asymmetric membranes has touched nearly every aspect of life including uses in water purification, food technology, biological separations, waste treatment, medical applications, and bioengineering, and this appears to be just the beginning.

I know that I speak for all of their many friends when I take this opportunity to wish Drs. Loeb and Sourirajan continued good health and, if possible, even more success in their future research and development efforts.

ALBIN F. TURBAK

Development of a Tomato Juice Concentration System by Reverse Osmosis

K. ISHII, S. KONOMI, K. KOJIMA, and M. KAI

Daicel Chemical Industries, Ltd., 1 Teppo-cho, Sakai-shi, 590, Japan

N. UKAI and N. UNO

Kagome Co., Ltd., 3–14–15, Nishiki, Naka-ku, Nagoya-shi, 460, Japan

There have been many studies on the application of membrane technology to food industries. Few have, however, reached a commercial success except those of dairy processes (1). DAICEL has been studying since 1971 the application of its cellulose acetate RO membranes and polyacrylonitrile UF membranes to food, pharmaceutical, medical, paper and other industries. As to the use of membranes in food industries other than dairy processes, only two cases were developed to a semicommercial scale, that is, grape juice concentration for wine must and tomato juice concentration for processing and storage of the juice till next harvest.

The RO concentration of fresh fruit juice has two diffculties. The one is that the high osmotic pressure of fruit juice prevents concentrating the juice to the required concentration, and the other is the loss of light flavor.

In case of tomato juice concentration, the required product sugar content is ca. 20%, which is exceptionally low enough to be attained by RO process. In addition, the loss of light flavor does not significantly spoil the commercial value. The expected advantages of membrane process over conventional evaporation process was the improvement of the product quality especially in taste and color. The major problem was to develop a system which produces high quality condensed juice without adding to the cost over that of the conventional process. A joint study started in 1971 at DAICEL's laboratory, and after three seasons' field tests at Kozakai, Fujimi and Ibaragi plants of Kagome Co., Ltd., a semicommercial equipment was built at Ibaragi plant in 1975. Since then it has been producing ca. 1 m^3/hr of concentrated fresh tomato juice.

Experimental

Tomato juice. Diluted canned tomato paste was used for laboratory experiments with 28 cm^2 flat membrane cells. For field tests with tubular membranes, sterilized fresh juice was used.

0097–6156/81/0154–0001$05.00/0

Membranes. Three different grades of DAICEL's cellulose
acetate RO membranes, DRS-97, DRS-95 and DRS-90 were used both in
flat sheets and tubes. Their NaCl rejection values were 97%, 95%
and 90%, respectively.

Apparatus and equipment. For laboratory experiments, two to
six flat membrane cells of 28 cm^2 effective area and 0.3 mm channel thickness were used in series with a plunger pump of variable
output up to 50 l/hr under the pressure of up to 100 Kg/cm^2. For
field tests, 12 to 192 membrane tubes (1.4 cm inner diameter and
4.5 m by length each) were used both in series and parallel with
one or two plunger pumps of variable output up to 2 m^3/hr under
the pressure of up to 70 Kg/cm^2. Both a single- and a two-stage
system were examined.

Measurement and analysis. The viscosity of tomato juice was
measured using Tokyokeiki BH type disc rotating viscosimeter.
     Sodium chloride concentration was measured using TOA HA5a
electric conductivity meter.
     Sugar concentration was determined by reversed phase liquid
chromatograph with a 4.6 mmϕ x 250 mm length column of Nagel Nucleosil 5NH$_2$ and a 70% acetonitrile aqueous buffer solution fed
at the rate of 1.5 ml/min at 25°C. Shodex RI-SEll refractometer
was used as the detector.
     Amino acids were quantitatively determined using Hitachi KLA5
amino acid autoanalyzer with a Hitachi Custom 2613 column and
citrate buffer solutions, pH values of which were 3.25 for phase
1, then 4.25 and 6.10 for phases 2 and 3, respectively. The flow
rate of the buffer solution was 1.0 ml/min and that of the reagent, ninhydrin, was 0.5 ml/min. The measurement was carried out
at 55°C.
     The sour tasting organic acids were separately measured by
using Shimadzu total organic carbon meter.
     In field tests, sugar content was determined by refractometry
and the total amount of amino acid nitrogen was measured by Kjeldahl method and the quantity of organic acids was determined by
titration.
     The color was measured using a color reference meter manufac-
tured by Nippon Denshoku Kogyo, Ltd. The taste was examined by a
panel composed of ten skilled persons.

Results and discussions

Solute retention. Firstly, the rejection characteristics of
principal solutes of tomato juice were measured with three cellulose acetate membranes of different sodium chloride rejections in
order to determine which grade of the membranes should be employed for the most efficient concentration. Solute rejection
characteristics of three grades of the membranes tested are listed in Tables 1, 2 and 3.

Table I MEMBRANE PERFORMANCE ON SUGAR AQUEOUS SOLUTION

SOLUTE	DRS-97 FLUX m/d	DRS-97 REJ. %	DRS-95 FLUX m/d	DRS-95 REJ. %	DRS-90 FLUX m/d	DRS-90 REJ. %
NaCl	.47	98.6	1.31	95.4	1.71	90.0
GLUCOSE	.37	>99.9	1.31	99.3	1.67	97.3
FRUCTOSE	.38	>99.9	1.24	99.2	1.64	96.7
D-RIBOSE	.36	99.8	1.13	96.8	1.43	91.8
SUCROSE	.40	>99.9	1.33	>99.9	1.64	99.3
RAFFINOSE	.49	>99.9	1.34	>99.9	1.73	99.6

CONDITIONS:
 MEMBRANE AREA: 28 cm^2
 CONCENTRATIONS: 0.35% (NaCl) & 2% (SUGARS)
 PRESSURE: 40 Kg/cm^2
 TEMPERATURE: 25°C

The sugar content of raw tomato juice is about 4.5% Refractive Index (RI). The sugar loss during the concentration up to 20% RI must not exceed 5% of the total sugar contained in raw juice. From the relationship between concentration ratio and solute retention shown in Figure 1, the sugar rejection of the membrane to be employed must be over 97%. As listed in Table 1, all the membranes tested has rejection values higher than ca. 97% for glucose, fructose and sucrose. The curves illustrated in Figure 1 were calculated from the equation 3 derived from mass balance equation 1 and the relationship between volumetric and cocentrational condensation ratios 2 assuming that the membrane rejection is uniform throughout the whole membrane area.

$$C_0 V_0 \times Retention (\%)/100 = CV \quad \dots \dots (1)$$

$$(C/C_0) = (V_0/V)^R \quad \dots \dots (2)$$

$$Retention (\%) = 100(V_0/V)^{R-1} = 100(C/C_0)^{1-1/R} \dots (3)$$

$$Loss (\%) = 100 - Retention (\%) \quad \dots \dots (4)$$

where V_0 = initial volume
 V = final volume
 C_0 = initial concentration
 C = final concentration
 R = rejection of the membrane

Table II demonstrates all the membranes tested have amino acid rejection values over ca. 97%.

Table II   MEMBRANE PERFORMANCE ON AMINOACID AQ. SOLN.

SOLUTE	CONTENT (mg%)	%RETENTION DRS-97	DRS-95	DRS-90
SERINE	10.1	99.6	99.1	97.6
VALINE	9.2	99.4	99.0	97.7
ARGININE	6.8	99.7	99.2	97.6
ASPARAGINE	6.6			
GLUTAMINE	6.6	99.9	99.6	98.8
GLYCINE	4.8	99.7	98.6	96.5
GLUTAMIC ACID	4.0			
PHENYLALANINE	2.4	99.8	98.9	96.7
LEUCINE	2.1	99.8	99.3	97.7
LYSINE	1.9	99.6	99.2	98.1

MEMBRANE AREA: 28 cm^2
CONCENTRATION: 10-20 mg%
pH: 4.2 (ADJUSTED BY ADDING CITRIC ACID)
PRESSURE: 40 Kg/cm^2
TEMPERATURE: 25°C

As for sour tasting organic acids, permissible loss up to 10% corresponds to the membrane rejection of no less than 93% which will be also fulfilled by all the membranes tested as shown in Table III, as more than 90% of the organic acid in tomato juice is citric acid.

Table III   MEMBRANE PERFORMANCE ON ACID AQ. SOLUTION

SOLUTE	DRS-97 FLUX (m/d)	REJ. (%)	DRS-95 FLUX (m/d)	REJ. (%) ˙	DRS-90 FLUX (m/d)	REJ. (%)
CITRIC ACID	.54	98.0	1.50	97.1	1.93	94.5
LACTIC ACID	.52	84.3	1.46	70.0	1.89	64.0

MEMBRANE AREA: 28 cm^2
CONCENTRATION: 0.1 wt%
PRESSURE: 40 Kg/cm^2
TEMPERATURE: 25°C
CIRCULATION RATE: 8 ml/min
CHANNEL THICKNESS: 0.3 mm

As to water flux, DRS-90 membrane showed the highest value in all cases; we concluded that DRS-90 is best suited for minimizing the membrane area.

By the way, relatively low flux and rejection values for D-ribose represented in Table I suggest that D-ribose might have a specifically strong interaction with cellulose acetate RO membranes.

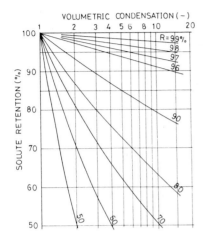

Figure 1. Retained solute as the function of membrane rejection and volumetric condensation

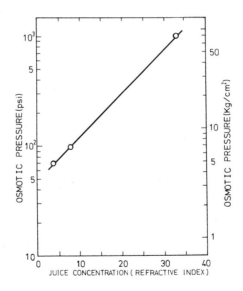

Figure 2. Osmotic pressure of tomato juice

Water flux. Secondly, the effects of factors which were anticipated to influence the membrane performance and the system efficiency were evaluated. They were the osmotic pressure and the viscosity of tomato juice as the function of juice concentration and feed velocity, and operating pressure. It was observed that the rise in temperature increases water flux.

Figure 2 shows that the osmotic pressure of tomato juice increases with concentration. The osmotic pressure of 20%RI tomato juice was about 20 Kg/cm^2.

Figure 3 illustrates that water flux decreases in proportion to the logarithm of juice concentration. This relationship suggests that tomato juice forms a gel layer which controls the water flux. In order to eliminate the influence of osmotic pressure which exponentially rises with juice concentration, a series of experiments was carried out, using a flat UF membrane which permeates sugars and salts completely. As illustrated in Figure 4, water flux is not significantly dependent on pressure. Considering that this UF membrane permeates water in proportion to pressure up to 3 Kg/cm^2 when pure water is fed, it can be supposed that water flux of tomato juice is governed by a gel layer.

The effect of juice velocity on water flux is demonstrated in Figure 5. This effect is smaller than anticipated from the data shown in Figure 4. One reason of this discrepancy might be the difference of the tomato juice used. Fresh juice was used to obtain the relationship summarized in Figure 5, while canned tomato paste was used in diluted form for the experiments shown in Figure 4. Another reason might be the difference in flow channels, 1.4 cm inner diameter tube and thin flat channel of 0.04-0.06 cm thickness. Although the exact reason is not clear, the results illustrated in Figure 5 suggest that it is not necessary to feed fresh tomato juice at high velocity to get high water flux.

Figure 6 represents the relationship between tomato juice viscosity and flow velocity. The measurement was done with the juice prepared from canned paste, using a disc rotating viscosimeter. The value, viscosity multiplied by velocity was nearly independent of the velocity. This suggests that the effect of flow velocity on the pressure drop would be small. This allows the variation of juice feed velocity in a wide range without significant change in pressure drop.

In Figure 7, the viscosity of tomato juice increases nearly exponentially with juice concentration. As anticipated from the results shown in Figure 7, pressure drop rises almost exponentially with increase in concentration when fresh tomato juice was fed in a thin tube of 0.4 cm inner diameter (Figure 8).

System design

If there were not a pressure drop along with feed flow! If so, it would be easy to concentrate any solution up to the con-

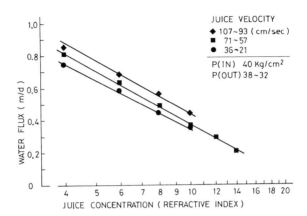

Figure 3.   Water flux as a function of tomato juice concentration observed by using 12 membrane tubes. Circulating the juice and discarding the permeate.

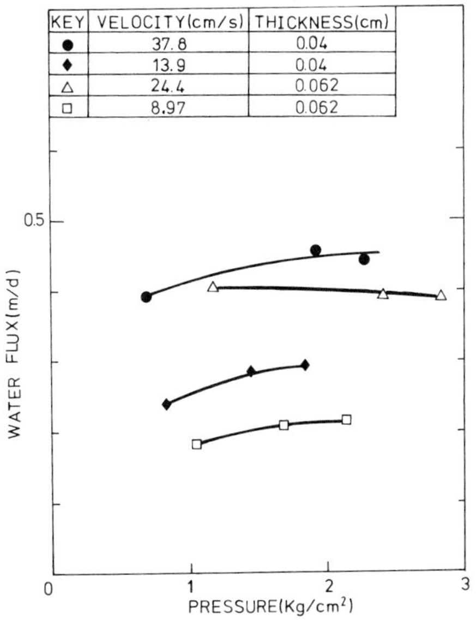

KEY	VELOCITY(cm/s)	THICKNESS(cm)
●	37.8	0.04
◆	13.9	0.04
△	24.4	0.062
□	8.97	0.062

Figure 4.   Water flux as a function of pressure. A UF membrane (DUY-L) was used. The cut-off molecular weight was 5 × 10 daltons.

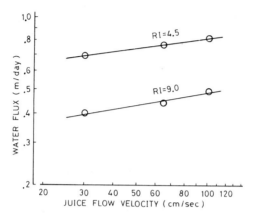

Figure 5.   Effect of tomato juice flow velocity on water flux observed by using 12 membrane tubes

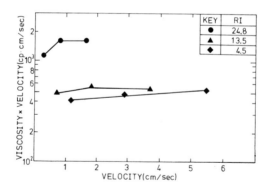

Figure 6.   The viscosity of tomato juice decreases in proportion to the reciprocal of juice velocity. Measured at 20°C by using a disc-rotating viscosimeter.

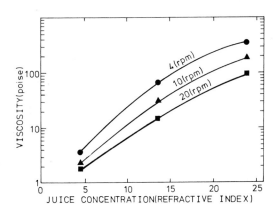

Figure 7.   The effect of tomato juice concentration on the viscosity observed at 20°C by using a disc-rotating viscosimeter

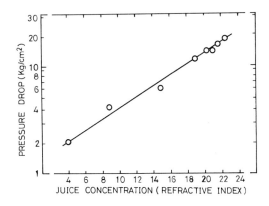

Figure 8.   The effect of tomato juice concentration on the pressure drop of the juice flowing through 4 mm × 4 mL tube at a velocity of 110 cm/s.   Temperature: 24°–30°C.

centration limited by the osmotic pressure of the feed solution, using a one-through single-stage system by simply extending the feed flow length. Practically, however, effective pressure goes down so much that the membrane performance and/or system efficiency are greatly decreased, and it is necessary to insert a second pump in the long flow line and add pressure and velocity to the flow. Some devices to match the divided flows is necessary. The loss of solutes can be decreased by replacing the second stage membrane with that of higher rejection. In a sophisticated scheme shown in Figure 9 (2), the water flux or the outlet concentration can be raised by employing a considerably low rejection membrane at the outlet stage, while the use of a high rejection membrane is required at the permeate discarding stage in order to minimize the solute loss to the permeate.

From the sanitary point of view, it is necessary to minimize the number of articles, such as reservoirs, pumps, valves, gages, etc., which may cause contamination and stagnation of flow, even if these articles are sanitary grade. Circulating the juice is also undesirable for sanitary reason since it yields the ever-staying-in-the-system portion of the feed juice. A circulating system generally requires more frequent cleaning and sterilization than a one-through system.

As already been discussed in the preceeding part of this paper, the water flux and the pressure drop are both strongly affected by the juice concentration, while they are insensitive to the feed flow rate. The latter characteristic allows to increase or decrease the feed flow velocity at will with slight change of water flux and pressure drop. This makes it possible to attain the required outlet concentration with one-through single-stage system by simply decreasing the feed rate. The decrease in feed rate enhances the ratio, water flux to feed rate, hence raises the volumetric concentration ratio as elucidated by equation 5:

$$(V_0/V) = V_0/(V_0 - F) = 1/[1-(F/V_0)] \ldots\ldots\ldots\ldots (5)$$

where V_0 = feed rate (m^3/hr) = feed velocity (m/hr) x cross
                                              section (m^2)
        V = outlet rate (m^3) = outlet velocity x cross section
        F = water removal rate (m^3/m^2hr) = water flux (m^3/m^2hr)
           x membrane area (m^2)

The only possible problem of decreasing the feed rate was whether the thickening of gel layer and concentration polarization due to the slow juice speed would raise the osmotic pressure on the membrane surface as high as the operating pressure before the bulk concentration reaches the required value.

After the operating conditions for producing 20% RI concentrated juice had been mastered by using a 12 to 96 tube single pass equipment (3), it was decided to build a semicommercial system consisted of 1440 tubes. The flow diagram of the semicommer-

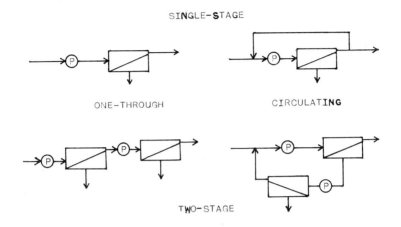

Journal of Applied Polymer Symposia

Figure 9.   Four types of concentration systems (2)

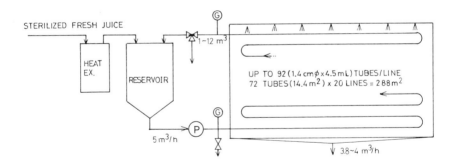

Figure 10.   Flow diagram of the semicommercial equipment built at Ibaragi Plant, Kagome Co., Ltd

cial system is shown in Figure 10. Approximately 5 m³/hr sterilized fresh juice is first cooled to 30°C. Reservoir is set in
order to absorb the temporary unbalance of flow rates. The juice
is then distributed to 20 lines, each equipped with 72 tubes.
Total membrane area is 288 m². About 4 m³/hr of permeate and ca,
1 m³/hr of product were expected. It is necessary to rinse the
outer surface of membrane tubes in order to prevent microbial
growth on it.

Performance of the semicommercial equipment

    In order to see how the juice concentration goes up and how
the pressure and the flow velocity go down as the juice courses
the 72 tubes, gages and sampling ports were built in 2 lines.
Typical observations are shown in Figure 11 and 12. Figure 11
demonstrates that the product concentration rises to 20% RI by
decreasing the feed velocity below 50 cm/sec (ca. 290 1/hr. tube)
under the inlet pressure not more than 65 Kg/cm. In case the
juice was fed at 45 cm/sec, the last several tubes hardly con-
tributed to concentration, perhaps due to both low pressure
caused by pressure drop and high osmotic pressure on the membrane
surface as the result of the higher concentration and lower velocity.
    As illustrated in Figure 12, the slower the feed velocity,
the more rapidly diminishes the operating pressure along with the
juice flow. This behavior corresponds to the experimental observation that the viscosity of the juice goes up nearly exponentially with increase in concentration and it goes down almost in
proportion to the reciprocal of feed velocity. Considering that
the concentration of the juice supplied at 45 cm/sec hardly rises
in the last several tubes, the osmotic pressure on the membrane
surface can be estimated to be 30 to 35 Kg/cm². While the osmo-
metric results shown in Figure 2 suggests that the osmotic pressure of the bulk flow juice must be about 20 Kg/cm.
    The relationship between water flux and juice concentration
(Figure 13) observed by the semicommercial equipment is nearly
the same to that observed in field tests summarized in Figure 3.
    Figure 14 shows that the juice velocity dependance of water
flux is similar to that observed by the field tests.
    As is seen in Figure 15, the pressure drop rose exponential-
ly with increase in juice concentration as had been observed in
the model experiments illustrated in Figure 8.
    The quality of the product is superior to that of the con-
ventional in color and taste as shown in Table IV.
    The retention of solutes is more than required as listed in
Table V.

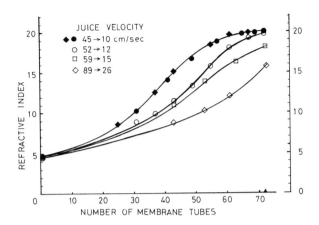

Figure 11.   Tomato juice concentration observed along the juice flow through 72 membrane tubes at various feed velocities

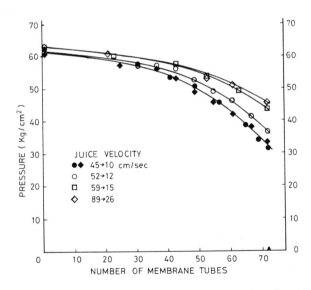

Figure 12.   Tomato juice pressure observed along the juice flow through 72 membrane tubes at various feed velocities

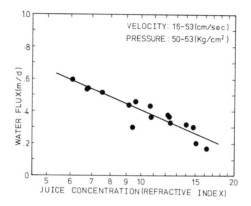

Figure 13. Water flux as the function of tomato juice concentration. Semicommercial plant (72 membrane tubes × 20 lines).

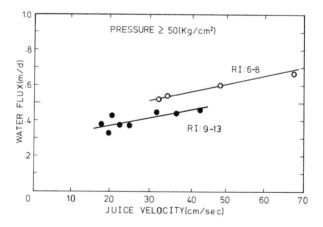

Figure 14. Effect of tomato juice flow velocity on water flux. Semicommercial plant (72 membrane tubes × 20 lines).

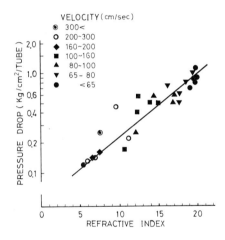

Figure 15.   The influence of tomato juice concentration on pressure drop (semi-commercial system)

Table IV   THE QUALITY OF RO-CONCENTRATED TOMATO JUICE

COLOR:	LIGHTNESS	26	(BETTER)
	REDNESS	29	
	YELLOWNESS	13	
	RED/YELLOW	2.2	(BETTER)
TASTE:	PANEL	BETTER	

Table V   THE SOLUTE RETENTION VALUES OF RO-CONCENTRATED
          TOMATO JUICE

SUGARS	97%
ACIDS	92%
AMINO ACIDS	94%
VITAMIN C	62%

Conclusion

Since the semicommercial equipment with 20 lines of 72 tubes each was built in 1975 at Ibaragi plant of Kagome Co., Ltd., it has been producing 1 m^3/hr of 20% RI condensed fresh tomato juice of the quality superior to that of the conventional product, with lighter and more reddish color and better taste.

The employment of the one-through single-stage system and some devices for sanitary maintenance prolonged the sterilization interval and reduced the running cost.

Further lowering of the total cost would be expected by the off-season use of the equipment.

References

1. S. Sourirajan (ed.), Reverse Osmosis and Synthetic Membranes, p. 417-458, 515, 518, National Research Council Canada, Ottawa, 1977.
   H. Ohya (ed.), Maku Riyo Gijutsu (Membrane Application Technology) Handbook, p. 221-470, Saiwai Shobo, Tokyo, 1978.
2. R. L. Merson & L. F. Ginnette, J. Appl. Polym. Symposia, 13, 309-322, 1970.
3. Unexamined Japan Patent No. 52-136942.

RECEIVED December 30, 1980.

Membrane Processes in Must and Wine Treatment

E. DRIOLI, G. ORLANDO, S. D'AMBRA[1], and A. AMATI[2]

Istituto di Principi di Ingegneria Chimica, University of Naples, Italy

Membrane processes are one of the most important separation technologies in food industry. The operate, at room temperature, require no addition of chemicals and are gentle and non-destruct ive. Their potentiality is confirmed by an annual growth rate of 37% (1). However the major area for ultrafiltration and reverse osmosis in food applications is mainly whey purification, and the dairy industry in general. This market has been estimated of 2 million US dollars in 1976 and 5 million US dollars in 1981.

Pressure driven membrane processes will play an important role in other areas typical of the food industry and in the treatment of must and wine.

Great progress has been made during the last few years in:
a) the development of new membranes with high resistance to solvents, pH, temperature, Cl_2 etc.
b) the development of membrane plant engineering;
c) in the better understanding of fouling and membrane deterior ation.

[1] Current address: D'Ambra Vini d'Ischia, Ischia, Italy.
[2] Current address: Istituto di tecniche agrarie, University of Bologna, Italy.

0097–6156/81/0154–0017$05.00/0

Wine technology now requires various separation techniques which could profitably be replaced   by membrane processes (2).

Certain enzymes present in grapes are responsible for wine problems such as clouding, darkening or an oxidized taste. To prevent this, wineries routinely treat must and wines with sulfur dioxide. In addition to its antimicrobial activity, SO_2 has an antioxidative property which prevents browning and taste defects. Polyphenoloxidase has detrimental effects on wine quality. However enzymes are also responsable for the formation of certain desir able esters which are essential to the aroma or bouquet of the wine.

Methods which reduce the undesirable effects of polyphenoloxid ases include pressing, centrifuging or settling musts, bentonite fining and thermal treatment (70°C for 3 min).

Depending of the type of grapes, the length of fermentation and the type of wine produced, the fresh wine after racking and rough filtration may still be cloudy because of suspended colloidal particles of grape or yeast components. This cloudiness may remain for a long time. It is unusual when a good wine becomes brilliant ly clear by natural settling. With present technology, such cloudi ness caused by grape of yeast proteins, peptides, pectins, gums, dextrans unstable grape pigments, tannins etc. may be removed from wine by the judicious use of small amounts of fining agents. These adsorb or chemically and physically combine with the colloidal particles or neutralize their electric charges causing them to agglomerate and gravitate to the bottom. Such treatment combined with subsequent filtration clarifies the wine. Bentonite, one of the most popular fining agents in winemaking, effectively removes protein materials. Activated carbon, gelatin, casein and poly(vinylpirrolidone) may also be used and aid in the removal of unstable tannins and other pigments. U.S. regulations however limit the use of fining agents. The clarifying agents must not remain in the wine.

After fermentation, wine becomes supersaturated with potassium bitartrate. The removal of this excess is necessary to avoid sedimentation after the wine is bottled. A cold stabilization technique where the wine is chilled just above its freezing point is generally used. Protective colloids, which prevent the crystall ization of the excess potassium bitartrate make a wine resistent to cold stabilization even during prolonged refrigeration. In those cases ion exchange treatment of the wine as been suggested to render the entire lot of wine potassium bitartrate stable when blended back (2). Electrodialysis has also been explored.

The inhibition of malo-lactic fermentation can be obtained by SO_2 ($\sim$ 30 mg/liter), maintainance of storage temperature at less than 18°C and adjustment of pH to at least below 3.3. Killing or removing the bacteria from wine is a more definite step to stabilize wine against malo-lactic fermentation. Pasteurization and particularly HTST treatment (high temperature, short time – 98°C for one second – with rapid cooling) is often used. Sterile filtration has also been used with 0.45 μm membrane filters.

In this paper preliminary experimental results obtained in a University-Industry joint research project are reported. The tests have been carried out in cooperation with a medium size well known winery. The aim was to analyze the potential of ultra filtration and reverse osmosis in solving some of the problems or in improving the existing technology in wine making. A diagram of the potential of pressure driven membranes in must treatment is presented in fig.1.

In this paper we will discuss the experiments on must staibliz ation avoiding SO_2 addition, and on the control of polyphenols and cations in the must. Various polymeric membranes in different configurations have been tested. The majority of them have already been commercially used in other food or biomedical applications.

EXPERIMENTAL

All the experiments described in this paper have been carried out on white must.

The majority of the ultrafiltration (UF) experiments have been performed using the laboratory unit shown in fig.2. The apparatus was constructed to use capillary membranes manufactured by the Berghof Institute (Tubingen, Germany). The physical properties of the membranes are given in Table I.

Table II shows the rejection for proteins,polyphenols and sugars measured using three different modulis. The must was filtered through a BMR 500515 modulus (cut-off 50.000 mw). The permeate was then ultrafiltered through a BMR 10515 (cut-off 10.000 mw) and the permeate from this step was ultrafiltered through a BMR 021.006 (cut-off 2.000 mw) modulus.

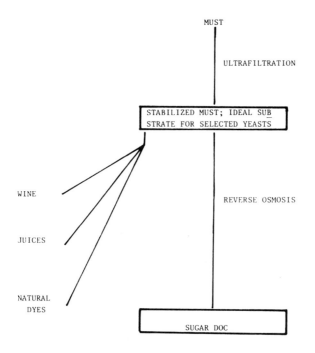

Figure 1.   Potentialities for UF and RO in must treatment

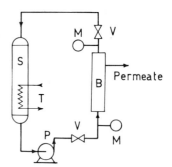

Figure 2.   Schematic of UF equipment:
B, capillary membrane modulus; S, must
reservoir; M, manometers.

TABLE I

Characteristics of the filtration units.

	cut-off (MW)	tubes diameter (mm)	membrane area (m^2)	max pressure (bar)	filtration capacity $(1/m^2h)$
1	50.000	1.5	0.5	1.2	300
2	10.000	1.5	0.5	1.2	120
3	2.000	0.6	1.0	2.0	10
4	18.000	25.4		4.0	150

type : (1) BMR 500515
       (2) BMR 100515
       (3) BMR 021006
       (4) HFM 180

TABLE II

	1		2		3		MUST
	c_p (g/lt)	R%	c_p (g/lt)	R%	c_p (g/lt)	R%	c_i (g/lt)
Total nitrogen	0.129	8	0.118	16	0.118	16	0.140
Total polyphen.	0.241	9	0.213	19	0.114	57	0.264
Sugar	162	0	162	0	162	0	162

conc. in permeate   rejection

Sugar rejection was always zero. Polyphenol rejection increased
from 9% to 57% with decreasing membrane cut-off. Difference in
polyphenol rejection have been observed when the must is ultra
filtered in the first UF step with the BMR 100515 and after with
the BMR 021006, as reported in table III. Fig.3 shows the typical
behaviour of the ultrafiltrate flux observed in these experiments.
A constant flux was generally obtained after two hours. Table IV
shows the final must ultrafiltrate flux values. All the
experiments were carried out at the same axial velocity and at
the same applied pressure. Table V shows results obtained with
tubular membranes (Abcor-USA).

Particular attention was devoted to the control of membrane fouling
and membrane cleaning. Acid-alkaline washing was tested and low
concentration chlorine solutions were also used. The recovery of
initial fluxes was generally 50% with the new modulus, and higher
then 95% with a used modulus. These results indicate the existence
of a certain irreversible fouling of the new membranes, which come
to steady state values, and does not increase with membrane reuse.

The must ultrafiltered with high flux membranes has also been
treated with membranes having intermediate or very high rejection
for electrolytes.Cellulose acetate and polyamide membranes were
used. The Reverse Osmosis apparatus shown in fig.4 was used.
The tests were carried out with high axial flow rate, sufficient
to promote a turbulent regime upstream from the semipermeable
membrane, for minimizing concentration polarization phenomena (4).

Table VI shows the rejection measured for total N_2, polyphenols
and sugars with DDS 800 and PA 300 membranes. Sugar rejections
increased from about 20% with DDS 800 to 100% with PA 300. Table
VII shows the rejections of various cations using the PA 300
membrane. The rejection for the majority of cations is higher
than 97%. Only Cu^{++} and Zn^{++} permeate easily through the membrane.
The rejections for these two cations is essentially zero. The
reason is attributed to a high specific interaction of Cu and Zn
with the polymeric materials forming the membranes and to Donnan
equilibrium.

Flux decay in the reverse osmosis test has been determined and
minimized using appropriate fluid dynamic regimes. Typical flux
decay with DDS 800 and PA 300 are shown in Figure 5 and 6. The
feed was must ultrafiltered through BMR capillary membranes.

TABLE III

	BMR 100515		BMR 021006		MUST
	c_p (g/1t)	R%	c_p (g/1t)	R%	c_i (g/1t)
Total nitrogen	0.218	20	0.151	45	0.274
Total polyphenol	0.674	8	0.618	15	0.731

TABLE IV

Must ultrafiltrate fluxes

P = 0.5 atm
T = 20°C

MEMBRANE	flux $1/m^2$ h
1	30
2	18
3	2,5

TABLE V

Membrane HFM 180

P = 2 atm
T = 25°C
J_∞ = 20,2 $1/m^2$h

	c_i	c_p	R%
Total nitrogen	741 mg/1	190 mg/1	74
Sugars	18%	18%	0

TABLE VI

	DDS 800		PA 300		FEED
	c_p(g/l)	R%	c_p(g/l)	R%	c_i(g/l)
Total Nitrogen	0.130	52	0.016	94	0.26
Total Polyphenol	0.243	45	0.012	98	0.51
Sugars	134	21	traces	100	166

TABLE VII

Membrane PA 300
P = 34 atm
T = 10°C

	c_i(mg/l)	c_p(mg/l)	R°(%)
N_2(total)	256	16	0.94
Polyphenols	576	12	0.98
Sugars	$163 \cdot 10^3$	//	1.00
K^+	1255	18	0.98
Na^+	77	4	0.95
Ca^{++}	123	4	0.97
Mg^{++}	74	1	0.97
Fe^{+++}	11.5	1.6	0.86
Cu^{++}	0.9	0.9	0
Zn^{++}	2.3	1.9	0.17
Mn^{++}	0.9	//	1.00

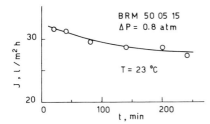

Figure 3. UF flux as a function of time: Feed, white must.

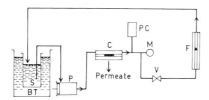

Figure 4. Scheme of RO laboratory apparatus: C, membrane cell; S, reservoir; P, volumetric pump.

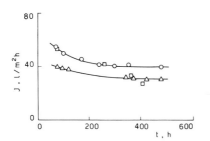

Figure 5. Typical flux decay with CA DDS-800 membranes. Feed: white must previously ultrafiltered through BMR-100515 modulus; T = 10°C, P = 35 atm.

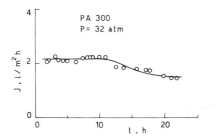

Figure 6. Typical flux behavior with PA-300 polyamide composite membranes. Feed: white must previously ultrafiltered through BMR-021006 modulus; T = 10°C.

Interesting effects have been observed on the ultrafiltered must
for what concerns color changes and wine stability. The analysis
of these effects are still in progress in cooperation with
specialist in winemaking.

DISCUSSION AND CONCLUSION.

The results described in this report show some of the uses that
pressure driven membrane processes offer in the treating virgin
must.
Polyphenol and protein concentrations can be controlled without
affecting the sugar content. The ultrafiltered must can be
concentrated by reverse osmosis with membranes up to 100% rejection
for sugars. Cu^{++} and Zn^{++} cations could be extracted from the
concentrated must.

Flux decays and rejection changes in the UF steps, depending upon
the feed concentration and experiment history, must be mainly
attributed to concentration polarization phenomena with consequent
gel layer formation of the pressurized membrane surface, for the
presence of proteins, colloids and in general high molecular
species in the feed (3).

LITERATURE CITED

1. Crull A.W., " The evolving membrane market" P.041 Business
   Communications CO., Inc., Conn.USA

2. Dinsmoor Webb A., Chemistry of Winemaking", A.C.S. Advances in
   Chem.Series 137, Washington DC (1974)

3. Drioli, E., Dynamically formed and transient membranes" in
   "Recent Advances in Separation Science", Ed.N.N.Li, vol.3,
   CRC Press Inc., (1977), p.343

4. Drioli, E., "Polarizzazione per concentrazione" in "Ricerche
   sul processo ad osmosi inversa", Quaderni IRSA, C.N.R.,
   vol.22 (1977), p.177.

RECEIVED February 18, 1981.

Industrial Application of Ultrafiltration and Hyperfiltration in the Food and Dairy Industries

OLE JENTOFT OLSEN

DDS–NAKSKOV, Division of the Danish Sugar Corporation, 4900 Nakskov, Denmark

The development started by Loeb and Sourirajan in 1960, has resulted in something quite different than desalination of sea and brackish water. I am quite certain that in those days they did not think of Feta cheese and low-alcohol beer. I have selected these products in order to show that membrane filtration is an accepted process in the food industry and not just a pipe dream of the future, on which we all based our hopes during the first years of the process.

Feta Cheese

Feta cheese originates from Greece, where it was originally produced from yew's milk. Today it is an important ingredient of the daily diet in Southeast Europe and the Arabic countries. In these countries the milk production is too low to sustain a level of self-sufficiency with this type of cheese. Consequently several North European countries, among them Denmark, have started a comprehensive production of Feta cheese for export purposes.

The principle of any cheese production is that the milk proteins are brought to an insoluble form by means of enzymes, the so-called coagulation. Then the coagulated protein is sifted from the components of the remaining milk. These components being water, salts, lactose, and the whey proteins lactalbumin and lactoglobulin. The whey proteins constitute up to 20% of the total protein content in milk. So these proteins are wasted during the process.

The principle of cheese production by ultrafiltration is that the proteins are concentrated by UF in the soluble form, i.e. before the enzyme treatment. The concentration is controlled in such a way that the composition of the concentrate as regards fat, protein, salts and water, is equivalent to the composition of the finished cheese. It is at this point the enzyme is added, causing the cheese to set in the form, into which it has been poured. The whey proteins, which were previously wasted during the traditional process, remain in the finished cheese, resulting in increased production and therefore higher profits. I shall revert to this later.

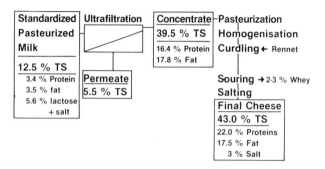

Figure 1.   The UF process for feta cheese

	Milk tons/day	Fat tons/day	Cheese tons/day	Sales price $/day
Traditional method	300		41	73,800
Ultrafiltration method	300	1.8	57	102,600
Extra Yield			16	28,800
Fat addition Operation Costs				÷ 6,700 ÷ 3,900
Profit by the UF process				18,200

Figure 2.   Economy in feta cheese production by UF

Figure 3.   Ørum Plant

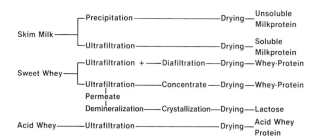

Figure 4.   UF of whey

Figure 5.   Denmark proteins (outside)

Figure 6.   Denmark proteins (inside)

Figure 1 shows, how ultrafiltration is incorporated in the process.

Today all Danish dairies producing Feta cheese, with one exception, base their production on ultrafiltration. The largest of these installations, built in 1977, is today treating 300,000 metric tons milk daily. Investment in UF plants amounts to approx. 1 mill. $. The economical side of the matter is as follows (see Figure 2). Indeed, a notable increase in profits as a result of the work carried out at UCLA in 1960 and followed-up by DDS in 1965.

Figure 3 shows the DDS UF-plant at the above mentioned Feta cheese factory. It comprises a total of 20 DDS UF modules, type 35, each with 27 m^2 (approx. 297 ft^2) membrane area. The membrane applied is of synthetic material with a nominal cut-off value of 20,000. The plant can operate round the clock, and the cleaning time is approx. 2 hours every 24 hours. The cleaning is carried out with a solution of hot 0.5% sodium hydroxide, followed by a solution of hot 0.3% nitric acid, and sterilization if necessary with Cl_2. The membrane life time is approx. 1 year.

Proteins

The introduction of membrane filtration in connection with dairy production has resulted in a wide range of new protein enriched products of which the whey proteins have attracted the largest amount of attention.

Figure 4 shows a few of the different products which are produced today.

The largest dairy company in Denmark, called "Dairy Denmark" is, as far as I know, the most progressive one in the world today with regards to the production of whey proteins by means of ultrafiltration. Figure 5 is a photo of a quite new protein factory, called "Denmark Proteins", whose sole purpose is to ultrafiltrate 1,000 metric tons of whey per day for the production of approx. 10 metric tons pure whey protein in powder form, and as a by-product approx. 50 metric tons of lactose. The plant was put into operation in May, 1980.

Up till now nothing has been released concerning the total economy of the plant, but I am convinced that "Dairy Denmark" have made sure that the economy is sound.

The essence of this plant is of course the UF plant itself, which is shown in Figure 6. It is a DDS plant of the same type as at the Feta cheese dairy, consisting of 45 modules, type 35, each with 42 m^2 (452 ft^2) membrane area. The plant is fully automatic, controlled by micro processors and integrated in a superior total control of the whole factory.

The principle of the plant construction is shown in Figure 7. If a higher purity is desired than achieved by normal ultrafiltration, water may be added during the process (diafiltration). In this way more impurities will pass through the membranes.

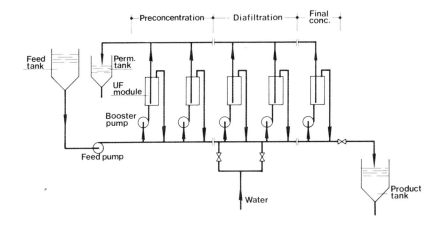

Figure 7.   Continuous UF Plant (principle)

Figure 8.   Brørup, HF of whey in Denmark

	tons vapour	kg fuel	kWh
		per ton water removed	
Evaporation of whey 5 % TS — 20 % TS	0.18	13.8	53.2
Hyperfiltration of whey 5 % TS — 20 % TS			6.8
Saving in %			88

Figure 9. HF of whey

Figure 10. HF plant for removal of alcohol

Figure 11. Development center in the dairy industry (outside)

Figure 12. Development center in the dairy industry (inside)

Figure 13.   DDS–NAKSKOV

The product composition, i.e. the proportion between protein and lactose in the final product, may be controlled from the central control room. Thus the factory is able to produce protein powder with compositions varying from approx. 35% protein of total solids to approx. 85% protein of total solids. The first mentioned is a product with a composition like cheap skim-milk powder, whereas the latter is an expensive product used for baby-food and dietetic food.

Concentration of Whey

Today direct concentration of whey is known and accepted as an exceedingly attractive supplement or alternative to evaporation.

Figure 8 shows a typical DDS RO plant consisting of 14 19 m^2 (205 ft^2) modules equipped with membranes of cellulose acetate, not very different from those developed in 1960. Around 6 metric tons are treated daily.

Fig. 9 shows a comparison of the energy consumption by evaporation and hyperfiltration (also called reverse osmosis).

Removal of the Alcohol in Beer

A new field is the removal of alcohol in beer by means of hyperfiltration. "De forenede Bryggerier" - perhaps better known under the names Tuborg and Carlsberg - have developed a process for removal of the alcohol in beer by means of the DDS hyperfiltration system. The advantages with this are that the alcohol percentage may be adjusted according to the different marketing areas - without having to change the brewing process.

Figure 10 shows a DDS plant for the hyperfiltration of Beer.

DDS Development

In order to emphasize how much we expect of the future DDS has built a new dairy for development purposes. The main objects being product and process development based on membrane filtration in the food industry. The dairy is shown in Figures 11 and 12.

DDS-Nakskov

Figure 13 shows the DDS production plant in Denmark for membrane filtration equipment. Around 250 people are working in this ever expanding company.

RECEIVED December 4, 1980.

Fouling in Whey Reverse Osmosis

B. R. SMITH

CSIRO Division of Chemical Technology, P.O. Box 310,
South Melbourne, Australia 3205

Reverse osmosis, although originally developed for water desalination (1), has been applied to numerous pollution control and
concentration problems, including industrial (2) and municipal (3)
wastewaters, pulp and paper waste streams (4), food processing
liquids (5), and dairy wastes (6).

Whey is a highly polluting waste stream (BOD$_5$ about 40,000
ppm) from cheese and casein manufacture. Historically, whey has
been disposed of by feeding it to pigs, by using it as a fertili-
ser, or by dumping it in sewers and watercourses. With increasing
environmental controls, there is now more interest in whey utilization. For whey concentration, reverse osmosis is attractive in
that the process operates at ambient temperatures, so that the
functional properties of the whey proteins are less affected and,
of course, the energy consumption is lower than for alternative
processes.

One of the important factors determining the process economics is the flux decline that is caused by a build-up of whey components at the membrane surface. It is the aim of this paper to
review the application of reverse osmosis to whey processing, and
in particular, to discuss the problem of membrane fouling.

Whey Properties

There are two types of whey, classified (7) according to
source: (i) "sweet" whey, which is derived from the manufacture of
products in which rennet-type enzymes are used to coagulate milk
(e.g. Gouda and Cheddar cheeses), and which has a minimum pH of
5.6, and (ii) "acid" whey, which is derived from acid-induced coagulation (e.g. cottage cheese and casein), and which has a maximum pH of 5.1.

Typical concentrations of the major constituents in each type
of whey are listed in Table I (8) :

0097–6156/81/0154–0037$05.00/0

Table I

	HCl casein whey	Cheddar cheese whey
lactose, g/l	51.4	48.7
protein, g/l	7.3	6.5
non-protein N, g/l	0.18	0.23
citric acid, g/l	1.93	1.56
calcium, g/l	1.11	0.47
phosphorus, g/l	0.78	0.54
pH	4.47	6.25

The osmotic pressure of whey is approx. 0.6 MPa (6)

Whey Production

    The scale of whey production is illustrated in Table II
(summarized from reference 9), which lists the quantities of whey
produced in various countries in 1977 :

Table II   (Units: kilotonnes)

Country	Sweet whey	Acid whey	Total
U.S.A.	13,720	1,920	15,640
Canada	1,210	158	1,368
Australia	788	420	1,208
New Zealand	785	1,282	2,067
E.E.C.	22,800*	2,200*	25,000*

    *1978 figures, approximate only

    In Australia, New Zealand and Ireland, where dairy cattle are
pasture-fed, whey production is highly seasonal; the peak monthly
production may be up to twice the average monthly production.
This results in a lower plant utilization in whey processing in
these countries, and consequently greater emphasis on process
efficiency.

Membrane Processing of Whey

    The development of commercial ultrafiltration equipment has
made recovery of the whey proteins economically feasible, and a
number of uses for the remaining lactose (the principal BOD source)

have been suggested in an attempt to achieve complete utilization
of the whey solutes. Concentration of the whey (or whey ultrafiltrate) is generally necessary at some stage, perhaps prior to
transport to a central processing facility, or prior to evaporation, or to produce a concentrate which can be used directly.
Several commercial whey reverse osmosis installations are in operation (10), notably in Northern Europe where escalation in fuel
costs has been a major factor. de Boer et al. (11) have shown
that reverse osmosis is more economic than evaporation up to a
volume reduction of 75%.

Reverse osmosis was first proposed as a method for the concentration of liquid foods some fifteen years ago (12), and since
that time, numerous studies have been reported on aspects of the
ultrafiltration and reverse osmosis of whey. A common observation has been the decline in flux rate through the membrane that
occurs during operation due to the accumulation of fouling layers
on the membrane surface.

Membrane Fouling Studies on Whey

Lim et al. (13) studied the reverse osmosis of cottage cheese
whey and showed that only part of the fouling layer could be removed with fluid shear, and that casein was the major component of
that which remained. The latter finding was ascribed to the lower
diffusion coefficient of casein relative to the other solutes.
The flux rates under various conditions were used to calculate the
hydraulic resistances of the various layers, following the approach of Markley et al.(14); these calculations showed that the
resistance of the fouling layer was five times the resistance of
the membrane at low feed velocities (Reynold's Number = 1500),
whereas it was less than the resistance of the membrane at higher
feed velocities (Reynold's Number = 5,900). The authors pointed
out that fouling of the membrane surface would retard diffusion of
the microsolutes, and so increase the microsolute concentration
polarization. Fouling thus reduced flux rates by contributing an
added hydraulic resistance, and by reducing the effective driving
force for water permeation through the membrane.

In an attempt to directly measure the amount of material in
the fouling layer, Dejmek et al. (15) studied the ultrafiltration
of ^{131} I-labelled casein. A very slow accumulation at the membrane surface was observed, superimposed on the expected changes
due to feed flow rate, applied pressure, etc.

Lee and Merson (16) studied the effects of chemical treatments of cottage cheese whey on membrane fouling in ultrafiltration. By examining the deposits obtained with scanning electron
microscopy, they were able to correlate flux rates with the nature
of the deposits on the membrane. Calcium sequestration gave
increased flux rates, as did raising the ionic strength of the
whey; these results indicated that fouling could be minimised by
dispersing the whey proteins, and so preventing their deposition
on the membrane.

More recently, Hiddink et al. (6), studied the reverse
osmosis of Gouda cheese whey, and concluded that the flux-limit-
ing factors were the osmotic pressure of the feed, and membrane
fouling. Fouling by protein was observed with deionized whey, and
with whey that had been adjusted to pH 4.6; in both cases, the
fouling was seen as a consequence of the lower stability of the
whey proteins resulting in aggregation at the membrane surface.
Calcium phosphate deposition was also noted if Gouda whey (pH 6.6)
was concentrated at 30°C over a concentration ratio of 1.6 : 1.
This source of fouling could be removed either by exchanging the
calcium in the whey for sodium, or by slightly lowering the pH of
the whey.

As noted by Matthews (17), the studies on membrane fouling
published so far would suggest that some of the protein components
causing fouling are affected by such factors as pH, ionic strength
and ionic composition (particularly calcium concentration).
Interactions between the various solutes are also important, as
shown by Peri and Dunkley (18). Their results on the reverse
osmosis of solutions of whey components showed little indication
of fouling; only whole whey gave a steady decline in flux rate
with time.

Whey Pretreatments to Reduce Fouling

The possibility of pretreating the whey before membrane
processing to reduce fouling may be commercially attractive,
provided that the product properties, such as the functionality of
the proteins, are not detrimentally affected. For whey ultrafiltration, pretreatment methods have been developed to remove the
lipid fraction (19, 20) which involve flocculation and gravity
settling.

Hayes et al. (21) studied the effects of pH variation on the
ultrafiltration of Cheddar cheese and HCl casein wheys. Their
earlier work had shown that both wheys gave low flux rates at pH
4.1 - 4.4, and high flux rates below pH 3. Flux rates improved
for Cheddar cheese whey above pH 5, but there was little improvement with HCl casein whey. Heat treatment (80°C for 15 seconds)
of the casein whey followed by pH adjustment to an optimum between
5.2 and 5.9 resulted in marked decrease in fouling. Demineralization of, or EDTA addition to, HCl casein whey also gave higher
flux rates. These results were explained in terms of a balance
between (i) a heat-induced interaction of casein with β-lactoglobulin and calcium, which formed aggregates which did not foul the
membrane, and (ii) increasing calcium phosphate precipitation as
the pH was raised, which would lead to lower flux rates.

Smith and MacBean (22) applied the pretreatments developed by
Hayes et al. (21) to the reverse osmosis of HCl casein and Cheddar
cheese wheys, but found that an increase in fouling occurred com-

pared to untreated whey. It was also found that the rate of flux decline decreased if the whey was demineralized and increased if sodium chloride was added. The rate of flux decline was much higher for HCl casein whey than for Cheddar whey. These results have been supported by those of Matthews et al. (23) for the reverse osmosis of ultrafiltrates from pretreated whey.

Hickey (8), following on from the earlier Australian work (21, 22), carried out detailed laboratory studies on the reverse osmosis and ultrafiltration of HCl casein and Cheddar cheese wheys in order to characterize the membrane fouling in these systems. Again, pretreatments involving combinations of heat, pH adjustments, and calcium or citrate additions led to essentially opposite effects in reverse osmosis compared to ultrafiltration. This was particularly evident with HCl casein whey. For untreated HCl casein whey, a minimum occurs in the curve of permeation rate versus pH. This likely to reflect the isoelectric point of the fouling proteins, as under these conditions the proteins are least soluble, and hence likely to form denser layers with higher hydraulic resistance. A similar flux minimum at the isoelectric point has been reported for the ultrafiltration of gelatin solutions by Akred et al. (24). In the reverse osmosis experiments, the flux minimum occurred at a higher pH than in the ultrafiltration experiments; this can be explained in terms of the higher ionic strength and/or local calcium concentration in the reverse osmosis boundary layer causing a shift in the isoelectric point of the fouling proteins to a more alkaline pH value.

Membrane Fouling Models

Merten et al. (25) found that the simple relationship

$$\Delta (\log \text{flux rate}) = \text{constant} \times \Delta (\log \text{time}) \quad \ldots \ldots (1)$$

described the flux decline due to membrane compaction. The same relationship has been used satisfactorily to express flux decline rates due to membrane fouling in the reverse osmosis of such feed streams as river water (26, 27), decondary sewage effluent (3, 28) and whey (22). In several theoretical studies of membrane fouling kinetics, equations containing exponential forms have been derived; it is likely that equation (1) is simply an empirical approximation to these more complex relationships.

Blatt et al.(29) developed what has become known as the "gel polarization" theory for ultrafiltration, in which the amount of macromolecular material in the fouling layer is controlled by its back-diffusion rate into the feed stream. The gradual decline in flux observed in some practical systems was explained in terms of an irreversible consolidation of the gel layer with time, leading to a reduction in the layer's permeability. Kimura and Nakao (2) used Blatt's approach to model the fouling of reverse osmosis membranes by the suspended solids in industrial wastewater, and were able to correlate their experimental results with the derived equations. More recently, Gutman (30) extended the "turbulence burst" model for particle re-entrainment from a smooth impermeable wall to fouling of reverse osmosis membranes. Both of these analyses showed that the flux decline depended on the flux of the unfouled membrane, the mass transfer coefficient of the foulant and its concentration, the feed velocity, and the density and specific hydraulic resistance of the fouling layer.

An effect not considered in the above models is the added resistance, caused by fouling, to solute back-diffusion from the boundary layer. Fouling thus increases concentration polarization effects and raises the osmotic pressure of the feed adjacent to the membrane surface, so reducing the driving force for permeation. This factor was explored experimentally by Sheppard and Thomas (31) by covering reverse osmosis membranes with uniform, permeable plastic films. These authors also developed a predictive model to correlate their results. Carter et al. (32) have studied the concentration polarization caused by the build-up of rust fouling layers on reverse osmosis membranes but assumed (and confirmed by experiment) that the rust layer had negligible hydraulic resistance.

A further complication arises when the foulant carries a fixed charge, such as whey protein in solutions with pH significantly different from the isoelectric point. Under these conditions, the fouling layer acts as a polyelectrolyte membrane in series with the reverse osmosis membrane, and changes in the salt concentration at the surface of the reverse osmosis membrane would be expected.

Conclusions

Membrane fouling in the reverse osmosis of whey is clearly a complex phenomenon, because of the range of solutes present - proteins, lactose and salts - and their interactions with each other. Few detailed studies have been reported, and although some insights can be gained from work on fouling in ultrafiltration, additional factors must be considered. The conditions in the fouling layer are, of course, somewhat different in reverse osmosis than in ultrafiltration. The applied pressure is an order of magnitude greater, and this may affect protein interactions (33). Probably more significantly, the ionic strength in the fouling layer will be considerably higher because of the rejection of low molecular weight solutes by the membrane and the reduction in the diffusion rate away from the membrane surface caused by the presence of the fouling layer. In particular, more highly rejected solutes such as calcium, phosphate, and lactose will have higher concentrations in the fouling layer relative to less well rejected solutes such as monovalent ions. Precipitation of calcium phosphate in the fouling layer is therefore a possible explanation for

the observed fouling (22), particularly with HCl casein whey because of its higher calcium content.

Altering the state of aggregation of the fouling material by
pretreatment of the whey caused little change in the reverse osmosis flux rates. This result, together with the effects of demineralization or salt addition mentioned above, would suggest that
the flux-determining process in the reverse osmosis of whey is the
concentration polarization which is increased by the presence of
the fouling layer. The aggregates formed by the pretreatment
procedure, whilst forming a more water-permeable fouling layer as
shown by the ultrafiltration results, do not lead to a significantly greater back-diffusion rate of solute from the membrane
surface.

It seems therefore, that the established procedures involving
high feed velocity across the membrane surface, additional turbulence promotion, etc., need to be applied and optimized. There is
a need for a model for fouling in reverse osmosis which incorporates such factors as the added concentration polarization caused
by the fouling layer, and Donnan exclusion effects due to charged
foulants. Clearly there is scope for more detailed experimental
work in this area.

Literature Cited

1. Loeb, S.; and Sourirajan, S; Sea water desalination by means
   of a semi-permeable membrane U.C.L.A. Dept. of Eng. Report
   No. 60-60, 1960.
2. Kimura, S.; and Nakao, S-I.; Desalination, 1975, 17, 267.
3. Winfield, B.A.; Water Research, 1979, 13, 561.
4. Jonsson, G.; and Kristensen, S.; Desalination, 1980, 32, 327.
5. Kennedy, T.J.; Monge, L.E.; McCoy, B.J.; and Merson, R.L.;
   A.I.Ch.E. Symposium Series, 1973, 69, (132), 81.
6. Hiddink, J.; de Boer, R.; and Nooy, P.F.C.; J. Dairy Science
   1980, 63, 204.
7. International Dairy Federation; Standards of identity for
   whey powders, Report D-Doc. 1978, 49.
8. Hickey, M.W.; Hill, R.D.; and Smith, B.R.; N.Z.J. Dairy. Sci.
   Tech., 1980, 15, 109.
9. Zall, R.R.; Kuipers, A.; Muller, L.L.; and Marshall, K.R.;
   N.Z.J. Dairy Science and Technology, 1979, 14 (2), 79.
10. Eriksson, P.; Nordeuropaesk Mejertidsskrift, 1977, 43, 238.
11. de Boer, R.; de Wit, J.N.; and Hiddink, J.; J. Soc. Dairy
    Technol., 1977, 30, 112.
12. Morgan, A.J.; Lowe, E.; Merson, R.L.; Durkee, E.L.;
    Food Technol., 1965, 19, 52.
13. Lim, T.H.,; Dunkley, W.L.; and Merson, R.L.; J. Dairy Sci.,
    1971, 54(3), 306.
14. Markley, L.L.; Cross, R.A.; Bixler, H.J.; Hunter, J.A.;
    Gillman, W.S.; and Johnson, S.; U.S. Dept. of the Interior,
    Office of Saline Water, Res. Dev. Report No. 281, 1967.

15. Dejmek, P.; Hallstron, B.; Klima, A.; and Winge, L; Lebensm.-Wiss. u. Technol., 1973, 6(1), 26.
16. Lee, D.N.; and Merson, R.L.; J. Food Science, 1976, 41, 778.
17. Matthews, M.E.; N.Z.J. Dairy Sci. and Technol., 1979, 14(2), 86.
18. Peri, C.; and Dunkley, W.L.; J. Food Science, 1971, 36, 25.
19. de Wit, J.N.; Klarenbeck, G.; de Boer, R.; Proc. 20th Int. Dairy Congress 1978, E, 919.
20. Attebery, J.M.; U.S. Patent 3 560 219, (2/2/71).
21. Hayes, J.F.; Dunkerley, J.A.; Muller, L.L.; and Griffin, A.T.; Aust. J. Dairy Technol., 1974, 29, 132.
22. Smith, B.R.; and MacBean, R.D.; Aust. J. Dairy Technol., 1978 33(2), 57.
23. Matthews, M.E.; Doughty, R.K.; and Short, J.L.; N.Z.J. Dairy Sci. Tech., 1978, 13, 216.
24. Akred, A.R.; Fane, A.F.; and Friend, J.P.; Proc. A.C.S. Symposium on Ultrafiltration membranes and applications, Washington, 1979. (in press).
25. Merten, U.; Lonsdale, H.K.; Riley, R.L.; and Voss, K.O.; U.S. Dept. of the Interior, Office of Saline Water, Res. Dev. Report No. 265, 1967.
26. Sheppard, J.D.; Thomas, D.G.; and Channabasappa, K.C.; Desalination, 1972, 11, 385.
27. Kuiper, D.; van Hezel, J.L.; and Bom, C.A.; Desalination, 1977, 15(2), 193.
28. Wechsler, R.; Water Research, 1977, 11, 379.
29. Blatt, W.F.; Dravid, A.; Michaels, A.S.; and Nelson, L.; in Membrane Science and Technology, ed. J.E. Flinn, Plenum Press p.47, 1970.
30. Gutman, R.G.; The Chemical Engineer, 1977 No. 322, 510.
31. Sheppard, J.D.; and Thomas, D.G.; A.I.Ch.E. Journal, 1971, 17(4), 910.
32. Carter, J.W.; and Hoyland, G.; Proc. 5th Int. Symp. Fresh Water from the sea, 1976, 4, 21.
33. Payens, T.A.J.; and Heremans, K.; Biopolymers, 1969, 8, 335.

Received December 30, 1980.

5

Development of a Cellulose Acetate Membrane and a Module for Hemofiltration

M. KAI, K. ISHII, Z. HONDA, and H. TSUGAYA
Daicel Chemical Industries, Ltd., 1 Teppo-cho, Sakai-shi 590, Japan

M. MAEKAWA, T. KISHIMOTO, and S. YAMAGAMI
Osaka City University Medical School, 1-5-7 Asahi-machi, Abeno-ku, Osaka-shi 545 Japan

Since Henderson opened the gate to the clinical application of ultrafiltration to renal failure as an alternative to hemodialysis and peritoneal dialysis, the ultrafiltration of blood, hemofiltration, has been increasingly attracting both clinical and pathological interest. In the course of hemofiltration studies, it has been amply confirmed that this new therapy is effective for treatment of hemodialysis-difficulties patients who are not compatible with hemodialysis due to serious syndrome. Various studies are being under way concerning the mechanistic differences between hemofiltration and hemodialysis.

In hemodialysis the transport of plasma solutes through membrane is controlled by concentration gradient and diffusion coefficient. Since diffusion coefficient decreases with molecular weight, the whole blood clearance (the amount of removed solute in unit time divided by the solute concentration in the blood) sharply diminishes with molecular weight as illustrated in Figure 1 (1). In hemofiltration, on the other hand, removal of solutes is almost independent of molecular weight up to the cutoff molecular weight of the membrane. This difference in the clearance for solutes larger than uric acid is related to the fact that hemofiltration is effective for hemodialysis-difficulties patients. For hemofiltration to be effective, the total amount of blood water to be ultrafiltered in one treatment is 20 to 23 liters depending on patients' conditions. To complete each treatment in five hours, hemofilter, UF module for hemofiltration, is required to permeate 66 to 77 ml/min of water. None of hemofilters so far in use meet this requirement. Daicel and Osaka City University Medical School started a joint study to develop a practically more feasible hemofilter. The required properties for a new hemofilter are specified in Table 1. It is to be noted in Table 1 that UFR, ultrafiltration rate, is not less than 70 ml/min.

0097-6156/81/0154-0045$05.00/0
© 1981 American Chemical Society

Table 1 REQUIRED PROPERTIES FOR A NEW HEMOFILTER

UFR		$\geq$70 ml/min
Transmembrane Pressure		$\leq$300 mmHg/cm^2
Permeation, of which molecular weight is:	$<1\times10^4$ $\geq5\times10^4$	100% $<0.1\%$
Priming volume (Blood holding volume)		$\leq$100 ml
Residual blood volume		<1 g
Blood compatibility		
Chemical stability		
Reasonable cost		

Membrane development

So far as membrane performance is concerned, an UF membrane suitable for hemofiltration could have been readily developed out of a series of acrylonitrile copolymer UF membranes being sold by Daicel. The cyano group in acrylonitrile, however, suggested that it would be more desirable to develop new membrane of other materials. Considering the requirements listed in Table 1, cellulose acetate was selected as a membrane material among other candiate polymers such as, polysulfone, polycarbonate, and other cellulosics. More specifically, cellulose diacetate was the material for our extensive studies. Cellulose diacetate is innert to human blood, resistant to sterilizing agents, mechanically strong and inexpensive. In addition, cellulose diacetate with its moderately polar nature, hydrophilic and hydrophobic properties and its solubility in a wide variety of solvents makes it an attractive material for superior membranes of various kinds. Of course, the advantage of having some experiences in handling this material would be helpful in the course of the development.

In order to obtain in a very short time an optimum casting dope composition which produces a membrane of required performance, a guide line listed in Table II was established, based on our previous experience of membrane research. Mixtures of high and low boiling, water missible solvents for cellulose acetate were employed as solvents for dope. As for additives to the dope

were employed mixtures of water and organic solvents of limited
water solubility.

Table II GUIDELINE TO AN OPTIMUM CASTING DOPE COMPOSITION

1.	Cellulose diacetate	ca. 13%
2.	Mixed solvent:	ca. 57%

    2.1 Low boiling, water missible solvent
         for CDA (eg. Acetone)

    2.2 High boiling, water missible solvent
         for CDA (eg. DMF)

3. Mixed additive: ca. 30%

    3.1 Partially water soluble solvent
         for CDA (eg. Cyclohexanone) or
         Swelling agent for CDA (eg. cel-
         losolve acetate)

    3.2 Nonsolvent for CDA
         (eg. Water, alcohols, glycols)

Experimental

    Membrane preparation. Membranes were formed on polyester
cloth under the conditions shown in Table III by casting a dope,
evaporating a portion of solvents, then immersing into chilled
water.

Table III CASTING CONDITIONS

Dope is cast continuously on polyester cloth by
casting machine.

As cast thickness	150 microns
Casting speed	5 cm/sec
Evaporation period	30 sec
Evaporation temperature	27°C
Precipitant	Water
Bath temperature	2°C

    Evaluation of membranes and modules. Membranes were evalu-
ated in thin channel flat cells of 25 cm^2 effective membrane area
and 200 micron channel thickness at the mean flow velocity of 1.3
x 10^2 cm/sec. A 0.2% ovalbumine aqueous solution was used with
marker solutes dissolved in it. Modules were tested by using the
same solution, bovine blood in vitro and subsequently with living
dog under various flow rates, pressures, temperatures and protein
concentrations.

Analysis. Ovalbumine (4.8 x 10^4 Dalton), bovine albumine
(6.8 x 10^4), canine albumine (>6x10^4), urea (60), creatinine
(113) and vitamin B_{12} (1355) were quantitatively determined either by high performance GPC using Shodex Ionpack S-803 column or
by high performance liquid chromatography using Nagel Nucleosil
7C-18 column. Inulin was measured by resorcinol-thiourea color-
imetry after other saccharides were removed by yeast fermentation. Solvents in gelation bath water were determined using FID
gas chromatography (JEOL, JGC-20K) with ethylene glycol succi-
nate-chromosorb W-AW column at 150°C.

Abbreviations.

        NB -- nitro benzene
        AP - acetophenone
        IP - isophorone
        BL - butyl lactate
       CHX - cyclohexanone
        FF - furfural
       MEK - methyl ethyl ketone
        CA - cellosolve acetate
     γ-BL - γ-butyrolactone
        EL - ethyl lactate
        DA - diacetone alcohol
       NMP - N-methyl pyrrolidone
       DMF - NN-dimethyl formamide
        CS - cellosolve

Results and discussions

     In Figures and Tables, values of water flux and ovalbumine
permeation are normalized to the standard values for the purpose
of compensating fluctuation of individual experiments.

     Effects of additives. The results are summarized in Figure
2 in terms of water solubility of additive solvent and membrane
performance evaluated with 0.2% ovalbumine aqueous solution. The
water flux rises very steeply from zero to $8.8x10^2$ml/min.m^2 in
correspondence with increase in the water solubility of additive
solvent from 1 to 4 g/dl. Contrary to the fact that the water
flux curve has a plateau for the additive water solubility larger
than 4 g/dl, the ovalbumine permeation values for some water missible additive solvents are undesirably higher than those for additive solvents, of which water solubility is in the range from
4 to 20 g/dl.
     Figure 3 illustrates that membrane thickness increases con-
sistently with water solubility of additive solvents.
     Figure 4 shows the relationship between membrane performance

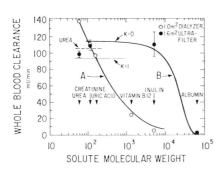

Journal of Laboratory and
Clinical Medicine

Figure 1. Whole blood clearance plotted against the logarithm of solute molecular weight (1)

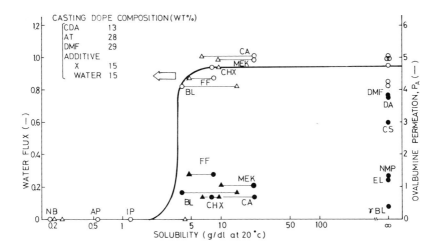

Figure 2. Relationship between membrane performance and water solubility of additive solvents: (○, ●) solubility of additive solvents in water; (△, ▲) solubility of water in additive solvents. Water flux is normalized to the standard value of 8.8 × 10² mL/min · m² and ovalubumine permeation is normalized to the standard value of 0.66%.

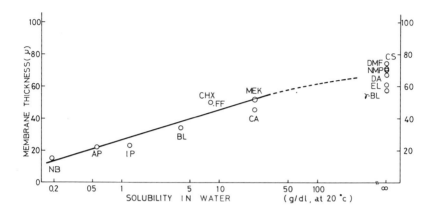

Figure 3.   Membrane thickness vs. water solubility of additive solvents

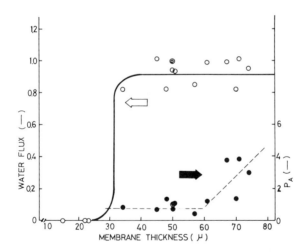

Figure 4.   Relationship between membrane performance and membrane thickness

and membrane thickness. Membranes from 30 to 60 microns in thickess give high water flux as well as sufficiently low ovalbumine permeation for maintaining the albumine loss under the required level. The membrane thickness from 30 to 60 microns are given by the additive solvents, of which water solubility ranges from 4 to 20 g/dl.

Effects of component ratio in casting dope. Among partially water soluble organic solvents which gave membranes from 30 to 60 microns in thickness, cyclohexanone was chosen as the standard additive solvent for studies varying casting dope component ratios. In Figure 5, each curve represents each relationship between membrane performance (water flux and ovalbumine permeation) and cyclohexanone content in a given amount of additive solution (cyclohexanone aqueous solution). As seen in Figure 5, water flux decreases very rapidly with increase in cyclohexanone content over ca. 60%. On the other hand, a synergistic effect is observed in ovalbumine permeation in the way that satisfactorily low permeation values are obtainable only in the range of 40 to 60% cyclohexanone content when the total amount of the additive solution was from 20 to 30% of the casting dope.

Similar behavior was observed in the relationship between membrane thickness and cyclohexanone content as shown in Figure 6. The membrane thickness comes to a minimum where permeation has the lowest value. Scanning electron microscope studies on membrane substrate structure revealed that a change from a finely pored sponge structure to a coarsely pored finger structure occurs at the point where the membrane thickness turns to go up with increase in cyclohexanone content as already shown in Figure 6.

Role of partially water soluble additive solvents. There have been published many studies on the membrane formation mechanism and the effects of solvents, additives (swelling agents or poreformers) and precipitants. Membrane performance and morphology are well correlated to polymer precipitation rate in nascent membrane (2). Low precipitation rate generally produces membranes of finely pored sponge substrate structure with low solute permeation. Remarks on solvent-precipitant interaction by Frommer et al. (3) is helpful to speculation on membrane formation. In the following paragraphs is discussed the role of partially water soluble solvent as a plasticizer of nascent membrane matrix.

As shown in Figure 5, the very steep drop of water flux corresponding to the rise of cyclohexanone content higher than 0.6 was caused either by decrease in water or by increase in cyclohexanone. In order to see which of these two components governs this sharp drop of water flux, numerical data on these descending lines are summarized in Table IV.

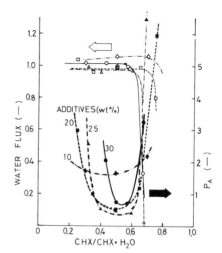

Figure 5. Membrane performance vs. cyclohexanone content in the additive solution. Numbers attached to each curve indicate the amount of additive solutions in weight percent of dope.

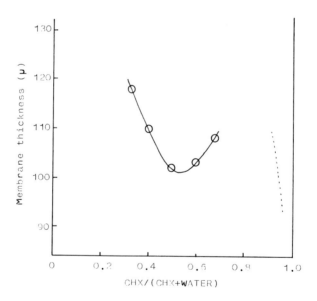

Figure 6.   Membrane thickness vs. cyclohexanone content in the additive solution of 25 wt % of dope

Table IV   NUMERICAL DATA ON CYCLOHEXANONE AND WATER

FOR CYCLOHEXANONE/WATER >2

Additive Solution (%)	Cyclo- hexanone (%)	Water (%)	Cyclo- hexanone/ water (-)	Water flux (-)	Permea- tion (-)
10	7	3	2.3	1.06	2.2
20	15	5	3.0	0.80	6.5
30	20	10	2.0	0.34	3.3

It is remarkable in Table IV, that water flux decreases with increase in water. This means the water flux promoting effect of
water as the only nonsolvent for cellulose acetate contained in
the casting dope was suppressed by the coexistence of partially
water soluble solvent, cyclohexanone.

Increase of water in the casting dope accelerates phase separation in the early stage of gelation and increases the number
of and decreases the size of precipitating polymer cores. A certain amount of water, therefore, is necessary to obtain a finely
pored membrane with low solute permeability (4). This explains
why the minimum permeation value for 10% additive is more than
twice those for 20 to 30% additives. At the same time, however,
the nascent polymer cores seem to rapidly lose flexibility resulting in the fixation of the membrane matrix at a relatively
early stage of gelation and thus giving a broad pore size distribution. The nascent membrane matrix, however, is likely to keep
flexibility to the relatively late stage of gelation by the existence of cyclohexanone, a portion of which may be left parti-
tioned to the precipitated polymer phase due to its limited solubility in water. Thus, enhanced polymer flexibility accelerates
the polymer network to contract so as to make interstices or
pores narrow enough to reject the passage of ovalbumine. Increase in water content, therefore, requires the augmentation of
cyclohexanone and the both ingredients work synergistically.
However, if the cyclohexanone content exceeds a certain level,
i.e., 1.5 times of water, excessive contraction of highly solv-
ated polymer networks occurs leading to collapse of the interstices. At the same time, this contraction of nascent membrane
matrix would cause the formation of some specific chasms or voids
and make them large enough to pass ovalbumine freely. In substrate where polymer concentration is considerably lower than
that of skin layer, tendency to contraction of polymer network
necessarily yields numbers of large sized voids, and hence, re-

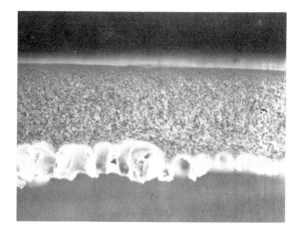

Figure 7. Membrane cross-section for cyclohexanone content of 32 wt % of additive solution

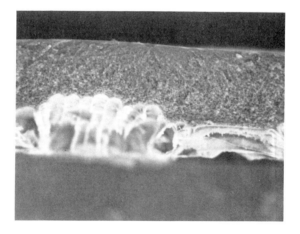

Figure 8. Membrane cross-section for cyclohexanone content of 40 wt % of additive solution

Figure 9.   Membrane cross-section for cyclohexanone content of 50 wt % of additive solution

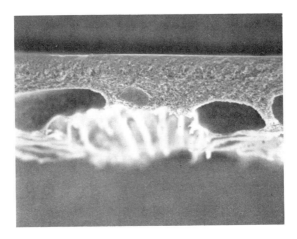

Figure 10.   Membrane cross-section for cyclohexanone content of 60 wt % of additive solution

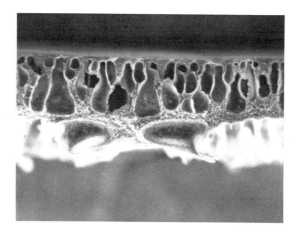

Figure 11.   Membrane cross-section for cyclohexanone content of 68 wt % of additive solution

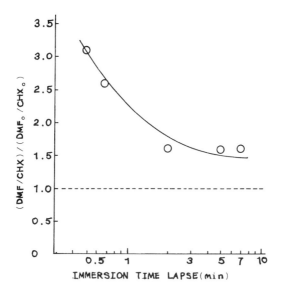

Figure 12.   Ratio of total extracted amount of DMF to that of cyclohexanone normalized to the ratio of initial contents in the casting dope. The casting dope is composed of 13 wt % CDA, 28 wt % acetone, 29 wt % DMF, 15 wt % cyclohexanone, and 15 wt % water.

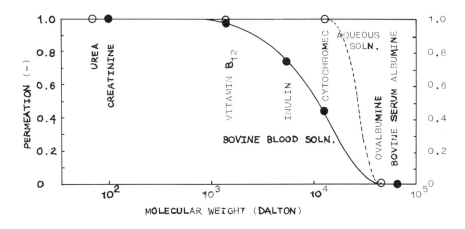

Figure 13. Separation characteristics of the developed membrane

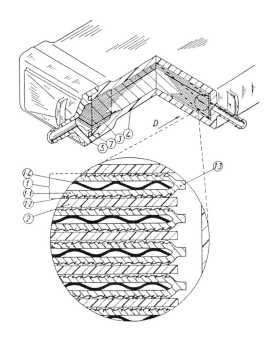

Figure 14. Structure of the developed module for hemofiltration, Daicel Hemo-Fresh: 1, unit compartment; 1.1, membrane; 1.2: substrate cloth; 1.3, heat-sealed side edge; 1,4, smooth-surfaced and corrugate-shaped blood compartment spacer; 2, PET spacer between unit compartments; 3, polyurethane end seal; 4, case; 5, cap.

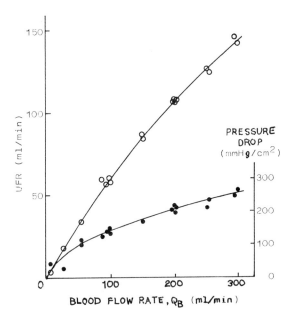

Figure 15.   UFR and pressure drop of the developed hemofilter as a function of blood feed rate, Q_B bovine blood in vitro. Testing conditions: hematocritt; 28%; total protein, 3 g/dL; temperature, 30°C; transmembrane pressure, 150–300 mm Hg/cm².

duces the degree of whole contraction. The whole membrane thickness, therefore, turns to increase at the point where water flux
begins to decrease due to undesirable contraction of polymer network in skin layer.

In order to confirm that cyclohexanone is extracted more re-
luctantly than other solvents, the concentrations of extracted
solvents in the gelation bath water were measured with immersion
time lapse by using gas chromatography. As illustrated in Figure
12, the extraction rate of cyclohexanone is less than 1/3 of
DMS's. In case of well-known acetone-formamide casting dope for
cellulose diacetate RO membrane, formamide is extracted faster
than acetone when as cast membrane is immersed into chilled water
(5). The role of formamide, therefore, seems to be limited to
evaporation stage and very early period of immersion.

As discussed above, the mechanism how the mixed additive,
nonsolvent (water) and partially water soluble solvent (cyclohexanone) works is supposedly different from that of well-known additives, such as formamide.

Separation characteristics of the membrane. Figure 13 shows
the separation characteristics of the membrane being used for
manufacturing hemofiltration module in Daicel. Thirteen thousand
molecular weighted cytochrome C in aqueous solution is able to
permeate through this membrane as well as small molecules, such
as urea. At the same time, blood albumine is retained almost
completely. With bovine blood solution, permeation values of intermediate molecular weighted solutes are somewhat reduced perhaps
due to partial clogging of pores with blood proteins and some retention in the protein gel layer formed on the membrane surface.
However, the permeation values are still higher than those of
other membranes so far available.

Module development

Figure 14 demonstrates a unique device to secure a uniform
blood flow throughout the whole membrane area in order to ensure
full performance. As is well-known, uniform and unstagnant blood
flow is indispensable for minimizing clotting and hemolysis as
well as ensuring full performance of the membrane used. In our
module, Daicel HemoFresh(a registered trademark), this is realized by inserting smooth-surfaced corrugate-shaped spacer in each
blood compartment. This hemofilter clears UFR of 100 ml/min when
bovine blood solution containing ca. 3.5-4.0 g/dl of protein is
fed at the rate of 200 ml/min under the transmembrane pressure of
150-300 mmHg/cm^2 as shown in Figure 15. It is confirmed by in
vitro and in vivo tests that UFR of 100 ml/min for said bovine
solution corresponds to UFR of 70 to 80 ml/min for clinical application.

Conclusion

A new cellulose acetate membrane for hemofiltration was developed by employing the mixtures of liquids of opposite properties for both solvent for cellulose diacetate and additive to the polymer solution. The additive was composed of water and organic solvents of limited water solubility. The role of the additive is likely to have somewhat different aspect from that of other additives known so far.

A new high performance module, Daicel HemoFresh (a registered trademark) for hemofiltration, is characterized by both superior membrane performance and good blood compatibility. It is now being confirmed clinically that this module is superior to other hemofilters so far available with regard to UFR, permeation of undesirable solutes, clotting, hemolysis and the amount of blood left behind in the module.

References

1. L. W. Henderson et al., J. Lab. Clin. Med., 85, 372, 1975.
2. J. L. Halary et al., Desalination, 13, 251, 1973.
   J. Vinit et al., ibid., 15, 267, 1974.
   J. Vinit et al., European Polym. J., 11, 71, 1975.
   H. Strathmann et al., Desalination, 16, 179, 1975.
   H. Strathmann et al., J. Appl. Polymer Sci., 15, 811, 1979.
3. R. Bloch and M. A. Frommer, Desalination, 7, 259, 1970.
   M. A. Frommer et al., ibid., 7, 393, 1970.
4. R. E. Kesting, Synthetic Polymeric Membranes, p. 120, McGraw-Hill, New York, 1971.
5. Unpublished data, Daicel Chemical Industries, Ltd., 1969.

RECEIVED December 4, 1980.

Pressure Control of the Ultrafiltration Rate During Hemodialysis with High-Flux Dialyzers and the Time Dependence of Membrane Transport Parameters

ALLEN ZELMAN, DAVID GISSER, GARY STRAIT, and VICTOR BASTIDAS

Center for Biomedical Engineering, Rensselaer Polytechnic Institute, Troy, NY 12181

ROBERT STEPHEN, CARL KABLITZ, JEFFREY HARROW, BARRY DEETER, and W. J. KOLFF

Division of Artificial Organs, University of Utah, Salt Lake City, UT 74112

Recent hemodialysis research has focused attention on the "middle molecule hypothesis" (1, 2) which suggests that solutes in the "middle molecular weight" spectrum of 500-3000 daltons include important uremic toxins. It appears that a significant fraction of the dialysis population could benefit from hemodialysis using a membrane with a larger pore size. However, if the diameter of the pore is doubled, the water loss will increase sixteen times. Thus, accurate and reliable ultrafiltration control is necessary when using so called "high flux membranes". The three extra-corporeal techniques used to remove middle molecules while controlling ultrafiltration are: 1) hemoperfusion (3, 4); 2) hemofiltration (5, 6, 7); and 3) dialysis with a dialyzer which contains a highly porous membrane capable of removing middle molecules, such as the Hospal RP-6 dialyzer (8, 9). Nevertheless, there are problems with all three techniques. Predilution hemo-filtration offers small molecule clearance comparable to hemodialysis and excellent (∿ 100 ml/min) middle molecule clearance. It is, however, quite expensive and technically complicated. Postdilutional hemofiltration offers good middle molecule clearance, but the small molecule clearance of 60-70 ml/min is marginal. Hemoperfusion has no capability for fluid removal and little capacity for urea removal; therefore, it fulfills only a supplementary role in the treatment of End Stage Renal Disease. Hemodialysis with a high flux membrane used in the standard counter-current mode requires either an expensive (∿ $4,500) ultrafiltration control system (in addition to the usual $6,000 dialysate delivery system) or a closed circuit 70 liter dialysate tank wherein the adequacy of urea removal is debatable: patients using the tank system average 22% higher BUNs than patients on standard single pass systems (10).

The mean transmembrane hydrostatic pressure drop, $\overline{\Delta P_m}$, primarily determines the rate of ultrafiltration and is given by

0097-6156/81/0154-0061$05.00/0
© 1981 American Chemical Society

$$\overline{\Delta P}_m = \frac{P_{Bi} + P_{Bo}}{2} - \frac{P_{Di} + P_{Do}}{2} \ . \tag{1}$$

$\overline{\Delta P}_m$ is related to the ultrafiltration rate, Q_v, by

$$Q_v = L_p (\overline{\Delta P}_m - \pi_p) \tag{2}$$

where L_p is the ultrafiltration index, π_p is the osmotic pressure of the plasma proteins, P_{Bi} and P_{Bo} are the hydrostatic pressures of the blood in and the blood out line respectively, P_{Di} and P_{Do} are the hydrostatic pressures of the dialysate in and dialysate out line respectively. Control of $\overline{\Delta P}_m$ obviously allows control of Q_v.

Consider Figure 1, which depicts the conventional hemodialysis system in counter-current mode. This dialyzer set-up maximizes the concentration difference across the membrane and thus ensures maximum solute transfer. However this configuration also maximizes the transmembrane hydrostatic pressure difference and thus, maximizes the water flux. During hemodialysis the hydrostatic pressure of the blood must always be higher than the pressure of the dialysate to ensure sterility in the event of a membrane rupture. One has the following constraints during counter-current flow $P_{Bi} > P_{Bo}$, $P_{Di} > P_{Do}$, $P_B > P_D$ (everywhere). From these constraints it is easy to see from Figure 1 that by setting dialysate and blood pressure at arbitrary values, a minimum $\overline{\Delta P}_m$ can only be generated to equal to $(P_{Bi} - P_{Do})$.

In the counter-current mode the magnitude of this difference is set by the construction of the dialyzer and the dialysate pressure control and is generally on the order of 50 mm Hg or greater. This minimum pressure will induce an absolute minimum ultrafiltration rate of 350 ml/hr for a typical high flux membrane. Thus, when the patient has lost sufficient water or perhaps when he does not need to lose any water during dialysis, the patient must continuously be given sterile saline to make up for the minimum ultrafiltration loses.

The purpose of this research was to develop a simple and inexpensive hemodialysis protocol with the following objectives: (a) to ensure maximum removal of the "middle molecules" by utilizing a highly porous membrane incorporated into so called "high flux dialyzers"; (b) to ensure normal removal of low molecular weight solutes by utilizing a single pass dialysis delivery system (11); (c) to ensure accurate control of ultrafiltration by maintaining the transmembrane hydrostatic pressure, ΔP_m, at appropriate small values easily read on standard dialysis equipment; and (d) to accomplish the above objectives without the use of expensive volumetric or other specialized equipment.

Description of a Simple Means of Controlling Ultrafiltration.

   Consider Figure 2 with co-current flows. When the hydrostatic pressures have reached a steady state, the net forces acting on
the membrane are balanced, i.e., mechanical equilibrium exists.
In a very simplified view, the mechanical force balance can be
written at any distance z along the length of the membrane as

$$P_B(z) = P_D(z) + \nu(z) \tag{3}$$

where $\nu(z)$ is the restoring force supplied by the membrane. If
$P_B(z)$ increases as a result of increased blood flow, then the membrane resists bending into the dialysate path by an amount $\nu(z)$.
Thus, the transmembrane pressure at z can be expressed by

$$\Delta P_m(z) = P_B(z) - P_D(z) = \nu(z) \tag{4}$$

   Now consider that if Q_{Bi} increases, then $P_B(z)$ increases and
the membrane will be forced into the path of the dialysate. The
restriction of dialysate cross section will cause the dialysate
pressure to increase when Q_{Di} is held constant, so equation 4 will
hold for new values of $P_B(z)$, $P_D(z)$ and $\nu(z)$. It is apparent that
when the membrane becomes very distensible or flexible, i.e., $\nu(z)$
tends toward zero, then $P_B(z) - P_D(z)$ tends toward zero also,
i.e., the membrane cannot support a hydrostatic pressure drop.
Thus if the membrane is free to move, the transmembrane pressure
drop will tend toward a minimum value.
   In the co-current mode $(P_{Bo} - P_{Do})$ can be made arbitrarily
close to zero by adjusting P_{Do}; this is a standard adjustment on
nearly all dialysate delivery systems. However, the delivery system must have the capability of providing a positive dialysate
pressure equal to the blood venous pressure ($\sim$ 80 mm Hg). The
pressure drop $(P_{Bi} - P_{Di})$ will automatically be adjusted to near
zero by the interaction of the co-current flows and distensible
membrane. Therefore by adjusting P_{Do} until $\overline{\Delta P}_m = \pi_p$, no matter
how porous the membrane, the ultrafiltration rate can be brought
to zero when the dialyzer is operated in the co-current mode.
   Because our system is a pressure control of ultrafiltration
rate, it is obvious that an accurate in vivo value of the ultrafiltration index, L_p, is required. Our first attempts at manual
determination of L_p (12) produced only a very small amount of data
compared to the enormous effort necessary to collect it. Thus, an
automated system was designed and constructed for collecting and
evaluating ultrafiltration data.

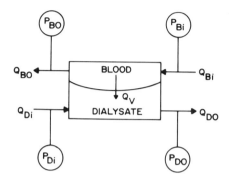

Counter - Current Flows

Figure 1.   Countercurrent dialyzer set-up

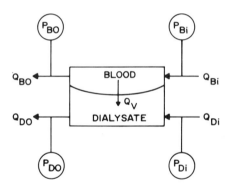

Co-Current Flows

Figure 2.   Cocurrent dialyzer set-up

Equipment and Methods.

The experimental set-up for finding the in vivo value of L_p is shown schematically in Figure 3. Blood is withdrawn from the patient at 225 ml/min. The dialysate input is 500 ml/min. The dialyzer is operated in the co-current mode. Two differential pressure transducers (Model CD 7, Celesco Transducer Products, Canoga Park, CA) monitor $(P_{Bi} - P_{Di}) = \Delta P_{BDi}$ and $(P_{Bo} - P_{Do}) = \Delta P_{BDo}$ to $\pm$ 1 mm Hg. The pressures are time varying due to patient unrest and the pulsatile nature of blood roller pumps. The analog signals of each pressure transducer demodulator is sent to the "ultrafiltration monitor" continuously.

The dialysate is delivered in the single pass mode, but the dialysate tanks are arranged to mimic a closed system. Dialysate reservoirs rest on a platform, the weight of which is continuously monitored to $\pm$ 2 g by an Aimex electronic weighing system (Aimex Corp., Boston, MA). Fresh dialysate flows from one tank through the dialyzer and returns to a drain tank. The total weight of these tanks may change only as a result of water loss by the patient or by compliance effects of the dialyzer. The Aimex weighing system sends a continuous analog signal indicating dialysate weight as a function of time to the ultrafiltration monitor. The ultrafiltration monitor is a hard-wired, digital signal processor. Its purpose is to average the input signals of weight and pressure and compute $\overline{\Delta P}_m(t)$, $Q_v(t)$ and $L_p(t)$. Figure 4 is a schematic of the operation of the ultrafiltration monitor. The time averaging systems operate in the following way. About once a sec a short data sample is collected from each input; after about 2 min, 128 data points are averaged and displayed on LED readouts. The average is updated for each sample. Since all variables during dialysis are slowly varying compared to 2 min and all noise is fast compared to 2 min, a 2 min time averaging system seemed to be a reasonable first try. The ultrafiltration monitor had the following ranges and in vitro accuracies as a function of time: dialysate weight changes $\pm$ 4 kg to $\pm$ 2 g; ultrafiltration rate $\pm$ 4000 ml/hr to $\pm$ 2 ml/hr; mean transmembrane hydrostatic pressure $\pm$ 250 mm Hg to $\pm$ 1 mm Hg; and the membrane hydraulic permeability (ultrafiltration index) 60 ml hr^{-1} mm Hg^{-1} to $\pm$ 0.8 ml hr^{-1} mm Hg^{-1}.

Q_v and $\overline{\Delta P}_m$ were continuously recorded on a 2 pen chart recorder to an accuracy of 10 ml/hr and 2 mm Hg per division (0.2 cm) at a chart speed of 30 cm/hr. Data was read from the chart at 2 min intervals. Data is excluded from analysis whenever changes in variables invalidate the averaging of the ultrafiltration monitor; approximately 50% of all data was excluded.

The mass transfer of each solute was computed from the standard clearance, C, formula

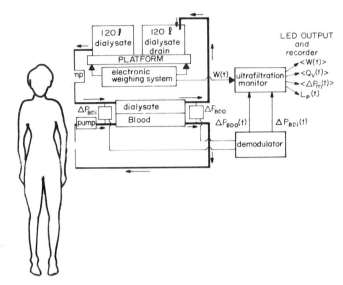

Figure 3.   Patient monitoring system. This apparatus was assembled only to determine the dialyzer UF index, L_p. Knowing L_p then allows safe high-flux dialysis without specialized equipment

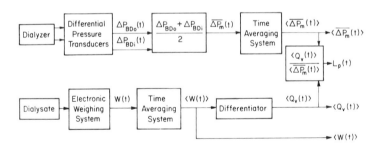

Figure 4.   Schematic of the UF monitoring system

$$C = (\frac{C_{Bi} - C_{Bo}}{C_{Bi}}) \, Q_{Bo} + Q_v. \tag{5}$$

All chemistries were determined by the clinical laboratory at the University of Utah Medical Center. A detailed error analysis shows the range of errors for clearance value to be between ± 10% at the start of dialysis and 15% at the end of dialysis. Oncotic pressures were measured with a colloid osmometer (Model 186, Instrumentation Laboratories, Boston MA) to ± 0.2 mm Hg.

Curve fitting was performed by standard statistical means. The linear regression used statistical package BMDPLR-Multiple Linear Regression, Health Science Computing Facility, University of California, Los Angeles, revised April 1977. The nonlinear regression used statistical package BMDP3R-Nonlinear regression, Health Sciences Computing Facility, University of California, Los Angeles, Revised April 1977. All data reduction was carried out at RPI using an IBM 3033 computer. All data collection was carried out at the University of Utah Medical Center.

Results

The equation assumed to properly predict volume flux is

$$Q_v(t) = L_p(t)(\overline{\Delta P_m}(t) - \pi_p(t)) \tag{6}$$

where

$$L_p(t) = L_p(1 - \alpha t) \tag{7}$$

and L_p is the hydraulic permeability (ultrafiltration index) prior to blood entering the dialyzer, α is a constant and t is time. There are two means for evaluating equation 6: 1) one may assume that $\pi_p(t) = \pi_o$ is a constant since $\pi_p(t)$ usually varies by no more than 4 mm Hg. One may then use non-linear regression and the measurement of $\overline{\Delta P_m}$ and Q_v to evaluate L_p, α and π_o, or; 2) one may measure $\pi_p(t)$ directly using a colloid osmometer and use a linear regression to evaluate L_p and α from the measurements of Q_v, ΔP_m and $\pi_p(t)$. These methods are compared in Tables I and II for the 1.36 M^2, Gambro high flux dialyzer.

The values in Table I are obtained by assuming that the oncotic pressure varies linearly between its initial value of 21.1 mm Hg and its final value of 24.8 mm Hg; the correlation co-efficient for the linear regression was 0.99 for 7 values of colloid osmotic pressure. Fifty-one values of (Q_v, $\overline{\Delta P_m}$ and π_p) spaced every 2 minutes or longer gave the curve fit indicated in Table I. The accuracy with which the equation represented the data is ± 37 ml/hr and the correlation coefficient, r^2, was 0.996.

TABLE I

Ultrafiltration Results - Gambro High Flux Dialyzer
Linear Regression, $\pi_p(t)$ Measured by Colloid Oncometer.

$Q_v(t) = L_p(1 - \alpha t)(\overline{\Delta P_m}(t) - \pi_p(t))$

$L_p = 15.2$ ml hr^{-1} mm Hg^{-1} ± 1.3%, $\alpha = 0.0591$ hr^{-1} ± 6.7%

$\langle\pi\rangle = 22.4 \pm 1.11$ mm Hg $(21.1 \rightarrow 24.8)$

$r^2 = 0.96$, $Q_v \pm 37$ ml hr^{-1}, $N = 51$ (1 Dialysis)

Of course, one cannot clinically measure the oncotic pressure
of the plasma proteins during each dialysis, so one needs an average value, π_o which is a reasonable approximation to $\pi_p(t)$. Table
II shows the results of determing π_o by non-linear regression from
the same $(Q_v, \overline{\Delta P_m})$ data used in Table I. The standard error in
the transport coefficients is somewhat greater than when measuring
$\pi_p(t)$ directly, but the error in ultrafiltration evaluation is
only slightly higher (2.7%).

TABLE II

Ultrafiltration Results - Gambro High Flux Dialyzer
Non-Linear Regression, π_o Determined by Regression

$Q_v = L_p(1 - \alpha t)(\overline{\Delta P_m}(t) - \pi_o)$

$L_p = 15.3$ ml hr^{-1} mm Hg^{-1} ± 4.1%, $\alpha = -0.0668$ hr^{-1} ± 9.4%

$\pi_o = 22.0$ mm Hg ± 7.2%, $Q_v \pm 38$ ml hr^{-1}, $N = 51$ (1 Dialysis)

The 1 m^2 RP610 dialyzer was characterized from data from 3
patients having one dialysis each. π_o in these experiments
represents an average patient oncotic pressure. Good data points
were taken every 2 minutes for nine out of 12 patient hours of
dialysis with roughly equal numbers of data points from each
patient. The results are given in Table III. The accuracy of
curve fit is ± 84 ml/hr.

TABLE III

Ultrafiltration Results - RP610 High Flux Dialyzer
Three Different Patients, 1 Dialysis Each,
Non-Linear Regression, π_o Determined by Regression

$$Q_v = L_p(1 - \alpha t)(\overline{\Delta P}_m(t) - \pi_o)$$

$$L_p = 17.3 \text{ ml hr}^{-1} \text{ mm Hg}^{-1} \pm 1.8\%, \; \alpha = 0.0806 \text{ hr}^{-1} \pm 5.2\%$$

$$\pi_o = 24.2 \text{ mm Hg} \pm 4.5\%, \; Q_v \pm 84 \text{ ml hr}^{-1}, \; N = 269$$

Data from two dialyses using the Gambro high flux dialyzer and three dialyses using the RP-610 dialyzer are depicted in Figure 5, 6 and 7. The decrease in L_p (called water permeability, hydraulic permeability, or ultrafiltration index) with time is depicted in Figure 5. Figures 6 and 7 show the effect of membrane-blood interaction. By initiating the plots at the same ultrafiltration rate, holding the pressure constant and comparing the decrease with and without normalized area, one can determine which membrane more readily changes its transport properties in the presence of blood.

Clearance values were taken at hourly intervals during dialysis. One group is reported, Table IV, where the ultrafiltration rate is brought to essentially zero by adjustment of mean transmembrane pressure to 21 mm Hg. A second group were taken at random ultrafiltration values and these are reported in Tables V and VI.

TABLE IV

In Vivo Data for 1.36 m^2 Gambro High Flux Dialyzer at
Zero Ultrafiltration Rate and Blood Flow at 225 ml/min

	Urea	Creatinine	Inorganic Phosphorus	Uric Acid
ml/min	136±7	121±8	119±6	110±8

N = 25 (3 Dialyses, 1 Patient)

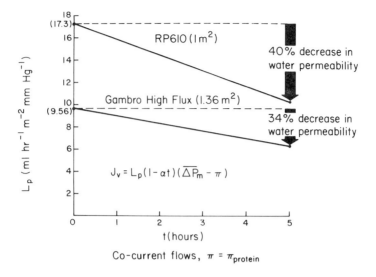

Figure 5.   In vivo UF index as a function of time

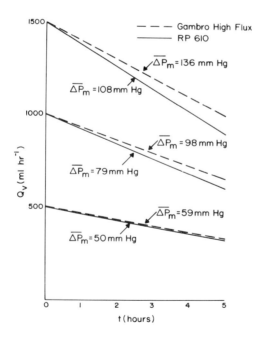

Figure 6.   Decay of UF rate with time at various fixed transmembrane hydrostatic
pressures

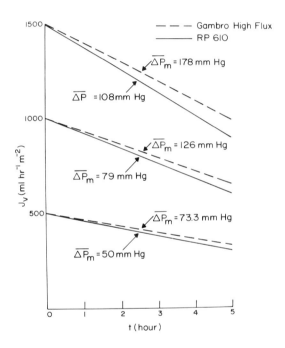

Figure 7.   Decay of UF rate with time at various fixed transmembrane hydrostatic pressures and per meters squared of membrane

TABLE V

In Vivo Data for 1.36 m^2 Gambro High Flux Dialyzer at Random
Ultrafiltration Rates and Blood Flow at 225 ml/min

	Urea	Creatinine	Inorganic Phosphorus	Uric Acid
ml/min	125±6	112±6	103±10	104±9

$\langle Q_v \rangle$ = 570 ± 321 ml/hr

$\langle t \rangle$ = 1.6 ± .6 Hours into Dialysis

N = 11 (2 Dialyses, 1 Patient)

TABLE VI

In Vivo Data for 1.0 m^2 RP610 High Flux Dialyzer at Random
Ultrafiltration Rates and Blood Flow at 225 ml/min

	Urea	Creatinine	Inorganic Phosphorus	Uric Acid
ml/min	126±4	110±4	96±5	88±6

$\langle Q_v \rangle$ = 1354 ± 418 ml/hr

$\langle t \rangle$ = 2.2 ± 1.4 Hours into Dialysis

N = 11 (2 Dialyses, 2 Different Patients)

Discussion

The results of this investigation which are clinically significant are; 1) an accurate and simple means for controlling
ultrafiltration during hemodialysis with "high flux" dialyzers has
been developed, and 2) a formula which can accurately predict the
ultrafiltration rate from measurement of hydrostatic pressures
alone has been determined. It is now possible for any hemodialysis clinic to benefit from the use of high flux dialyzers by
implementing the pressure control of ultrafiltration as described
here.

The physical interpretation of these results is rather
straightforward. We have shown equation 6 as an accurate
representation of ultrafiltration during hemodialysis. The effective solute transmembrane osmotic pressure differences given by
$\Sigma \sigma_i \Delta \pi_i$, where σ_i is the Staverman reflection coefficient have been
experimentally determined to be neglible in these systems;

measurement of π_p directly and numerical determination of π_o from the ΔP and Q_v data gives essentially the same results. This is not surprising since one is dealing with highly porous and highly hydrated membranes. These data therefore indicate that the decrease in ultrafiltration rate is solely due to a decrease in the ultrafiltration index, L_p, not a change in osmotic pressure across the dialyzer. There are at least 2 models to explain this: 1) a gel of protein is building up on the surface of the membrane; 2) the protein is binding to the membrane and plugging pores. If one considers the pore blocking model using Poiseuille flow and the Fick diffusion equation as rough approximations for volume and solute flow respectively, it is easily seen that the solute flow is proportional to the pore radius squared, but that the volume flow is proportional to the fourth power of the radius. A 40% decrease in water flow would indicate a 23% decrease in solute flow. The gel model would also predict a decrease in clearance because the diffusion pathway through the membrane-gel layer would increase. The clearance data indicates that there was no statistically significant change in clearance relative to either ultrafiltration rate or time. That is to say the magnitude of the clearance was sufficient to ensure proper dialysis for patients, but the random error in determining the clearance value was sufficiently large to void further analysis.

Figure 6 indicates that the ultrafiltration index of the RP-610 dialyzer decreased more rapidly than that of the 1.36 m^2 Gambro high flux dialyzer. When the ultrafiltration rates are normalized for unit area of membrane, the effect is more pronounced as seen in Figure 7. Apparently the membrane of the RP-610 dialyzer accumulates more "gel layer" than the Gambro high flux dialyzer when both are run at the same ultrafiltration rate. This may indicate less protein-membrane interaction or a better internal design giving high sheer rates for the Gambro. However, both dialyzers will remove significantly greater amounts of solutes in the 1000 MW range than conventional dialyzers.

It is hoped that this investigation will lead to a better understanding of dialyzer performance and a better therapy for hemodialysis patients.

Acknowledgement

This research was supported in part by the generosity of Mr. Peter Thompson, President of Aimex Corp., Boston, MA 02109; the Division of Artificial Organs, University of Utah Medical Center; and PHS-NIH grant #1 RO1 HL24466.

Literature Cited

1. Babb, A.L., Popovich, R.P., Christopher, T.G., and Scribner, B.H. American Society for Artificial Internal Organs, 17:81, 1971.

2. Scribner, B.H., Farrell, P., Milulinovic, J., and Babb, A.L. Proc 5th Int Cong Nephrol, 3:190, 1972.

3. Chang, T.M.S., Gonda, A., Dirks, J., and Malave, N. Trans Am Soc Artif Int Organs, 17:246, 1971.

4. Chang, T.M.S., Chinito, E., Barre, B., Cole, C., and Hewish, M. Trans Am Soc Artif Int Organs, 21:502, 1975.

5. Bosch, J.P., Geronemus, R., Glabman, S., Lysaght, M., Khan, T., and Albertini, B.V. Artificial Organs, 2:339, 1978.

6. Quellhorst, E., Schuenemann, B., and Borghardt, J. Artificial Organs, 2:334, 1978.

7. Henderson, L.W., Ford, C.A., and Lysaght, M.J. Contractors Conference, Artificial Kidney Chronic Uremia Program, NIAMDD, pp. 132, 1976.

8. Brunner, H., Mann, H., Essers, V., Schulthesis, R., Byrne, T., and Heintz, R. Artificial Organs, 2:375, 1978.

9. Man, N.K., Granger, A., Jungers, P., Rondon-Nucette, M., Zingraff, J., Sausse, A., and Funch-Grentana, J.L. E.D.T.A., 1973.

10. Ventelon, J., Perrone, B., Jcannot, F., Laurial, F., and Schrameck, E. Communication Presented to the Swedish Nephrology Society Fund, April 25, 1975.

11. Zelman, A., and Gisser, D. Journal of Dialysis, 3(2&3):237, 1979.

12. Zelman, A., Bulloch, E., Stephen, R., Kablitz, C., Duffy, D., and Kolff, W.J. To be published in J. Artificial Organs, 1980.

RECEIVED December 4, 1980.

Ultrafiltration Rates and Rejection of Solutes by Cellulosic Hollow Fibers

E. KLEIN, F. F. HOLLAND, and K. EBERLE
Gulf South Research Institute, P.O. Box 26518, New Orleans, LA 70186

R. P. WENDT
Gulf South Research Institute and Loyola University, New Orleans, LA 70118

A major objective of fundamental studies on hollow-fiber hemofilters is to correlate ultrafiltration rates and solute clearances with the operating variables of the hemofilter such as pressure, blood flow rate, and solute concentration in the blood. The mathematical model for the process should be kept relatively simple to facilitate day-to-day computations and allow conceptual insights. The model developed for Cuprophan hollow fibers in this study has two parts: (1) intrinsic transport properties of the fibers and (2) a fluid dynamic and thermodynamic description of the test fluid (blood) within the fibers.

Transport Properties. Important transmembrane transport parameters of the fibers are L_p, the hydraulic conductivity; P_m, the diffusive permeability for a given solute; σ, the solute reflection coefficient; and R, the solute rejection. These coefficients appear in the following equations, which are assumed to be valid at the steady state at each position Z along the fiber wall:

$$J_v = L_p (\Delta P - \sigma \Delta \pi) \tag{1}$$

$$J_s = J_v (1-\sigma) C_w + \frac{J_v (1-\sigma)(C_w - C_p)}{e^\beta - 1} \tag{2}$$

$$\beta = J_v (1-\sigma)/P_m \tag{3}$$

$$R = 1 - (C_p/C_w) \tag{4}$$

Here J_v and J_s are the transmembrane fluid and solute flux densities; ΔP and $\Delta \pi$ are the hydrostatic and osmotic pressure differences (inside minus outside) across the fiber wall; C_w is the "wall" concentration; i.e., solute concentration immediately adjacent to the solution-membrane interface within the fiber annulus; C_p is local filtrate or product concentration at the outer surface of the fiber; and β is the transmembrane Péclét

0097–6156/81/0154–0075$08.50/0

number. For a solute such as albumin, to which Cuprophan is
virtually impermeable, $\sigma = 1$ and volume flux is given by

$$J_v = L_p(\Delta P - \pi) \tag{5}$$

Lower-molecular-weight solutes such as myoglobin and inulin,
have $0 < \sigma < 1$, and exhibit a finite solute flux during ultrafiltration. Local filtrate concentration, Cp, is then given by

$$Cp = J_s/J_v \tag{6}$$

Substitution of Equation 6 in Equations 2 and 4 yields the
Spiegler-Kedem rejection equation ($\underline{1}$)

$$R = \sigma(e^\beta - 1)/(e^\beta - \sigma) \tag{7}$$

The response of R to β is illustrated in Figure 1, for several
values of σ. For $\beta \ll 1$, R is much less than σ because transmembrane diffusion dissipates the concentration difference created
by the convective sieving term, $J_v (1-\sigma) C_w$ in Equation 2. For
$\beta > 3$, $R \to \sigma$ because diffusion is dominated by convection.

Three factors can complicate this theoretical behavior of R
when applied to hollow fibers. First, the volume flow J_v, and
hence β and R, may decrease with distance along the fiber, because
of either an appreciable axial pressure drop or an increasing
back osmotic pressure exerted by accumulated solute within the
fiber. Hence, an overall observed value for R will be an integrated average along the fiber length.

A second complicating factor in hollow-fiber experiments is
that it is virtually impossible to measure either the local wall
concentration, C_w, in situ within a hollow fiber of small diameter
(e.g., 0.02 cm) or C_p, the local filtrate concentration at the
exterior surface of the fiber. Instead, the accessible quantities
are the entering feed stream concentration, C_o, and an average
concentration, $\bar{C}_p$ of filtrate collected from the entire fiber.
In terms of these measurable concentrations, the observed rejection, R_{obs}, is defined as

$$R_{obs} = 1 - (\bar{C}_p/C_o) \tag{8}$$

A concentration boundary layer theory clearly is needed to relate
C_w to C_o, so that membrane properties such as L_p, σ, and P_m can
be correlated with R_{obs} at various operating conditions. Also,
since π in Equations 1 and 5 is an independently determined
function of C, a boundary layer theory could correlate the observed filtrate velocity, $\bar{J}_v$ (averaged along the fiber length),
with average applied pressure ΔP. For sufficiently high axial
flow velocities, $C_w \approx C_o$, and a major theoretical barrier to data
analysis is removed. Some early work in reverse osmosis ($\underline{2}$) was
done with flat-sheet membranes and large feed stream velocities,
on the order of 100 cm/sec, so that $R_{obs} \approx R$. But for hollow

fibers used in this work, axial flow velocities were less than
about 4 cm/sec to avoid large axial pressure drops which might
rupture the fibers or result in a significant decrease of ultrafiltration with length. Thus, the search for an appropriate and
relatively simple boundary layer theory for hollow fibers became
a necessary part of this study.

A third possible complicating factor in rejection measurements, especially with protein solution, is physical interaction
of the solute with the membrane surface. Solute adsorption, for
example, could alter the parameters L_p, σ or P_m and cause anama-
lous rejection. An earlier search (3) for adsorption effects by
a cellulosic membrane was negative. Although other investigators
have reported such effects with non-cellulosic membranes, the
effects with Cuprophan fibers were not observed, and adsorption
parameters were not included in this transport model.

Another solute-membrane interaction, formation of a precipitated gel at the solution-membrane interface, is also not
considered in our model. Gel formation during protein ultrafiltration is a major premise of many theoretical and experimental studies, but as is discussed later, there was no evidence for
gel formation during the experiments with protein containing
systems. All of our mathematical modeling and data analysis is
for the pregel region of hemofiltration.

Boundary Layer Theory. The Reynolds number for flow-through
hollow fibers during our experiments was at most about 0.02 cm
(diameter) x 4 cm/sec (velocity) x 1.0 g/cm^3 (density)/ 0.007
poise (viscosity) $\simeq$ 11; therefore, a boundary layer theory is
needed for laminar flow in tubes. Because of its simplicity, the
most attractive available theory is an approximate result of
thin-film theory. This theory is restricted to a description of
boundary layers that are thin in comparison to the tube radius.
Furthermore, the ultrafiltrate velocity, J_v, must not vary along
the tube length (uniform-wall-flux theory). At the centerline or
axis of the fiber, the impermeable solute concentration $C = C_o$
(the entering feed stream concentration), but within the thin
boundary layer C_w for a totally impermeable solute is given by
the following approximate results (4, 5, 6,)

$$C_w = C_o e^{1.219(Pe^2E)^{1/3}} \tag{9}$$

$$Pe = J_v r/(2D) \tag{10}$$

$$E = 2J_v Z/(U_o r) \tag{11}$$

$$= 1-U_Z/U_o \tag{12}$$

$$= Q_v(Z)/Q_B \tag{13}$$

Here Pe is the wall Péclét number, a dimensionless variable for
the radial convective-diffusive process in solution within the
fiber annulus, which should be distinguished from β, the transmembrane Péclét number given previously for transport across the
fiber wall; r is the fiber radius; D is the solute diffusivity
in bulk solution; and E is the extraction ratio at a distance Z
along the fiber from the feed stream entrance of the fiber. As
given by Equation 12, E is the fractional change in average axial
flow (averaged over the fiber cross-sectional area normal to the
axis), where U_Z and U_o are axial flow velocities at Z and the
entrance, respectively. E is also the ratio of total ultrafiltrate flux up to Z, Q_v (Z), to flow rate of feed stream entering
the fiber, Q_B. For the processes considered in this study, Pe
can be thought of as a reduced ultrafiltrate velocity. For the
general cases of solutes with R $\leq$ 1, it can be shown ($\underline{5}$, $\underline{6}$)
that

$$(C_w/C_o)_{R<1} = (C_w/C_o)_{R=1}/[R+(1-R)(C_w/C_o)_{R=1}] \qquad (14)$$

where $(C_w/C_o)_{R<1}$ is the boundary layer modulus when R<1, and
$(C_w/C_o)_{R=1}$ is the modulus given by thin film theory for impermeable
able solutes (Equation 9).

The above equations, after transformation to rectangular
channel geometry and appropriate integration along the channel
length, have been used successfully to correlate R_{obs} with R (σ,β)
for rejection experiments in a flat-plate cell for conditions
where E<0.1 ($\underline{7}$). Equation 14 has also been tested against exact
thin-film film theory for the flat-plate geometry and found to be
in good agreement (within 10%) for R = 1 when Pe^2 E<0.33 and for
R = 0.75 where Pe^2 E<2.7 ($\underline{5}$). A similar theoretical test has not
been performed for the tubular geometry, although an exact theory
for imperfect rejection is available ($\underline{8}$). This theory requires
extensive computation and is not suitable for general data
analysis.

All of the thin-film theories, approximate and exact, are
restricted to the description of developing boundary layers that
have not penetrated to the channel center line. For our experiments at large extraction ratios (E>0.3), the boundary layer is
believed to be fully-developed, i.e., the center line concentration is greater than C_o. Fortunately, there are available simple
analytic forms for the boundary layer modulus that describe both
the developing and fully developed regions ($\underline{9}$, $\underline{10}$). They were
derived for the case of uniform wall-flux ultrafiltration out of
perfectly impermeable (R = 1) tubular membranes. These equations
were examined to see how they could be adapted to the case of
imperfectly rejecting membranes.

For rejection of tracer solutes out of saline solutions, the
uniform-wall-flux restriction is not a problem, because the axial
pressure drop is generally less than 10% of the average transmembrane pressure. Constant J_v with length along the tube is not
expected for experiments with protein solutions because protein

builds up the back osmotic pressure at the wall; π should increase with Z, and J_v should decrease, since $\Delta P \simeq$ constant (Equation 5). Nonetheless, over the range of pressure and axial flows used in our experiments with calf serum and bovine serum albumin, the average J_v at a given ΔP was independent of fiber length, suggesting that the condition of uniform wall flux holds even for protein solutions. Thus, the uniform wall flux equations for developing and fully developed boundary layers were applicable for all experiments.

The analytical forms derived by Dresner (11) for rectangular channels were converted for tubular geometry (9, 10). By comparison with exact results obtained by infinite series methods, a semi-empirical form was derived (12) to extend Dresner's analytical result beyond the entrance region. For our experiments the following results are important:

$$C_w/C_b = 1 + 1.219 \ (Pe^2E)^{1/3}$$

when $Pe^2E < 0.04$ (15)

$$C_w/C_b = 1 + 0.5 \ Pe^2E + 5[1-\exp \ (-Pe^2E/6)^{1/2}]$$

when $Pe^2E > 0.04$ (16)

$$(C_w/C_b)_{AS} = 1 + 0.916 \ Pe + 0.348 \ Pe^2 + 0.592 \ Pe^3$$

where $Pe < 3.3$ (17)

The boundary layer modulus is now C_w/C_b, with C_w reduced by C_b instead of C_o. Here C_b is the local bulk or mixing-cup concentration, the axial flow-weighted average across the fiber cross-section:

$$C_b = \frac{\int CudA}{(UA)}$$

         (18)

where U is the cross-sectional average of the axial velocity at Z. For a perfectly rejecting membrane,

$$C_b = C_o U_o/U$$

         (19)

Equation 17 gives the asymptotic limit of the boundary layer modulus in the far-downstream region of the fully developed region; i.e., for a given value for the wall Péclét number, the modulus C_w/C_b eventually becomes independent of E and hence Z and U_o, and dependent only on Pe and hence J_v. To replace Equations 15 and 16 an exponential form was found to be accurate within 10% for C_w/C_b,

$$C_w/C_b = e^{1.219 \ (Pe^2E)^{1/3}}$$

         (20)

where $Pe^2E < 1.3$.

Graphs for Equations 15, 16, and 20 are shown in Figure 2, and
for Equation 17 in Figure 3. Horizontal lines in Figure 2 represent the asymptotic limit for C_w/C_b for an experiment with a
given Péclét number. For example, for a rejection experiment of
myoglobin from saline solution, $D = 0.172 \times 10^{-5}$ cm/sec, $r =$
0.011 cm, and $J_v = 1.88 \times 10^{-4}$ cm/sec (constant with axial
distance); thus, $Pe = 0.6$. If C_w/C_b were computed with increasing
distance, Z, along the fiber length, or equivalently, with increasing E, then Equation 20 would be used up to the value $(Pe^2 E)^{1/3} =$
0.43, or $E = 0.22$ for the given Péclét number. If $E > 0.22$, then
C_w/C_b would begin losing its dependence on E at $E \gg 0.22$, to reach
eventually a value $(C_w/C_b)_{As} = 1.688$ as given by Equation 17. It
is not clear yet exactly when the switch should be made from
Equation 20 to Equation 17 as integration occurs along the
fiber. Rather rapid "peeling away" (9) occurs from Equations 15
and 16 for $Pe < 2$, but we have not tried to connect the two equations
by a smooth curve for every value of Pe. Instead, in the computations described later, we calculate a critical value for the
extraction ratio, E_c, beyond which the asymptotic form $(C_w/C_b)_{As}$
must be used. The criterion for switching for totally rejected
solutes at a fixed Péclét number is,

$$C_w/C_b \text{ (Eq. 20)} = (C_w/C_b)_{As} \text{ (Eq. 17)} \qquad (21)$$

or

$$E_c = 0.552 \, (1/Pe^2)(Log(C_w/C_b)_{As})^3 \qquad (22)$$

All of the above equations were originally derived for
perfectly rejecting membranes, $R = 1$. For the general case, $R < 1$,
the observation (10) was used that to a good approximation any
boundary layer modulus for imperfect membranes, $(C_w/C_b)_{R<1}$, is
related to that for perfect membranes, $(C_w/C_b)_{R=1}$, by

$$(C_w/C_b)_{R<1} = (C_w/C_b)_{R=1}/[R+(1-R)(C_w/C_b)_{R=1}] \qquad (23)$$

This general and useful equation is identical in form to Equation 14
given earlier for the special case of thin film theory. The
modulus $(C_w/C_b)_{R=1}$ is given by any of the Equations 15 through 17
or 20. It was shown to be accurate within 10% for $R = 0.8$ with
Pe as large as 74 (10) as compared with exact theories for the
developing region. Now, for imperfect membranes, the critical
extraction ratio can be defined as that value for E which causes

$$(C_w/C_b)_{R<1} = (C_w/C_b)_{As, R<1} \qquad (24)$$

This criterion when inserted into Equation 23 algebraically implies the criterion given before for perfect membranes,

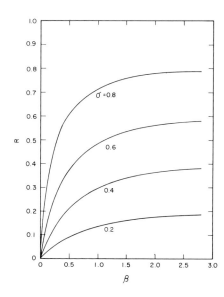

Figure 1. R vs. β for several σ

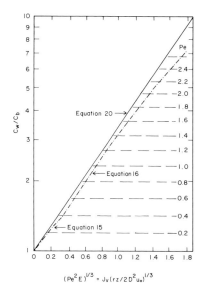

Figure 2. Comparison of equations for uniform wall flux boundary layer modulus

$$(C_w/C_b)_{R=1} \text{ (Eq. 20)} = (C_w/C_b)_{As, R=1} \text{ (Eq. 17)} \tag{25}$$

To summarize, the proposed boundary layer theory for rejection experiments across imperfect membranes involves analytic expressions for two regions of boundary layer development, corrected for R<1 by Equation 23, and corrected by the condition for switching, Equation 22. How integrations are performed to obtain an implicit relation between R_{obs} and R is shown later. Values calculated for R at various values for J_v are then used to calculate σ and P_m for the fiber membrane, according to Equation 7. For experiments with proteins, this theory, together with data for osmotic pressure, also aids in explaining the rather unusual response of ultrafiltration rate to pressure and the virtual independence of this response from fiber length and axial flow velocity. Osmotic pressure data are available in the literature for bovine serum albumin at pH 7.4 (3), and osmotic pressure measurements of moderate accuracy were made by the authors on bovine calf serum.

Data Reduction

Working Equations for Rejection Experiments in Saline. Raw data from the rejection experiments are Q_v (total filtrate rate, cm^3/sec), Q_B (total inlet feed stream flow rate, cm^3/sec), C_o (feed stream inlet concentration, g/cm^3), and $\bar{C}_p$ (average filtrate concentration, g/cm^3). R_{obs} is calculated according to Equation 8, and E_L (total extraction ratio for entire fiber length) is given by Equation 13 with $Q_v(L) = Q_v$. If J_v is constant along the fiber, then it is calculated from

$$J_v = Q_v/(2\pi rLN) \tag{26}$$

where N is the number of fibers per bundle. The average axial velocity is given by

$$U_o = Q_B/(\pi r^2 N) \tag{27}$$

A relation is needed between these measurable quantities and R, the intrinsic rejection coefficient defined by Equation 4. First, J_s^a is defined as the local axial solute flux averaged over the fiber cross-section with axial diffusion negligible,

$$J_s^a = UC_b \tag{28}$$

At the steady state for solute within the fiber,

$$\frac{\partial C_b}{\partial t} = 0 = -\frac{\partial J_s^a}{\partial Z} - 2J_s/r \tag{29}$$

where the last term represents solute loss across the wall. By
using Equation 4 and 6 we find

$$J_s = C_w(1-R)J_v \tag{30}$$

or

$$J_s = (C_w/C_b)C_b(1-R)J_v \tag{31}$$

Also, since total fluid volume within the fiber is conserved,

$$\frac{\partial U}{\partial z} = -2J_v/r \tag{32}$$

After the derivative in Equation 29 is taken by using Equations 31
and 32, the mass balance equation for solute can be written

$$dC_b/C_b = (2J_v/r)[1- (1-R)(C_w/C_b)]dZ/U \tag{33}$$

Integration along the fiber length yields

$$\text{Log } (C_b^L/C_b^o) = (2J_v/r)\int_o^L dZ/U-(1-R)\int_o^L (C_w/C_b)dZ/U \tag{34}$$

R_{obs} is introduced by using another form of the mass balance
equation for the fiber,

$$C_o U_o \pi r^2 = C_b UL\pi r^2 + 2\pi r J_v \bar{C}_p L \tag{35}$$

where

$$\bar{C}_p = (1/L)\int_o^L C_p dz \tag{36}$$

Also, from Equation 8,

$$\bar{C}_p = C_o (1-R_{obs}) \tag{37}$$

Thus Equation 35 can be rearranged to read

$$C_b^L/C_b^o = [1-E_L(1-R_{obs})]/(1-E_L) \tag{38}$$

where we have used (compare Equation 32)

$$U = U_o - 2J_v Z/r \tag{39}$$

and Equation 12 for E_L at $U = U_L$. Therefore, Equation 34 is an
implicit function of R, with C_b^L/C_b^o related to R_{obs} by Equation 38,
and C_w/C_b given by Equation 23. For convenience we integrate
$\int^L dZ/U$ directly using Equation 39, and change variables so that
Equation 34 becomes a function of Pe and E_L:

$$\text{log } [1-E_L (1-R_{obs})] = -(1-R)\int_o^{E_L} (C_w/C_b)_{R<1}dE/(1-E) \tag{40}$$

If for a given experiment a critical length or extraction ratio
exists, i.e., E_c (calculated from Equation 22) $<E_L$, then the
above integration along the fiber length must be done sequentially,
first over the region $0<E<E_c$ where C_w/C_b is given by Equation 23
and 20, then over the asymptotic region $E_c<E<E_L$ where the boundary
layer modulus is given by Equations 23 and 17. The latter integration can be performed analytically, and Equation 40, with all
terms brought on one side, becomes

$$f(R) = 0 = \log[1-E_L(1-R_{obs})] + (1-R)\int_0^{E_c} \frac{(C_w/C_b)dE}{[R+(1-R)(C_w/C_b)](1-E)}$$

$$+ \frac{(1-R)(C_w/C_b)_{As}}{[R+(1-R)(C_w/C_b)_{As}]} \log [(1-E_c)/(1-E_L)] \tag{41}$$

Here C_w/C_b and $(C_w/C_b)_{As}$ are given explicitly by Equations 20 and
17, respectively, and E_c is calculated according to Equation 22
for the given Péclét number. The computational problem is to
find the root R of $f(R)$ at the data point R_{obs}, J_v, E_L. Since no
analytical form was discovered for the integral in Equation 41,
it must be evaluated either numerically or by using an accurate
approximation.

An iterative scheme would involve guessing a value for R,
evaluating the integral and other terms in Equation 41, testing
the calculated value for $f(R)$, and systematically adjusting R
until $f(R)$ is sufficiently close to zero. To find the most
efficient way to evaluate the integral so that an iterative
scheme based on the method of interval halving could be used with
a desk-top computer to calculate R, Simpson's 1/3- rule and the
Gaussian quadrature were tried. About 20 intervals for the 1/3
rule and 5 intervals for the quadrature were sufficient to achieve
better than 0.5% accuracy over the entire range of useful values
for E (0→0.99) and Pe (0→3). A third procedure was tried, called
the "mid-point" approximation. This method leads to an analytic
form for the integral and a consequent quadratic form for $f(R)$
which can be solved algebraically for R. According to the mid-
point method, the average value, $\bar{I}$, of the integral from 0 to E_c
is approximated by the integral evaluated at $E_c/2$,

$$I = \int_0^{E_c} \frac{\exp[1.219(Pe^2E)^{1/3}]dE}{[R+(1-R)\exp(1.219(Pe^2E)^{1/3})](1-E)} = E_c\bar{I} \tag{42}$$

$$\simeq E_c\bar{I}_{mp} = \frac{E_c\exp(1.219(Pe^2E_c/2)^{1/3})}{[R+(1-R)\exp(1.219(Pe^2E_c/2)^{1/3})](1-E_c/2)} \tag{43}$$

Percentage errors in this approximation as a function of E are
illustrated in Figure 4 for Pe = 1.0 and for R = 0.1 and 0.9.

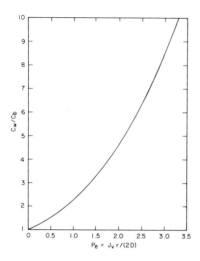

Figure 3.   Asymptotic limit of boundary layer modulus in fully developed region (see Equation 17)

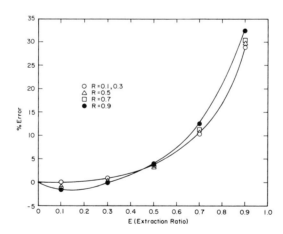

Figure 4.   Errors in I (see Equation 42) incurred by using midpoint approximation at Pe = 1.0

For E less than 0.4 the errors are less than about 2%, a tolerable error for analysis of most of our data. The root R of the
quadratic function f(R), which is obtained when E_c $\bar{I}_{mp}$ is substituted for the integral in Equation 41, is given by Equation 1A
(Appendix A). We used this equation for all of our calculations
including those with E_c >0.4, since sample calculations performed
iteratively and with I evaluated by Simpson's rule, gave final
values of R differing by less than 1% from those found by using
the mid-point approximation for I.

Finding R with either method requires a value for E_c.
Figure 5 is a graph of E_c versus Pe calculated according to
Equation 22. There was some concern about the sensitivity of the
calculated value for R to the choice of E_c. The asymptotic form
for the boundary-layer modulus, Equation 17, was used for $E > E_c$
even though that form is truly exact at $E >> E_c$ for a given wall
Péclét number. Locally, the exponential form for C_w/C_b at $E > E_c$
can be much larger than the asymptotic function, $(C_w/C_b)_{As}$, and
the choice of E_c would seem to be quite critical. But it is the
sum of the integrals along the entire fiber length that helps
determine R, not the local values. To test the sensitivity of R
to the choice of E_c, the sum of integrals in Equation 41 which
help determine R was calculated,

$$I_s = \int_0^{E_A} \frac{(C_w/C_b) dE}{[R+(1-R)(C_w/C_b)](1-E)} + \frac{(C_w/C_b)_{As} \log[(1-E_A)/(1-E_L)]}{[R+(1-R)(C_w/C_b)_{As}]} \quad (44)$$

Here (C_w/C_b) and $(C_w/C_b)_{As}$ are given by Equations 20 and 17,
respectively; E_A is an assumed value for $E > E_c$, and E_L is E for a
given experiment. In Figure 6 is a graph of the percentage error
in I_s incurred by using $E_A > E_c$, $[I_s(E_A) - I_s(E_c)] \times 100/I_s(E_c)$,
versus E_A, for R = 0.5, P_e = 0.5 and E_c = 0.340. Three values of
E_L were used. A remarkable insensitivity to the choice of $E_A > E_c$
is shown for these conditions, which are in the midrange of
values for most of the saline experiments. Thus, although all of
the data was reduced by using Equation 41 with E_c given by
Equation 22, for most experiments the choice of E_c was not critical. Only for values of E_L >0.5 can the choice cause appreciable
error in calculations of R from R_{obs}. In fact, for experiments
with E_L <0.5, the concept of an asymptotic limit could be dispensed
with without affecting calculations of R by much more than the
experimental error in measuring R_{obs}.

Values calculated for the intrinsic rejection coefficient at
each value for J_v were used to find σ and P_m in Equation 7,
according to a Newton-Rhaphson iterative least-squares procedure
previously described (7).

Ultrafiltration Experiments. There is no boundary layer
theory for ultrafiltration of proteins in tubes for the general
case of applied pressures comparable to reverse osmotic pressures.
The process involves complete rejection of protein, and most

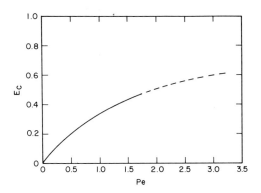

Figure 5. E_c *vs.* Pe

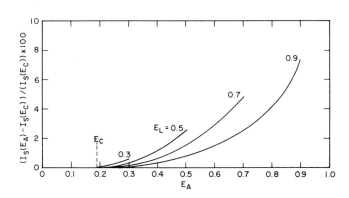

Figure 6.   *Errors incurred by choice of* E_c *for* $R = 0.5$ *and* $Pe = 0.5$

likely, non-uniform wall fluxes. The theory for the pregel
region derived (13) using an integral method comes closest to our·
needs, but it applies to ultrafiltration cells with thin rectangular channels; furthermore, it is limited to the developing boundary
layer region where solute concentration at the center line retains
its original inlet value. A similar theory is needed for tubes,
to extend through the fully developed region. However, as the
presented data shows, the graphs of J_v versus $\bar{P}$ for calf serum
and BSA are remarkably independent of the fiber length and the
axial flow velocity. This independence from length for the
average J_v suggest the possibility that the local J_v is approximately independent of distance Z; consequently the simple equations
from uniform wall flux theory given earlier may be valid for
protein ultrafiltration. The independence from axial velocity
further suggests that the process may be in the asymptotic region
of the fully developed boundary layer, because there C_w is a weak
function of axial velocity and fiber length. The exponential
form for C_w/C_b from uniform-wall-flux theory, (Equation 20) will
not be applicable because according to D'arcy's Law (Equation 5)
a constant J_v with Z would imply a constant π with Z when $\Delta P \simeq$
constant with Z. If π is independent of Z, then so must be the
average wall concentration C_w. But this average would be given
approximately by $\bar{I}_{mp}$, the mid-point approximation (cf. Equation
43 with $R = 1$ for proteins and E_c E_L). A constant $\bar{I}_{mp}$ implies
that $Pe^2 E_L/2 = J_v r Z/(4U_o D^2)$ is independent of Z for a given J_v
and U_o; this requirement is impossible unless D^2 is allowed to
vary directly with Z. It appears then, that the asymptotic
result is the only equation from uniform-wall-flux theory that
can possibly correlate our ultrafiltration data.

The range of Pe for protein as a solute is about 0.5 to 2
for our experiments, implying E_c = 0.2 to 0.5. Extraction ratios,
E_L, for most experiments were below this range, and asymptotic
behavior would not normally be expected on the basis of uniform-
wall-flux theory. However, the strong dependence of π on C for
protein solutions may result in a rapid buildup of solute and
back osmotic pressure immediately downstream from the fiber
entrance; this buildup opposes the constant applied pressure to
obtain a nearly uniform wall flux and asymptotic boundary layer
for most of the fiber length.

Analytic expressions for the protein osmotic pressure were
needed to test the applicability of uniform wall flux theory.
Vilker's data (3) at pH 7.4 were used for BSA, interpolated over
our range of interest and converted to our concentration units
(g/1 of solution) by using a protein partial specific volume of
0.746 cm^3/g. The data were fit by the method of least squares to
a polynomial; the resultant expression for BSA at 37°C is

$$\pi(atm) = 3.464 \times 10^{-4} C \, (1 + 1.284 \times 10^{-2}C + 1.135 \times 10^{-5}C^2 +$$
$$2.078 \times 10^{-7}C^3) \tag{45}$$

Our own osmotic pressure data for calf serum at 37°C can be expressed by a 2-parameter power series (14).

$$\pi(\text{atm}) = (25.451/M)C(1+\Gamma C + 0.625\Gamma^2 C^2 + 0.2869\Gamma^3 C^3 +$$
$$0.1103\Gamma^4 C^4 + 0.03806\Gamma^5 C^5 + 0.0138\Gamma^6 C^6) \qquad (46)$$

where

$C < 340$ g/l

$(M = 53438, \ \Gamma = 3.574 \times 10^{-3} \ 1/g)$

Graphs of π versus C for calf serum and BSA are shown in Figure 7. No exact theory for protein ultrafiltration is available to test the asymptotic theory against; therefore, its validity can only be inferred by how well it correlates data. The test of the data used only one adjustable parameter, the protein diffusivity. The value calculated for D for BSA systems was compared with that in the literature. For calf serum there are no published diffusion data, and internal consistancy of results was the primary criterion for success. A patterned search program was used to find the least value of the sum $\Sigma[(\overline{P} - \overline{P}_{Calc})/\overline{P}]_i^2$ for several sets of values for $\overline{J}_v$ and $\overline{P}$ measured at a given axial velocity flow through a particular hollow-fiber bundle. $\overline{P}_{calc}$ is defined by a rearrangement of Equation 5,

$$\Delta P = \overline{P}_{calc} = \overline{J}_v/L_p + \pi \qquad (47)$$

where L_p is the hydraulic conductivity measured separately in saline solution. To start the search, values for Pe were calculated at each data point by using an initial guess for protein diffusivity, D. Equation 17 was then used to find C_w, with the arithmetic mean for the bulk concentration (between inlet and exit) related to the known inlet concentration by

$$\overline{C}_b = C_o(1-0.5 \ E_L)/(1-E_L) \qquad (48)$$

Resultant values for C_w were used to calculate π according to Equations 46 or 47, which led to values for $\overline{P}_{calc}$ (Equation 47) to be used in the least-squares sum. According to its internal criterion, the patterned-search program then systematically changed D until its optimum value was found for the given set of several measured values for J_v and $\overline{P}$.

Rejection Coefficients for Protein Ultrafiltration Experiments. Since the data for ultrafiltration rates seem to imply the condition of uniform wall flux, the calculation procedure for finding R for these experiments was identical with that used for saline solutions. No doubt the diffusivity of the small solutes within

the concentrated protein boundary layer will differ from that
used for saline systems, but in the absence of factual knowledge
of that difference the saline values for D for each solute were
used.

Experimental

Samples. Cuproammonium cellulose fibers made by Enka
Glanzstoff AG were used in the study. The fibers designated
Cuprophan HDF, (Table I) are intended for application in hemofiltration and generally are characterized by having 5 to 10
times the hydraulic permeability of similar fibers made for
hemodialysis. Fiber samples were tested in dog-bone shaped
experimental dialyzers having fiber lengths of 20.5 cm and filament
numbers of 2940, 5870, and 8800. With a nominal inside fiber
diameter of 0.0215 cm, surface areas of these devices were
0.4 m^2, 0.8 m^2, and 1.2 m^2. Fibers were also tested as small
test bundles containing up to 250 filaments and lengths from 10
to 40 cm.

TABLE I. PROPERTIES OF CUPROPHAN FIBER BUNDLES

Bundle number	Number of fibers N	I.D. cm	O.D. cm	Length cm	Area cm^2	$Lp \times 10^5$ cm/atm-5
I	160	0.0263	0.0326	11.5	132	23.1
II	160	0.0263	0.0326	18.5	245	23.1
III	160	0.0263	0.0326	41.5	549	23.1
IV	8800	0.0263	0.0326	20.5	1.49×10^4	22.5
V	160	0.0259	0.0336	20	260	44

Measurement of J_v and R. To test solute rejection and
volumetric flux by the walls of hollow fiber potted in small test
bundles, the device shown in Figure 8 was used. The solute was
circulated from a nitrogen pressurized reservoir through the
fiber bundle and returned. Circulation was effected by a calibrated peristaltic pump. A bubble trap was provided at the inlet
header, and the inlet pressure and return pressure were measured
with calibrated test gauges. The exterior of the fibers was set
at atmospheric pressure, and transmembrane pressure was calculated
from the mean of the inlet and outlet pressure. By using the
pressurized reservoir, transmembrane pressure and axial flow rate
were varied independently. Ultrafiltrate was collected in a
tared weighing dish so that flux could be calculated from the
collection time and final mass of the dish. This gravimetric
flux determination gave higher precision (for the small sample
collected in these studies) than a volumetric method. The solute
reservoir and ultrafiltrate collection vessel were immersed in a
37°C water bath.

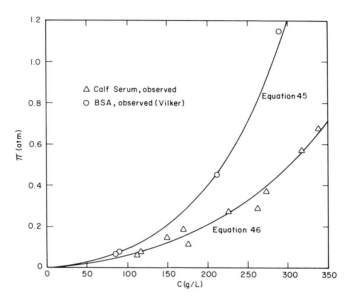

Figure 7.   Osmotic pressure for calf serum and BSA

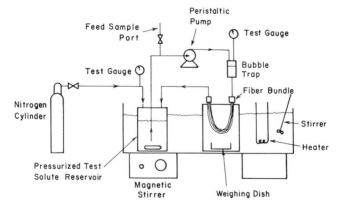

Figure 8.   Schematic of apparatus used to test bundles

Test solutes were dissolved in 0.85% NaCl stabilized with
200 ppm NaN_3. The rejection of four test solutes was measured:

	MW	Concentration	$D \times 10^5$ (cm^2/u)
Vitamin B-12	1355	0.005%	0.379
Myoglobin	17000	0.01%	0.172
Inulin	5200	0.01%	0.215
Cytochrome C	13500	0.01%	0.198

Vitamin B-12 and myoglobin and inulin and cytochrome C were
paired in solution so that only two separate solutions had to be
filtered. Vitamin B-12, myoglobin, and cytochrome C (Sigma
Chemical Co.) concentrations were followed spectrophotometrically,
and inulin was followed by liquid scintillation counting of the
C-14 labeled tracer (New England Nuclear). Vitamin B-12 absorbance
was read at 361 nm maximum and myoglobin was read at 415 nm. To
separate the small absorbance overlap for these two solutes at
their respective peak maximums, simultaneous equations describing
the total absorbance were solved by using independently measured
absorptivity coefficients for each pure solute. Cytochrome C
absorbance at 410 nm was used for analysis. Rejection data were
collected as a function of transmembrane volumetric flux (J_v).
The volumetric flux was calculated from the test bundle surface
area and rate of ultrafiltration.

The observed rejection (R_{obs}) was calculated from the solute
concentration in the recirculating reservoir C_o and ultrafiltrate
$\overline{C}_p$ using Equation 2:

$$R_{obs} = 1 - (\overline{C}_p/C_o) \tag{49}$$

The UFR and solute rejection for test dialyzers were measured
by using the experimental apparatus shown in Figure 9. The test
solution containing either vitamin B-12 and myoglobin or inulin
and cytochrome C in saline solution was circulated by a variable
speed peristaltic pump. A calibrated Rotometer was used to
measure feed solution flow rate. Pressures on the inlet and
outlet flow streams were measured by test gauges. Care was taken
to maintain the solution level in bubble traps even with the
dialyzer midpoint and solution in the reservoir to avoid syphoning
effects. The ultrafiltrate flow was continuously measured by
another calibrated flow meter placed in the collection tube.
Transmembrane pressure was varied by a metering valve restricting
the feed solution return line flow. The test solution reservoir
contained 2 liters of solution; it was immersed in a waterbath
and continuously stirred by means of a magnetic stirrer. Solute
concentration in the feed solution and ultrafiltrate was analyzed
after the system had come to equilibrium. Ultrafiltrate flow
rate, and feed inlet and outlet pressures were read just before
the samples were withdrawn for analysis. A sample volume of only
0.5 ml was required for analysis.

Each test dialyzer was evaluated at inlet feed flow rates of
200, 300, and 400 ml/min and transmembrane pressures up to 22 psi

(1.5 atm). From this data set, the following parameters can be calculated: ultrafiltration rate Q_v (ml/sec), volumetric flux J_v = Q_v/A (cm/sec), observed rejection R_{obs} = $1 - (\overline{C}_p/C_o)$, and feed flow rate Q_B (ml/sec).

In both the test dialyzers and test bundles, the solvent used was 0.85% saline buffered with sodium phosphate (0.05M) or membrane filtered (0.45 μm) fetal calf serum (Biologicals, Kansas City) (6-7% protein). Protein analysis was performed by the method of Lowry.

Measurement of Osmotic Pressure. Osmotic pressure as a function of serum protein concentration was measured by a membrane technique. Bovine calf serum solutions containing varying protein concentrations from 3.85 g/100 ml of solution to 41.7 g/100 ml of solution were prepared by dilution or concentration from normal bovine calf serum. The concentrated solutions were prepared by ultrafiltration using a stirred cell (Amicon Model 52) loaded with a high flux Cuprophan membrane (molecular weight cut off <20,000 Daltons). The solutions were assayed for total protein by the method of Lowery and were then loaded into smaller stirred cell (Amicon Model 12), and the ultrafiltration rate was measured at varying applied pressures. During this measurement, changes in protein concentration due to fluid loss were minimzed by use of a micropipet to collect ultrafiltrate. The low ultrafiltration rate used in these experiments and high shear achieved in the small radius rapidly stirred (1200 rpm) cell effectively minimized boundary layer concentrations of protein at the membrane wall as shown by linear plots of ultrafiltration rate (ml/sec) as a function of applied pressure. From these plots the osmotic pressure at each protein concentration was obtained as the abscissa intercept (Q_v = 0). All data were taken at 37°C.

Results

Rejection Experiments. In Figures 10 through 15 and in Table II, typical data of rejection versus J_v are given for four solutes in saline and serum systems. For myoglobin and cytochrome C the observed values for R (open circles and triangles) rise to a maximum and then fall off with further increase in J_v. Experiments with inulin and B-12 (open squares and x's) were not performed at sufficiently high volume fluxes to produce maxima in R_{obs}. Corrected values for R, calculated from observed values by using Equation 41, are entered on the graphs as shaded or closed circles, triangles, etc. If the boundary layer theory is valid, then according to Figure 1 for the Spiegler-Kedem equation, each graph of R (corrected) versus J_v should asymptotically approach a horizontal line, R → σ, at large J_v, and vary linearly with J_v as J_v → 0. This behavior is followed by myoglobin and cytochrome C in serum, and for inulin and B-12 in saline. Anomalous behavior is shown by inulin and B-12 in serum: The graphs intersect the J_v-axis far short of the origin at J_v = 0. In saline the corrected values for R for myoglobin and cytochrome C tend to eventually

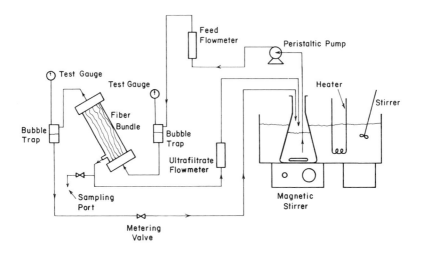

Figure 9.   Schematic of apparatus used for test dialyzers

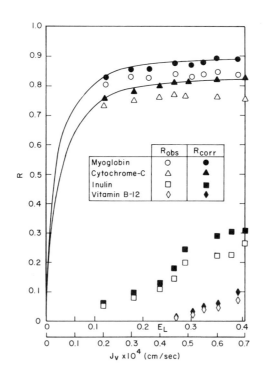

Figure 10.   R vs. J_v in serum: L = 41.5; U_o = 0.92 cm/s; L_p = 23.1 × 10^{-5}

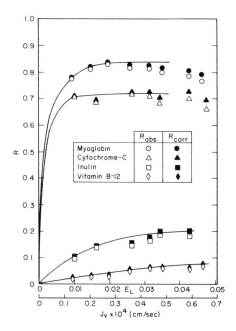

Figure 11.   R *vs.* J_v *in saline:* L $=$ *18.5;*
$U_o =$ *3.06 cm/s;* $L_p =$ *23.1* $\times$ *10^{-5}*

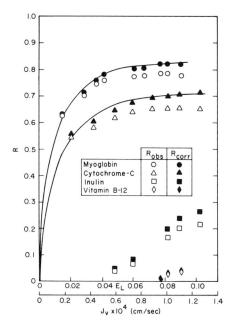

Figure 12.   R *vs.* J_v *in serum:* L $=$ *20*
cm; $U_o =$ *3.06 cm/s;* $L_p =$ *44* $\times$ *10^{-5}*

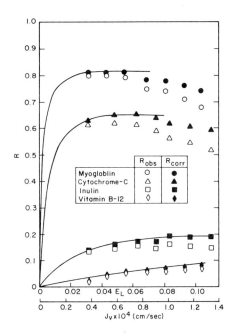

Figure 13. R *vs.* J_v *in saline:* L $= 20$ *cm;* $U_o = 3.06$ *cm/s;* $L_p = 44 \times 10^{-5}$

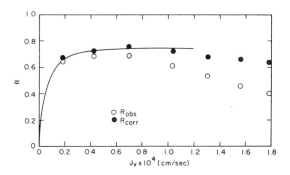

Figure 14. R *vs.* J_v *for myoglobin in saline:* L $= 20.5$*;* $U_o = 0.70$ *cm/s;* $L_p = 22.5 \times 10^{-5}$

TABLE II. DATA FROM REJECTION EXPERIMENTS

P(O)	P(L)	$\bar{P}$	$Q_v \times 10^3$	R_{obs}	Pe	E_c	E_L	R	R_{TF}
			atmospheres cm³/s						

System 3, Bundle III: Myoglobin in Serum
$Q_B = 0.082$ cm³/s

P(O)	P(L)	$\bar{P}$	$Q_v \times 10^3$	R_{obs}	Pe	E_c	E_L	R	R_{TF}
0.197	0.163	0.180	10.1	0.808	0.0703	0.029	0.123	0.827	0.820
0.279	0.245	0.262	14.3	0.828	0.0996	0.041	0.174	0.853	0.844
0.361	0.340	0.351	17.5	0.826	0.122	0.050	0.213	0.856	0.845
0.497	0.470	0.484	21.8	0.840	0.152	0.062	0.266	0.874	0.862
0.592	0.579	0.586	24.5	0.829	0.171	0.069	0.299	0.870	0.855
0.722	0.708	0.715	26.5	0.837	0.185	0.075	0.323	0.879	0.864
0.824	0.824	0.824	28.8	0.845	0.201	0.081	0.351	0.889	0.873
0.960	0.960	0.960	32.2	0.837	0.224	0.090	0.393	0.889	0.870

System 14, Bundle V: Cytochrome -C in Saline
$Q_B = 0.263$ cm³/s

P(O)	P(L)	$\bar{P}$	$Q_v \times 10^3$	R_{obs}	Pe	E_c	E_L	R	R_{TF}
0.116	0.054	0.085	5.3	0.546	0.067	0.028	0.020	0.560	0.557
0.225	0.157	0.191	9.2	0.580	0.116	0.048	0.035	0.603	0.598
0.334	0.265	0.300	12.8	0.617	0.161	0.066	0.049	0.647	0.641
0.449	0.388	0.419	15.8	0.640	0.199	0.080	0.060	0.677	0.669
0.572	0.511	0.542	18.9	0.652	0.238	0.095	0.072	0.695	0.686
0.694	0.647	0.671	21.8	0.656	0.274	0.109	0.083	0.705	0.695
0.810	0.762	0.786	23.6	0.655	0.297	0.117	0.090	0.708	0.697
0.967	0.939	0.953	26.9	0.652	0.338	0.132	0.102	0.713	0.700

System 10, Bundle IV: Inulin in Saline
$Q_B = 6.67$ cm³/s

P(O)	P(L)	$\bar{P}$	$Q_v \times 10^3$	R_{obs}	Pe	E_c	E_L	R	R_{TF}
0.113	0.077	0.095	333	0.087	0.068	0.029	0.050	0.093	0.092
0.192	0.159	0.178	525	0.103	0.108	0.045	0.079	0.121	0.112
0.263	0.236	0.250	775	0.139	0.159	0.065	0.116	0.163	0.156
0.344	0.317	0.331	1000	0.139	0.205	0.083	0.150	0.171	0.162
0.401	0.377	0.389	1208	0.146	0.248	0.099	0.181	0.187	0.175
0.472	0.447	0.460	1442	0.153	0.296	0.117	0.216	0.206	0.182
0.540	0.514	0.527	1642	0.180	0.337	0.132	0.246	0.251	0.227
0.603	0.579	0.605	1883	0.165	0.386	0.149	0.282	0.242	0.217
0.675	0.653	0.664	2133	0.158	0.438	0.167	0.320	0.245	0.216
0.739	0.710	0.725	2383	0.134	0.489	0.184	0.357	0.223	0.192

decrease at higher values for J_v. Whether these are theoretical
or experimental anomalies cannot be ascertained, especially for
the complex serum systems where the assumption of uniform-wall-
flux is not likely to be entirely valid. However, in saline
systems this assumption probably is valid, since $P(0) - P(L) << \overline{P}$
(Table II). Failure of the boundary layer theory at large values
for J_v is probably because $(C_w/C_b)_{R<1}$ cannot be simply and accurately related to $(C_w/C_b)_{R=1}$ by Equation 23.
    In calculations of σ and P_m from values for R and J_v anoma-
lous data points, such as R for myoglobin, Figure 11, for
$J_v > 0.4 \times 10^{-4}$ cm/sec were not used. Data subject to this exclusion procedure such as those shown in Table II were used to calculate values for σ and P_m given in Table III. Since fiber
bundles I through IV are composed of fibers with essentially the
same L_p, they are expected to have similar transport properties.
    Fiber bundle V, with an L_p almost twice that of the other
bundles, has values for σ and P_m for the four solutes that are
only slightly less than that found for bundles I through IV. For
all bundles, the relatively large uncertainties in σ and P_m for
inulin and B-12 result from the low transmembrane Péclét numbers,
β, for those solutes, which makes it difficult to reach the
plateau region of the R versus J_v graph where σ can be determined
with greater accuracy. Conversely, it is difficult to get good
accuracy in P_m for large solutes, because β will be large even at
small J_v and the graph of R versus J_v will have few points in the
rapidly rising region near the origin.
    For high-flux membranes, it is difficult to get independent
measurements of P_m from a "pure" diffusion experiment where
solution circulates through the fiber lumen, since appreciable
convective flux will always accompany diffusion. For the low-
flux dialysis membranes of an earlier study (7) a comparison was
possible between values for P_m measured independently in diffusion
and rejection experiments; the agreement was good, implying
probable accuracy to the present results which were also obtained
by curve-fitting to the Spiegler-Kedem equation.
    The effect of serum on rejection of solutes, as compared
with rejection measured out of saline, can be addressed in light
of data for cellulosic membranes. Figures 10 and 11 demonstrate
an effect consistently observed for the solutes myoglobin and
cytochrome C. The observed and corrected rejection values fell
off at approximately $J_v > 0.6 \times 10^{-4}$ cm/sec from a plateau when
saline was the solvent, whereas in serum the R versus J_v graphs
were as predicted from the Spiegler-Kedem equation. The relative
effects of serum or BSA on R_{obs}, and on resultant values for σ
and P_m for the two large solutes, are small. For cytochrome C in
serum and saline the difference between values is at most 11%,
and for myoglobin the difference is about 4% (Table III). In
summary, protein in the solvent results in negligibly small
increases in solute rejection by the cellulosic membranes studied
in this work.
    Finally, we note the rather small differences given in
Table II between R calculated according to uniform-wall-flux

TABLE III. VALUES FOR σ AND P_m MEASURED IN REJECTION EXPERIMENTS.

System No.	Bundle No.	Solvent	U_0 cm/s	B-12 σ	B-12 $P_m \times 10^4$	Inulin σ	Inulin $P_m \times 10^4$	Cytochrome-C σ	Cytochrome-C $P_m \times 10^4$	Myoglobin σ	Myoglobin $P_m \times 10^4$
1	I	Serum	0.92	0.10 ± 0.39	1.10 ± 6.4	–	–	0.79 ± 0.02	0.04 ± 0.01	0.84 ± 0.05	0.05 ± 0.01
2	I	Serum	3.06	–	–	–	–	0.82 ± 0.01	0.04 ± 0.01	0.89 ± 0.03	0.03 ± 0.03
3	II	Serum	0.92	–	–	–	–	0.85 ± 0.02	0.06 ± 0.03	0.88 ± 0.02	0.04 ± 0.01
4	II	Serum	3.06	–	–	–	–	0.83 ± 0.03	0.05 ± 0.01	0.87 ± 0.01	0.02 ± 0.01
5	II	Saline	3.06	0.14 ± 0.02	0.90 ± 0.60	0.24 ± 0.03	0.28 ± 0.10	0.72 ± 0.01	0.01 ± 0.02	0.84 ± 0.01	0.01 ± 0.01
6	III	Serum	0.92	–	–	–	–	0.83 ± 0.04	0.04 ± 0.02	0.89 ± 0.05	0.04 ± 0.02
7	III	Serum	3.06	–	–	–	–	0.82 ± 0.03	0.04 ± 0.02	0.91 ± 0.03	0.04 ± 0.01
8	IV	BAS (0.5%)	1.40	0.24 ± 0.16	1.30 ± 1.26	–	–	–	–	0.81 ± 0.02	0.03 ± 0.02
9	IV	BAS (10%)	0.70	–	–	–	–	–	–	0.86 ± 0.03	0.02 ± 0.02
10	IV	Saline	1.40	0.18 ± 0.11	1.70 ± 1.79	0.31 ± 0.17	0.70 ± 0.66	0.63 ± 0.07	0.09 ± 0.09	0.77 ± 0.03	0.02 ± 0.02
11	IV	Saline	0.70	0.10 ± 0.03	0.86 ± 0.69	0.62 ± 1.27	1.73 ± 4.28	0.66 ± 0.06	0.07 ± 0.04	0.76 ± 0.04	0.04 ± 0.02
12	V	Serum	0.92	–	–	–	–	0.75 ± 0.05	0.09 ± 0.03	0.85 ± 0.05	0.07 ± 0.03
13	V	Serum	3.06	–	–	–	–	0.73 ± 0.03	0.10 ± 0.03	0.84 ± 0.03	0.09 ± 0.03
14	V	Saline	3.06	0.11 ± 0.04	0.81 ± 0.60	0.25 ± 0.05	0.55 ± 0.30	0.71 ± 0.10	0.06 ± 0.08	0.82 ± 0.02	0.03 ± 0.02

theory, and R_{TF}, calculated from the R_{obs} according to Equations 8,
9 (with $E = E_L^{TF}/2$), and 14. Appreciable differences occurr only
for $E_L > 0.2$.

Protein Ultrafiltration Experiments. In Table IV and in
Figures 16 through 19, typical data obtained in ultrafiltration
experiments with serum and BSA are shown. Values for π in
Table IV were calculated by using a rearrangement of Equation 5,

$$\bar{\pi} = \bar{P} - J_v/L_p \tag{50}$$

with $\bar{P} = \Delta P$, the average transmembrane pressure and J_v the average
filtrate velocity. Graphs of π versus C for serum and BSA
(Figure 7) were used to calculate the average wall concentration,
C_w, which produced the reverse-osmotic pressure and the consequent
reduction of filtrate velocity of protein systems below that
obtained in saline at comparable pressures (cf dashed lines in
Figures 16 through 18). For pressures applied in those systems,
C_w never was larger than about 350 g/ℓ for serum or BSA. For BSA
the solubility has been independently measured to be about 580
g/ℓ (17), well above the estimated wall concentrations in our
experiments. Also, the graphs of J_v versus $\bar{P}$ never reach a
horizontal plateau region where J_v becomes independent of $\bar{P}$.
Therefore, there can be no justification for invoking a gel-layer
hypothesis to explain the observed graphs of J_v versus $\bar{P}$. Instead,
as explained previously, a boundary layer theory must be used to
predict C_w, π, and hence J_v at the given operating conditions.

The remarkable independence of the J_v versus $\bar{P}$ graphs from
axial velocity and fiber length, illustrated in Figures 14 through
17, suggests the existance of an asymptotic boundary layer region
of fully developed flow. Calculated values for D, obtained by
using the uniform-wall-flux are shown in Tables V and VI. For
serum, data points for $\bar{P} > 0.5$ atm were excluded; for BSA, data
points at all pressures were included to calculate D. For serum
(Table V) there is a small trend to increase D while increasing L
and decreasing U_o, but an average value, $D = 1.41 \times 10^{-7}$ cm^3/sec,
correlates all of the serum data for bundles I-III well for
$\bar{P} < 0.5$ atm (cf solid lines in Figures 14 and 15). Results for D
calculated from data for BSA at four concentrations are shown in
Table VI. There is a definite and strong increase of D with C_o,
but again, as with calf serum, only a small dependence on U_o.
Except for D at $C_o = 195$ g/ℓ, the calculated diffusivities are
below the range $6-8 \times 10^{-7}$ previously measured for BSA by a
light-scattering technique (15).

Lines drawn in Figure 18 were calculated by using the respective values for D at each concentration. The tangential approach
of the curve for $C_o = 5$ g/ℓ to the curve obtained with saline
supports the view that these cellulosic membranes do not strongly
absorb proteins on their surface.

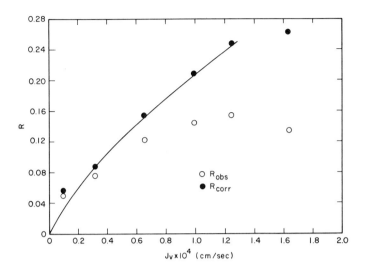

Figure 15. R *vs.* J$_v$ *for insulin in saline:* L $= 20.5$; U$_o = 0.70$ cm/s; L $= 22.5 \times$ 10^{-5}

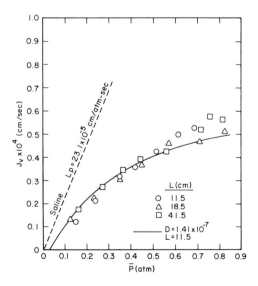

Figure 16. J$_v$ *vs.* P *for calf serum through fibers of three lengths at* U$_o = 0.92$ cm/s

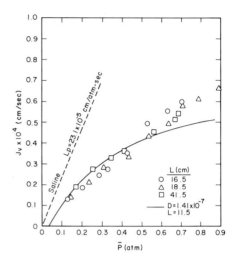

Figure 17. J_v vs. $\overline{P}$ for calf serum through fibers of three lengths at $U_0 = 3.06$ cm/s

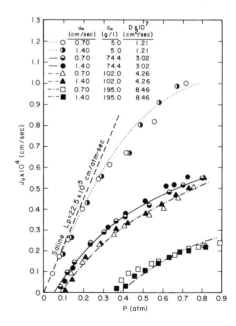

Figure 18. J_v vs. $\overline{P}$ for BSA in large ENKA bundle

TABLE IV. TYPICAL DATA FROM ULTRAFILTRATION EXPERIMENTS

P(0)	P(L) atmospheres	$\bar{P}$	$Q_v \times 10^3$ cm^3/s	$\bar{\Pi}$ atm	$\bar{C}_w$ g/l
\multicolumn{6}{c}{Bundle III: 55.7 g/l Calf Serum at $U^O = 0.92$ cm/s}
0.184	0.143	0.164	9.6	0.088	123
0.285	0.252	0.269	14.8	0.152	166
0.381	0.347	0.364	19.0	0.214	202
0.470	0.442	0.456	21.4	0.287	237
0.579	0.545	0.562	23.3	0.378	269
0.722	0.708	0.715	28.6	0.489	301
0.824	0.810	0.817	31.1	0.572	320
0.967	0.967	0.967	33.8	0.700	348
\multicolumn{6}{c}{Bundle IV: 74.4 g/l BSA (pH 7.4) at $U^O = 0.70$ cm/s}
0.108	0.068	0.088	40	0.076	92
0.140	0.099	0.119	145	0.076	92
0.174	0.135	0.155	213	0.091	100
0.255	0.223	0.240	355	0.133	121
0.321	0.287	0.304	433	0.174	137
0.379	0.349	0.364	512	0.211	151
0.426	0.391	0.408	542	0.246	162
0.546	0.516	0.531	625	0.344	189
0.647	0.615	0.631	722	0.416	203
0.715	0.684	0.700	767	0.471	215
0.813	0.785	0.800	817	0.555	228

TABLE V. PROTEIN DIFFUSIVITIES CALCULATED FROM
ULTRAFILTRATION DATA FOR CALF SERUM

Bundle	L (cm)	Uo (cm/s) 0.92	Uo (cm/s) 3.06	
I	11.5	1.39	1.20	$D \times 10^7$
II	18.5	1.47	1.36	(cm^2/s)
III	41.5	1.57	1.48	

TABLE VI. BSA DIFFUSIVITIES CALCULATED FROM
ULTRAFILTRATION DATA OBTAINED IN BUNDLE IV

Cl (g/1)	Uo (cm/s) .70	Uo (cm/s) 1.40	
5.0	1.21	1.15	$D \times 10^7$
74.4	3.02	2.97	(cm^2/s)
102	4.26	4.03	
195	8.46	7.02	

Conclusions

The boundary-layer theory used here to correct observed
rejection coefficients is an improvement over thin-film theory,
but it appears limited to filtrate velocities, J_v, below about
0.5×10^{-4} cm/sec for highly rejected solutes. An exact theory
for incomplete rejection by hollow fibers is needed to define the
validity of Equation 23, over the range of conditions of the
experiments.

As a one-parameter correlation of ultrafiltration data at a
given C_o, the osmotic/asymptotic method does an excellent job.
The parameter, D, calculated is probably strongly related to a
true protein diffusivity, but an exact boundary layer theory for
protein solutions is needed to accurately establish that relationship. However, irrespective of a theoretical explanation, the
observed independence of graphs of J_v versus $\overline{P}$ from axial velocity
and fiber length is a new region of the protein ultrafiltration
process that should be investigated further.

It seems clear from the rejection and ultrafiltration data
that there is no appreciable protein adsorption on the cellulosic
fibers. The transport properties measured in saline are of good
predictive value for both serum and BSA experiments.

LIST OF SYMBOLS

J_v Transmembrane filtrate velocity (cm/s)
L_p Membrane hydraulic conductivity (cm/atm-s)
P Hydrostatic pressure (atm)
Π Solution osmotic pressure (atm)
C_p Solute concentration in filtrate (g/cm^3, g/l)
C_w Solute concentration at feedstream-membrane interface
        (g/cm^3, g/l)
J_s Transmembrane solute flux (g/cm^2-s)
σ Reflection or Staverman coefficient
R Rejection coefficient (Equation 4)
P_m Diffusive permeability coefficient (cm/s)
β Transmembrane Péclét number (Equation 3)
R_{obs} Observed rejection coefficient (Equation 8)
C_o Solute concentration in feedstream (g/cm^3, g/l)
C_b Bulk or mixing-pot concentration (g/cm^3,g/l)
P_e Wall Péclét number (Equation 10)
r Fiber radius (cm)
D Solute diffusivity in solution (cm^2/s)
Z Distance along fiber axis (cm)
U_o Average axial velocity of entering feedstream (cm/s)
U_z Average axial velocity of feedstream at axial position Z
        (cm/s)
E Extraction ratio up to axial position Z (Equations 11 - 13)
Q_v Filtrate flow rate (cm^3/s)
Q_B Entering feedstream flow rate (cm^3/s)
E_c Critical extraction ratio (Equation 22)
L Length of fiber (cm)
N Number of fibers per bundle
$J_s{}^a$ Average axial solute flux (g/cm^2-s)
E_L Extraction ratio over entire length of fiber
I Integral, defined by (Equation 42)

Appendix

Equation 43 for the integral I is inserted into Equation 41, the substitution:

$$R = \delta/(1+\delta) \qquad (1A)$$

is introduced, and the positive root of F (δ) is found:

$$\delta = (-b+(b^2-4c)^{\frac{1}{2}})/2 \qquad (2A)$$

$$b = \Theta(1+E_c/(1-E_c/2)G)+(C_w/C_b)_{as}(1-B/G) \qquad (3A)$$

$$c = \Theta(C_w/C_b)_{as}[1-B/G+E_c/(1-E_c/2)G] \qquad (4A)$$

$$G = \log \left[1 - E_L(1 - R_{obs})\right] \qquad (5A)$$

$$B = \log \left[(1 - E_L)/(1 - E_c)\right] \qquad (6A)$$

$$\Theta = e^{1.29(Pe^2 E_c/2)^{1/3}} \qquad (7A)$$

Abstract

Solute rejection for four solutes and ultrafiltration rates for two protein solutions have been measured for high-flux cellulosic hollow-fiber bundles of three lengths.

Myoglobin, cytochrome-C, inulin, and vitamin B-12 were the solutes studied in saline, calf serum, and BSA systems at 37°C and pH 7.4. Observed solute rejections were corrected to intrinsic values by using uniform-wall-flux boundary layer theory for the developing and fully-developed asymptotic regions. The Spiegler-Kedem equation (1) for rejection versus volume flow was used to calculate reflection coefficients and diffusive permeabilities for each solute. There was no significant difference between rejection parameters measured in saline and protein solutions.

Ultrafiltration velocities of the protein solutions at each transmembrane pressure showed a remarkable independence from fiber length (L) and axial flow velocity (U_o). This new region of the hemofiltration process is distinguished from the familiar pregel and gel regions where ultrafiltration velocities depend strongly on L and U_o. Data for this new region were successfully correlated at a given protein concentration by using osmotic pressure data and the equation from uniform-wall-flux theory for boundary layer concentrations in the asymptotic region of fully developed flow. The one floating parameter, D (protein diffusivity), in this correlation had a smaller value than expected for BSA and depended strongly on the concentration of BSA.

Acknowledgment

This work was supported by Contract NO1-AM-2-2221 from the Artificial Kidney-Chronic Uremia Program of the National Institute of Arthritis, Metabolism and Digestive Diseases, National Institute of Health.

The authors are grateful to W.N. Gill of The State University of New York at Buffalo for his suggestion to use uniform-wall-flux-boundary-layer theory in the developing and asymptotic regions, together with the relation between $(C_w/C_b)_{R<1}$ and $(C_w/C_b)_{R=1}$, to analyze rejection data. The authors also appreciate the helpful interest of M.R. Doshi of the Institute of Paper Chemistry in the protein ultrafiltration work and gratefully acknowledge the help of P. Beduerftig, T. Sulli, J. Hamaker, and J. Harrell for their help in the preparation of this manuscript.

Literature Cited

1. Spiegler, K.S., and Kedem, O., Desalination, 1966, 1, 327.

2. Johnson, J.S.,Jr., Dresner, J., and Kraus, K.A., "Hyperfiltra-
    tion (Reverse Osmosis)," in "Principles of Desalination,"
    K.S. Spiegler (Ed.), Academic Press: New York, 1966.

3. Vilker, V.L., "The Ultrafiltration of Biological Macromole-
    cules," Ph.D. Thesis, MIT, Cambridge, Mass., 1976.

4. Bird, R.B., Stewart, W.E., and Lightfoot, E.N., "Transport
    Phenomena," John Wiley: New York, 1970.

5. Dorzansky, L.J., "An Experimental Study of Reverse Osmosis
    in a Horizontal Tube: Combined Free and Forced Convection,"
    Ph.D. Thesis, Clarkson College of Technology, Potsdam, New
    York, 1973.

6. Derzansky, L.J., and Gill, W.N., A I Ch E J, 1974, 20, 751.

7. Wendt, R.P., E. Klein, Bresler, E.H., Holland, F.F., Serino,
    R.M., and Villa, H., J. Membrane Sci 1979, 5, 23.

8. Mastrominico, C., "Reverse Osmosis in Laminar Flow in Annuli,"
    M.S. Thesis, Clarkson College of Technology, Potsdam, New
    York, 1968.

9. Sherwood, T.K., Brian, P.L.T., Fisher, R.E., and Dresner,
    L., Ind. Eng. Chem. Fund., 1965, 4, 113.

10. Gill, W.N., Derzansky, L.J., and Dishi, M.R., "Convective
    Diffusion in Laminar and Turbulent Flow Hyperfiltration
    (Reverse Osmosis) Systems," in "Surface and Colloid Science,"
    Vol. 4, E. Matijeric (Ed.), Wiley-Interscience: New York,
    1971.

11. Dresner, L., "Boundary Layer Buildup in the Demineralization
    of Salt Water by Reverse Osmosis," Oak Ridge National Labora-
    tory Report 3621, 1964.

12. Fisher, R.E., Sherwood, T.K., and Brian, P.L.T., "Salt
    Concentration at the Surface of Tubular Reverse Osmosis
    Membranes," Office of Saline Water, U.S. Department of the
    Interior, Research and Development Progress Report No. 141,
    1965.

13. Leung, W., and Probstein, R.F. Ind. Eng. Chem. Fundam.,
    1971, 18, 274.

14. Ross, P.D., and Minton, A.P., J. Mol. Biol., 1977, 112, 437.

15. Phillies, G.D.J., Benedek, G.B., and Mayer, N.A., J. Chem. Phys., 1976, 65, 1883.

16. Klein, E., Holland, F.F., and Eberle, K., J. Membrane Sci., 1979, 5, 173.

17. Kozinski, A.A., and Lightfoot, E.N., A. I. Ch. E. J., 1972, 18, 1030.

RECEIVED December 4, 1980.

Dialysis Processing of Cryopreserved Red Blood Cells

ALLEN ZELMAN, DAVID GISSER, and DEXTER SMITH

Center for Biomedical Engineering, Rennsselaer Polytechnic Institute, Troy, NY 12181

ROBERT STEPHEN

Division of Artificial Organs, University of Utah, Salt Lake City, UT 74112

Red cells, frozen in the presence of glycerol, can be stored for years at $-80^{\circ}C$ with excellent post-thaw recovery and in vivo survival.

Today, three approaches to red cell freezing and deglycerolization are in clinical use: the agglomeration method (1), the low glycerol method developed in the United States (2, 3) and in Europe (4) and the high glycerol procedure (5) modified and adopted by the American Red Cross (6). Estimates of the extent to which these three procedures are used in North America, based on sales of glycerol solutions during 1976 by United States manufacturers, total 25,000 units processed by agglomeration, 30,000 by the low glycerol method and 165,000 by the high glycerol procedure. All procedures yield a product of essentially equivalent quality (7, 8). Differences in the rate of use to some extent reflect differences in processing costs as well as the very large impact of the Red Cross Blood Program which processes an estimated 50% of all units frozen in North America.

Of all the uses for frozen red cells probably the most important and far reaching would be their use for inventory control. First, in regional blood centers, cells collected during peak collection times of the year could be maintained in storage for use in times of deficit. Second, small isolated hospitals, because of irregular needs, now must either tolerate an excessive rate of outdating or engage in an extensive exchange program with a distant regional center. Frozen red cells would be a solution for both of these inventory control problems but only provided that the glycerolization procedure was rapid, simple and economical.

Some of the problems surrounding the removal of glycerol from the high glycerol preparation have been overcome through the use of cell washing devices. One of these, developed by the Haemonetics Company (Braintree, MA) and based on the Cohn Fractionator, performs a continuous flow wash in a disposable bowl. The other apparatus developed by the IBM Corporation, conducts an automated batch wash in a disposable bag. Although effective,

0097–6156/81/0154–0109$05.00/0

these devices add considerable cost to the use of frozen cells.
The capital equipment ranges from over $5,000 to over $17,000
with the disposable plastic components ranging from about $8.00
to over $20.00. The washing protocols require roughly 30 minutes
per unit and these devices will wash only a single unit at a
time.

Advantages of Frozen Red Cells Using Current Processing Methods.

Long term preservation is the most obvious asset of frozen
red cells and one which in earlier days was assumed to be the only
novel virtue. This extended shelf life has proven invaluable for
the preservation of rare types and cells for autotransfusion. Inventory control is an important application as well, but one whose
full potential has been limited by the high cost of frozen cells.
Reduced incidence in non-hemolytic transfusion reactions, as
Tullis, Haynes et al. (9) correctly observed, is one of the fringe
benefits of deglycerolizing red cells. Washing for deglycueroliza-
tion removes virtually all the plasma, the platelets, and most of
the leukocytes. White cells are less permeable to glycerol than
red cells and the glycerolizing procedure used for red cells is
damaging to leukocytes. Most of these cells are destroyed by
glycerolization alone with additional destruction occurring during
freezing and thawing. Valeri (10) has shown that the proportion
of intact white cells remaining following deglycerolization decreases with 4° storage of the blood prior to freezing. After
10 days, 1% or less of the leukocytes will remain following
deglycerolization.
Sensitization to histocompatibility antigens is presumed to
be reduced in frequency in patients receiving leukocyte-poor deglycerolized cell suspensions. To a considerable extent, it is
the presumption that reducing sensitization should be beneficial
to transplant recipients that has led to widespread use of frozen
red cells in dialysis centers. Reports have both supported and
contradicted these conjectures and the immunological virtues of
frozen red cells for dialysis patients remains uncertain.
Reduction in the incidence of post-transfusion hepatitis has
been reported as a result of conversion to frozen red cells. With
exception of the study by Tullis (11), the observations are retro-
spective, uncontrolled and fail to provide unequivocal evidence
that red cell freezing is a defense against this disease. The
study by Tullis, although well-designed, is generally considered
to comprise too few cases of hepatitis to be conclusive.
Mandatory testing has resulted in a substantial reduction of
type B hepatitis as a transfusion problem (12). The dominant
clinical disease now involves a virus which is neither type A nor
type B so that it cannot be predicted with confidence that the
virus or viruses involved in present day post-transfusion hepatitis will respond like the type B virus to freezing and
deglycerolization.

Low temperature storage accounts for the simplicity of the
current procedure. Storage at -80°C in mechanical freezers is
easily obtainable even though the equipment is expensive and maintenance and repair require specialized experience. The imminent
availability of a procedure permitting storage at -20°C (13)
essentially eliminates storage facility obstacles to the use of
frozen cells.

Disadvantages of Frozen Red Cells Using Current Processing
Methods.

Processing time, from the removal of a unit from the freezer
to the removal of deglycerolized cells from the washing apparatus,
requires an absolute minimum of 30 minutes (14). Time of processing is an effective obstacle to the use of frozen red cells
for emergency applications under most circumstances. On the other
hand, when frozen cells are routinely deglycerolized on a large
scale within a hospital, the diversion of deglycerolized cells
for emergency use appears to be entirely feasible, and at least
two large general hospitals have reported outdating rates of 5%
(15) and 1% or less (16), respectively.

The 24 hour outdating period constitutes one of the major
problems with frozen red cells today. This is particularly true
when cells are deglycerolized at a blood center and delivered to
a hospital at some distance. A unit of cells specifically directed to a particular patient, and then not used, frequently cannot
be crossmatched for some other recipient within the 24 hour limit.
The 24 hour outdating is imposed because of the hazard of bacter-
ial contamination during processing.

Processing of multiple units imposes a special hardship where
more than one unit has been deglycerolized in the Haemonetics disposable bowl. Blood centers preparing frozen red cells under
Federal license are required to use a variety of safeguards to
assure that all units washed through the same bowl are delivered
to a single recipient. Changes in the design of the Haemonetics
apparatus could obviate the need to prepare multiple units with
the same bowl. But acceptable economics and more rapid and simultaneous deglycerolization are a necessary goal of blood banking.

Cost continues to be the predominant disadvantage of frozen
red cells, although one large general hospital reports that, since
converting almost entirely to frozen or washed red cells, the cost
per thousand units of matched, frozen cells is only 44% more than
matched whole blood. At the present time, disposable supplies for
glycerolization and deglycerolization total at least $35.00 per
unit. The present scale of red cell freezing is already
sufficient to obtain cost reductions from volume production and it
seems unlikely that substantial further reductions in the costs of
disposables can be anticipated.

Hemolysis during deglycerolization accounts for up to 12%
loss of the red blood cells. The various sterile solutions used

in RBC washing lowers the osmolality too fast for the cells to
accomodate and the cells rupture. These losses are obviously a
major cost factor.

A New Method for Adding and Removing Cryoprotective Agents.

   We propose a new method for both glycerolization and
deglycerolization, based on the use of a blood bag composed entirely of semi-permeable membrane material, as shown in Figure 1.
Because the membrane itself would form an absolute barrier for
pyrogens, viruses and bacteria, costly sterile solutions are
totally avoided. Since the blood could be collected and maintained in a sterile environment, the 24 hour outdating period could
probably be greatly increased. The process could be easily automated and carried out without technician attendance. Processing
of multiple units simultaneously could be accomplished without
fear of cross contamination inasmuch as each blood unit would be
contained within its own membrane system and lastly, the cost
would undoubtedly be greatly decreased because membrane material
is not very expensive and none of the sterile solutions would be
needed. Objections to using membranes comparable to those used in
hemodialysis for such a procedure would be that hemoglobin and
cell fragments formed during the freezing-thawing process could
not be washed out as in present methods. If hemolysis could be
eliminated by a more gentle washing procedure, the only objection
to this membrane process would be the retention of white cell
fragments: however, administration of whole blood has similar
consequences.

Methods.

   Figure 2 is a schematic of the transport cell which holds the
blood bag. The bag is placed in a "waffle iron" like cell which
allows the cell to be easily opened and closed. Dialysate enters
the bottom, travels through a plastic mesh which acts both as a
"dialysate mixer" and as a membrane support. The dialysate exits
and then re-enters at the bottom. In this manner both sides of
the blood bag are washed by the single dialysate stream. The bag
volume is designed to "fill" the compartment; this prevents osmosis, due to plasma proteins, from swelling the bag and diluting
the red blood cells. The bag is formed by heat-sealing polycarbonate membrane (American Membrane, Covina, CA). For the in vitro
experiments reported here, the bag is filled with 350 ml of outdated, human blood which has been glycerolized according to
standard procedures set by the American Red Cross. The bags have
960 cm^2 area on each side. The transport cell is mounted on a
shaker (Eberbach Corp, Ann Arbor, MI) and is shaken at 160 revolu-
tions per minute to enhance mixing of the blood in the blood bag
during dialysis.
   The primary considerations in the design of the apparatus

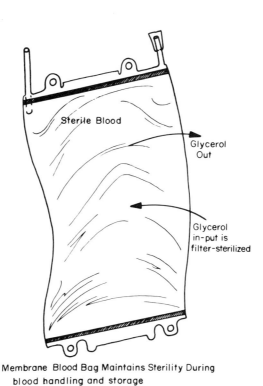

Membrane Blood Bag Maintains Sterility During
blood handling and storage

Figure 1.   Schematic for a membrane blood bag for maintaining sterility during glycerolization and deglycerolization

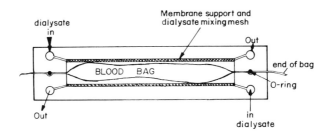

Transport Cell made like a "Waffle Iron"

Figure 2.   Schematic of the transport cell that holds the blood bag

are: 1) to have the dialysate flowing as fast as practical, without wasting salt, to facilitate mass transfer, and 2) to lower the
dialysate osmolality smoothly from ≃ 4000 mosm to 265 mosm during
a time span sufficiently fast to be efficient, but not so fast as
to cause osmotic hemolysis.

Figure 3 shows schematically the principle components of the
system. Tap water is drawn by a dialysate delivery system (B-D
Drake-Willock, Portland, OR) commonly used for hemodialysis. This
system produces dialysate at rates of up to 600 ml/min at 38°C by
diluting a concentrate with tap water. The freshly made dialysate
is piped to a mixing flask containing ≃ 2500 ml of 4500 mosm
dialysate. As the dialysate is forced into the flask the dialysate leaving the flask and entering the transport cell varies in
osmolality with time according to Table I.

TABLE I

Exponential Decay of Dialysate Osmolality

$$C_D(t) = C_D(o) + (C_{Conc} - C_D(o)) \, \text{Exp}(\frac{Q_D \, T}{V_{Tank}})$$

$$C_D(o) \quad \rightarrow \quad C_{Tank}(t) \quad \rightarrow \quad C_D(t)$$

Dialysate	Concentrate	Dialysate to
Delivery	Tank	Transport
System		Cell

T is time, Q_D is the constant rate of volume flow to the
transport cell, V_{Tank} is the volume of the concentrate tank, $C_D(o)$
and $C_{Conc}(o)$ are the incoming dialysate and initial tank concentrate concentrations respectively and are constant in time. This
method of dialysate delivery produces a very smooth exponential
decay from very high osmolality to that of standard dialysate.
The salt concentrations of the blood bag after deglycerolization
will be essentially that of the dialysate and are listed in Table
II for these experiments. Other concentrations can be easily substituted for those chosen here.

TABLE II

Composition of Dialysate at 265 mosm

Na^+ 130 meq/L	Cl^- 102 meq/L
K^+ 2 meq/L	Ac^- 31 meq/L
Kg^{+2} 1 meq/L	Glucose 200 mg%
	(11.1 m M)

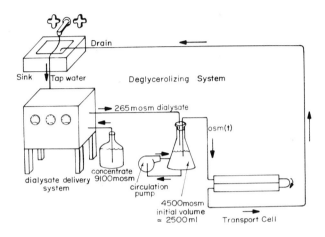

Figure 3. Schematic of the laboratory set-up for deglycerolization

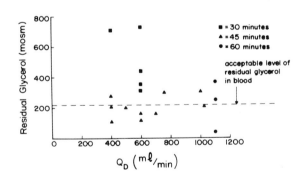

Figure 4. Residual glycerol left in 350 mL of red blood cells after deglycerolization

Having passed through the transport cell, the glycerol dissolved
in the dialysate is put in the sink drain. The circulation pump
on the flask maintains a well mixed solution.

These experiments were aimed to determine three variables for
optimization of this process: 1) What should be the initial
dialysate osmolality in order to prevent hemolysis? 2) What is
the fastest rate at which the osmolality may be lowered without
hemolysis? 3) How long should dialysis continue before the
glycerol is at acceptable levels (< 200 mosm)?

Since we knew that initiating dialysis with an osmolality
above that of the initial glycerol would prevent hemolysis, we
simply initiated a research program to determine an optimum value
of $(\frac{Q_D T}{V_{Tank}})$ as given in Table I.

Results With Discussion.

Figure 4 shows the results of deglycerolization using our
first prototype transport cell of 960 cm^2 area for each side of
the membrane bag, i.e., 1920 cm^2 total area. It is clear that
about 50% of the samples were properly deglycerolized. Dye tests
on the flow patterns in the test cell indicated that the scatter
in data was more likely due to irregular dialysate flow paths
rather than to biological irregularity. But these results do indicate viability of the process and point directly toward construction of an improved dialysis system.

After each experiment the extracellular fluid was checked for
plasma hemoglobin. In our last 29 experiments, 11 showed zero
hemolysis with an average change in plasma hemoglobin of 183 mg %
± 203 mg % with a range of (0 - 500 mg %). The American Red Cross
sets the limit of plasma hemoglobin for reinfusion at 500 mg %.
Thus even with the outdated blood, which is very fragile, our
method excels in preventing red cell losses.

The long term goals of this project are to deglycerolize
400 ml of red blood cells in about 30 minutes. These preliminary
data indicate that this goal can be met by proper design of the
transport cell. At the time of this writing a new prototype cell
is being assembled with a membrane area of 1419 cm^2 (each side)
and with dialysate flow patterns designed to ensure uniformity of
fluid distribution across the surfaces of the blood bag. This new
test cell will certainly achieve our goal. Our primary need now
is for a bag composed of a pinhole free membrane material. The
bag must be pinhole free to ensure sterility; perhaps a double
layer membrane would meet this goal. We can expect that in the
near future membrane technology will play a far greater role in
the blood banking and blood processing industry.

Acknowledgement

This research could not have been conducted without the help, encouragement and criticism of Dr. H. Meryman, ANRC, Washington, D.C., Dr. A. Britten, ANRC, Albany, N.Y., and Dr. J. Eisenmann, Baker Bros., Stroughton, MA. This research is supported in part by Public Health Services grant #NIH 3 R01 HL24466.

Literature Cited

1. Huggins, C.E. Science, 139:504, 1963.

2. Pert, J.H., Schork, P.K., Moore, R. Clin. Res., 11 (1):197, 1963.

3. Rowe, A.W. In: Red Cell Freezing. AABB Workshop, pp. 55-71, 1973.

4. Krijnen, H.W., Goudsmit, R., deWit, JJ Fr M. Bibl. Haemat., 29 (3):807-813, 1968.

5. Tullis, J.L. (Proceedings 9th) Conference on the Plasma Protein Cellular Elements of the Blood, p. 17-18. Cambridge, MA, Protein Foundation, 1954.

6. Meryman, H.T. and Hornblower, M. Transfusion, 16:159, 1976.

7. Meryman, H.T. and Hornblower, M. Transfusion (in press).

8. Valeri, C.R. In: Red Cell Freezing: A Technical Workshop. AABB. pp. 1-30, 1973.

9. Tullis, J.L., Haynes, L.L., Pyle, H.M. Arch. Surg. (Chicago) 81 (1):169-172, 1960.

10. Crowley, J.P. and Valeri, C.R. Transfusion, 14 (3):196, 1974.

11. Tullis, J.L., Hinman, J., Sproul, M.T. JAMA 214:719-723, 1970.

12. Conrad, M.E. Am. J. Hematol., 1:357-365, 1976.

13. Meryman, H.T. and Hornblower, M. (Presented at the 15th Annual Meeting) Society for Cryobiology. Tokyo, August 6-10, 1978.

14. Meryman, H.T. In: Red Cell Freezing: A Technical Workshop. AABB. pp. 73-86, 1973.

15. Meryman, H.T. Am. Journal. of Med. Tech., 41:265-282, 1975.

16. Huggins, C.E. In: Red Cell Freezing. AABB Workshop, pp. 31-53, 1973.

RECEIVED December 4, 1980.

Effect of Gel Layer on Rejection and Fractionation of Different-Molecular-Weight Solutes by Ultrafiltration

SHIN-ICHI NAKAO and SHOJI KIMURA

Institute of Industrial Science, University of Tokyo, Tokyo 106, Japan

It is well known that the gel layer of high molecular substances or suspended matters tend to form on the membrane surface, which sometimes controls the overall phenomena, that is, it limits the permeate flux and affects the rejection nature of membranes. As a result it happens that different membranes behave almost same after the gel layer formation, even though the manufacturers claim that their own membrane have better quality.

In the usual applications of membrane processes, such as water desalination, suspended matters are removed from feed solutions by applying many types of pretreatments. But in the application for food processing or medical use, the adoption of pretreatment is usually meaningless, and the deposition of the gel layer is unavoidable. Thus it becomes necessary to understand the nature of gel layer and to know how to control it. But so far this kind of research is scarce and the analytical treatment is inconclusive.

We have been studying this problem as an extension of our research on the fouling of membrane by the deposition of suspended matters (1). We first studied on the resistance of gel layer to permeation (2), next on the characterization of ultrafiltration membranes (3) regarding the solute rejection, and lastly on the effect of gel layer on the solutes rejection and fractionation. Though this paper is mainly concerned with this last aspect, we want to quickly review the previous results.

The concentration and the resistance of gel layer

The concentration profile in the boundary layer on the membrane surface with gel layer is shown in Fig. 1. At steady state most of the solute conveyed by flow to the membrane diffuse back due to the concentration gradient and the rest permeate through the membrane. This mass balance is given as

$$J_s = J_v \cdot C - D\frac{dC}{dx} \qquad (1)$$

Boundary conditions are

$$x=0; \ C=C_b$$
$$x=\delta; \ C=C_g \qquad (2)$$

Solutes flux through membrane J_s is given as

$$J_s = J_v \cdot C_p \qquad (3)$$

Using Equations (2) and (3), Equation (1) is integrated as follows:

$$J_v = k \cdot \ell n(\frac{C_g - C_p}{C_b - C_p}) \qquad (4)$$

where k is mass transfer coefficient defined as

$$k = \frac{D}{\delta} \qquad (5)$$

In Equation (4), if the membrane has a very high rejection of so-lutes, the term C_p can be neglected. Then

$$J_v = k \cdot \ell n(\frac{C_g}{C_b}) \qquad (6)$$

Eq. (6) is usually called gel polarization equation and the value of C_g, which can be obtained by extrapolation of $J_v \to 0$ in the plot of J_v against log C_b, is considered as constant; that dependent on the solute material but not dependent on the experimental conditions.

After we started to analyse the data of ultrafiltration experiment, we came to conclusion that this assumption is not correct. So we decided to measure directly C_g at each experiment by scratching out the gel layer from membrane after measuring steady state flux. Solutes used were polyvinyl alcohol(PVA) and ovalbumin. It was found that C_g is not constant, but was dependent on the experimental condition as shown in Fig. 2, where a case of PVA is plotted.

By the measurement of C_g value it became also possible to obtain k value using Eq. (6). Using this k, Sherwood No. obtained are plotted against Reynolds and Schmidt No. in Fig. 3, where the solid line gives the Deissler correlation, that is valid in the large Schmidt No. range and given as

$$N_{Sh} = 0.023 N_{Re}^{0.875} N_{Sc}^{0.25} \qquad (7)$$

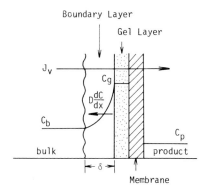

Figure 1.   Gel polarization schematic (2)

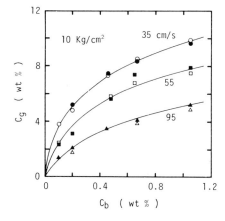

*Figure 2.   Gel layer concentrations of
PVA 224 measured directly as a function
of bulk concentration and feed velocity
using   T4/A(black)   and   T2/A(white)
membranes (2)*

These facts show that the actual C_g value can be calculated by Eq. (6) by knowing appropriate k value.

From the other point of view the ultrafiltration flux is given by the resistance law as

$$J_v = \frac{\Delta P}{R_m + R_g} \qquad (8)$$

where R_m and R_g are the resistance of membrane and gel layer, respectively. Although Eq. (6) and (8) both give flux, their relation has not been investigated. When R_g is plotted against C_g, the relation were found to exist as shown in Fig. 4, where R_g is proportional to $C_g^{1.7}$. Precise meaning of this relation is not yet known, but it enables now to predict J_v at given conditions. One example is given in the following. Fig. 5 shows the typical plot following the gel polarization model as suggested by Eq. (6) with the assumption that C_g is constant. Fig. 6 shows the same data but solid lines are obtained in this case by the calculation using Eqs. (6), (8), Deissler's correlation and the relation shown in Fig. 4. These figures clearly show the difference of the assumption regarding the value of gel layer concentration.

Characterization of ultrafiltration membrane

Before discussing the rejection characteristics of membrane with gel layer, the property of membrane without gel layer should be determined. Various transport equations have been used, some of which are based on the particular mechanism, the others are based on the phenomenology. According to the latter the following equations are presented (4).

$$J_v = L_p(\Delta P - \sigma \Delta \Pi) \qquad (9)$$

$$J_s = P(C_m - C_p) + (1-\sigma)J_v\bar{C} \qquad (10)$$

In these equations, the membrane characteristics are described by three parameters, pure water permeability L_p, solute permeability P and reflection coefficient σ. The determination of these parameters is very important. The term $\bar{C}$ in Eq. (10) shows the average concentration on both sides of a membrane and the logarithmic mean is usually used.

In the case of high rejection membrane, the value of ΔC is so large that the logarithmic mean concentration does no longer correspond to correct average. To solve this problem, Spiegler and Kedem (5) divided the membrane into differential elements in the direction of its thickness and applied Eq. (10) in it as the form of differential equation. The result of integration is expressed as

$$R = \frac{\sigma(1-F)}{1-\sigma F} \qquad (11)$$

where

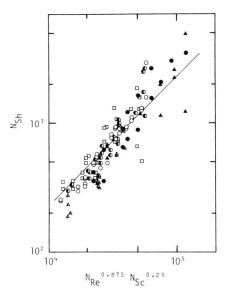

$$N_{Re}^{0.875}\ N_{Sc}^{0.25}$$

American Institute of
Chemical Engineers Journal

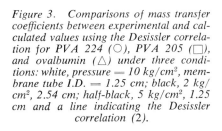

Figure 3. Comparisons of mass transfer coefficients between experimental and calculated values using the Desissler correlation for PVA 224 ($\bigcirc$), PVA 205 ($\square$), and ovalbumin ($\triangle$) under three conditions: white, pressure = 10 kg/cm², membrane tube I.D. = 1.25 cm; black, 2 kg/cm², 2.54 cm; half-black, 5 kg/cm², 1.25 cm and a line indicating the Desissler correlation (2).

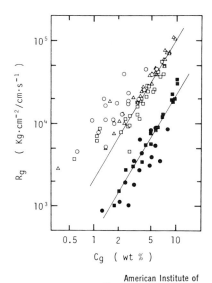

American Institute of
Chemical Engineers Journal

Figure 4. Relationships between the resistance to a flow and the concentration of gel layer for PVA 224 (white) and ovalbumin (black) under various conditions: pressure = 2 kg/cm, membrane diameter = 2.54 cm ($\bigcirc$); 5 kg/cm², 1.25 cm ($\square$); 10 kg/cm², 1.25 cm ($\triangle$) (2).

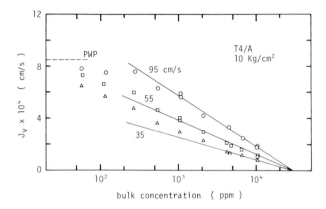

American Institute of Chemical Engineers Journal

Figure 5.   Experimental fluxes for the T4/A membrane, with a 1.25-cm diameter, treating PVA 224 aqueous solutions under three kinds of feed velocities (2)

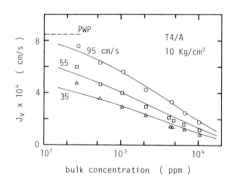

Figure 6.   Comparisons between experimental and calculated fluxes for PVA 224 aqueous solutions under three kinds of feed velocities.   Curves are calculated from Equations 6, 7, and 8, and the relation shown in Figure 4 (2).

American Institute of
Chemical Engineers Journal

$$F = \exp\left(-\frac{1-\sigma}{P} \cdot J_V\right) \qquad (12)$$

Equation (9) does not change by the same treatment. The applicability of these equations to ultrafiltration membrane is not fully established and the determination method of parameters in these equations from the experimental data is not fixed yet. For such purposes the following experiments were conducted.

Two kinds of cellulose acetate ultrafiltration tubular membranes (T2/A and T4/A) produced by Paterson Candy International, Limited, England, were employed in this study. Six kinds of solutes, polyethylene glycol (PEG#4000), vitamin B_{12}, raffinose, sucrose, glucose, and glycerin, were used. Molecular weights, diffusivities and molecular radii of these solutes are shown in Table 1. The experimental apparatus is shown schematically in Fig. 7.

Two kinds of experiments were performed. In one kind of experiment, four feed velocities (38, 58, 100, 140 cm/s) were employed and the pressure was kept constant at 8 atm. In the other, various pressures between 2 and 12 atm were employed and the velocity was kept constant at 58 cm/s. The temperature of feed solution was controlled at 25°C by a thermostat throughout all the experimental runs. The concentration of the feed solution ranged from 100 to 2000 ppm.

Three parameters, L_p, σ and P, which describe the membrane characteristics were determined in the following manner.

Pure water permeability L_p was obtained from the experiment of pure water permeation using Eq. (9), in which the osmotic pressure difference $\Delta\Pi$ is zero.

Two parameters σ and P were first determined by using the logarithmic mean concentration $C_{\ell m}$. Equation (10) is rewritten as

$$\frac{J_s}{\Delta C} = P + (1 - \sigma) \cdot \frac{J_V C_{\ell m}}{\Delta C} \qquad (14)$$

where $\Delta C = C_m - C_p$ is the concentration difference. As illustrated in Fig. 8, there is good linear correlation between $J_s/\Delta C$ and $J_V \cdot C_{\ell m}/\Delta C$, and the parameters σ and P were obtained from the slope and intercept. Then, to examine the accuracy of these parameters, the real rejection R was calculated by means of Eqs. (11) and (12) using these values, and plotted R versus $1/J_V$ as dotted lines in Fig. 9. In the region of low flux, the calculated lines agreed well with the experimental data, but in the high flux area, the agreement between both values were not good. The use of logarithmic mean concentration, therefore, is only valid in the low flux region.

In Eqs. (11) and (12), $F \to 0$ at high flux and hence the reflection coefficient σ is the limiting value of R.

$$J_V \to \infty; R \to \sigma \qquad (13)$$

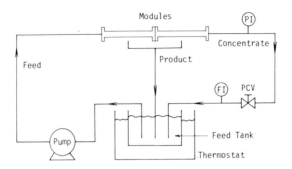

American Institute of Chemical Engineers Journal

Figure 7.   Schematic flow sheet of the experimental apparatus (2)

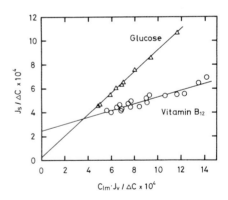

Figure 8.   Determination of σ and P of
T4/A membrane by using the logarith-
mic mean concentration

This fact has been used for the determination of σ by plotting R vs. J_V or R vs. $1/J_V$ and by extrapolating $J_V \to \infty$ or $1/J_V \to 0$. But it was only in the case of high or low rejected solutes that this plot became a straight line, as illustrated in Fig. 9., and the values of σ extrapolated were not accurate.

The direct curve fitting of Eqs. (11) and (12) was also attempted. When σ is assumed to have a certain value, the average and standard deviation of P for all experimental data of one solute and membrane can be calculated using Eqs. (11) and (12). By calculating the standard deviation at a different value of σ, its most suitable value is determined when the standard deviation becomes minimum. P is then given as the average of all data. The best fitting curves are illustrated in Fig. 9 as solid lines and the values of σ, P and its standard deviation listed in Table 2. The calculated lines agreed very well with the experimental data for all solutes.

It is apparent from all these results that the Spiegler and Kedem equations, Eqs. (11) and (12), were suitable as transport equations of ultrafiltration and the curve-fitting method was the best for the determination of the membrane parameters, σ and P.

The rejection of solutes by gel

Our next step is to determine σ and P values of gel layer. To do that equations are needed, which deal with the case that the two different membranes are in series, which were developed by Jagur-Grodzinski & Kedem (6). Following this treatment rejection of series membranes is given by

$$R = \frac{(1-F_g)(1-\sigma_m)+F_g(1-\sigma_g)(1-F_m\sigma_m)-(1-\sigma_g)(1-\sigma_m)}{(1-F_g)(1-\sigma_m)+F_g(1-\sigma_g)(1-F_m\sigma_m)} \qquad (15)$$

where

$$F_g = \exp\{-\frac{J_V(1-\sigma_g)}{P_g}\} \qquad (16)$$

$$F_m = \exp\{-\frac{J_V(1-\sigma_m)}{P_m}\} \qquad (17)$$

Suffix g corresponds to gel layer and m corresponds to membrane, and σ_m and P_m are already determined. So the next step is to obtain σ_g and P_g from the experimental data by the curve fitting method explained previously.

The experimental apparatus and membranes used are same as before. As a gel layer forming solute ovalbumin, and as the other solute vitamin B_{12} were used.

Since the gel layer thickness changes depending on the pressure, feed velocity and bulk concentration, it is necessary to specify the thickness to obtain σ_g and P_g of the gel layer. Only

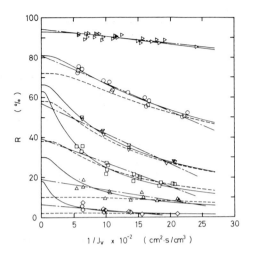

Figure 9.   Plot of R vs. $1/J_v$: (———) determined by the method of curve fitting; (— — —) determined by using the logarithmic mean concentration; (— — — —) extrapolation of $1/J_v \rightarrow 0$ for the determination of σ. PEG#4000 (▷); Vitamin B (○); raffinose (▽); sucrose (□); glucose (△); glycerin (◇).

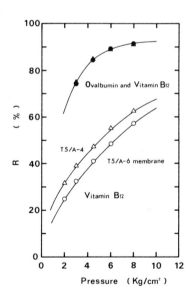

Figure 10.   Rejection of Vitamin B_{12} vs. pressure

Table 1   Molecular weights, diffusivities
and Stokes radii of solutes

Solute	Molecular weight	$D \times 10$ (cm^2/s)	$r_s \times 10^8$ (cm)
PEG #4000	3000	1.5	16.3
Vitamin B_{12}	1355	3.3	7.4
Raffinose	504	4.2	5.8
Sucrose	342	5.2	4.7
Glucose	180	6.9	3.6
Glycerin	92	9.5	2.6

Table 2   Parameters σ and P, and its standard
deviation of the T4/A membrane determined
by the method of curve fitting

Solute	σ	$p \times 10^4$ (cm/s)	Standard deviation
PEG #4000	0.93	0.52	1.7×10^{-5}
Vitamin B_{12}	0.81	3.0	3.1×10^{-5}
Raffinose	0.66	7.8	3.9×10^{-5}
Sucrose	0.63	17	1.8×10^{-4}
Glucose	0.30	17	4.5×10^{-4}
Glycerin	0.18	55	1.7×10^{-3}

Table 3   Values of σ_g and P_g of ovalbumin
gel layer. Solute; vitamin B_{12}.

R_g $(atm/cm.s^{-1})$	σ_g	$P_g \times 10$ (cm/s)
40000	0.99	1.4
20000	0.99	2.9
10000	0.99	5.6
8000	0.99	6.8

Values of σ_m and P_m of a membrane are;

$$\sigma_m = 0.89, \quad P_m = 1.1 \times 10^{-3} \quad (cm/s)$$

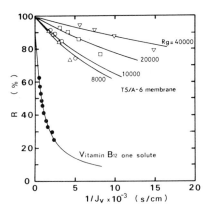

Figure 11. Plots of rejection of Vitamin B against 1/J_v: (——) determined by a method of curve fitting; black, Vitamin B_{12} single solute; white, ovalbumin + Vitamin B_{12} two solutes.

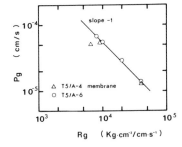

Figure 12. Relationship between P_g of Vitamin B_{12} and R_g

index to specify the thickness is the gel layer resistance, R_g. To determine σ_g and P_g values it is necessary to measure the rejection at different volume flux, J_v, that means it is necessary to perform experiment at different pressures. And at different pressures R_g changes, when the bulk concentration is kept constant. To keep R_g value constant at different pressure it is necessary to change bulk concentration or the feed velocity. In our experiment the latter was kept constant, while the bulk concentration was adjusted to keep R_g constant. Even so it is hard to keep R_g precisely constant. Therefore finally the experimental relations between R_g and rejection, R, were obtained by plotting data on the graph and R values were read at appropriate R_g by interpolation.

   After obtaining the original data it is necessary to correct the effect of the concentration polarization. In the mixed solutions it is not certain whether it is possible to use the mass transfer coefficient determined in a single solution. Here this value are used since no other correct method is known. Values of rejection, R, thus obtained are shown in Fig. 10 for vitamin B_{12} only and for the case with ovalbumin gel layer. In this figure it is shown the rejection of different membrane are same due to the gel layer formation of ovalbumin.

   The plot of R against $1/J_v$ is shown in Fig. 11. In the figure solid lines are drawn by curve fitting using Eq. (15) at each R_g value. Values of σ_g and P_g are shown in Table 3. σ_g is 0.99 and not dependent on R_g, but P_g is dependent on R_g. The relation between P_g and R_g is shown in Fig. 12, which shows P_g is inversely proportional to R_g. That means P_g is inversely proportional to the gel layer thickness, which is considered to be the reasonable conclusion. Further progress is being attempted to check these results with other solutes-gel layer systems.

Conclusion

   It was found that the gel layer concentration is not constant, but variable, which can be predicted by using the ordinary concentration polarization model with appropriate mass transfer coefficient. Also this concentration has a particular relation with the gel layer resistance. Using this relation the flux through the membrane can be calculated for the case of gel layer formation.

   Rejection characteristics of ultrafiltration membrane were analysed and method to determine the transport coefficients is developed. Also the rejection characteristics of membrane with gel layer were analysed and it is found that the transport coefficients of gel layer have a definite relation with the gel layer resistance, and perhaps with gel layer thickness.

Notation

C = concentration of solute, wt%
D = diffusivity, cm^2/s
J_S = permeation velocity of solute through membrane, cm/s
J_V = volume flux through membrane, $cm^3/cm^2 \cdot s$
k = mass transfer coefficient, cm/s
L_p = pure water permeability, $cm^3/cm^2 \cdot S \cdot atm$
N_{Re} = Reynolds number
N_{Sc} = Schmidt number
N_{Sh} = Sherwood number
ΔP = pressure difference, Kg/cm^2
P = solute permeability, cm/s
R = resistance to a flow, $Kg \cdot cm^{-2}/cm \cdot s^{-1}$

   or

R = real rejection
X = distance, cm
δ = boundary layer thickness, cm
$\Delta \Pi$ = osmotic pressure difference, atm
σ = reflection coefficient

Subscripts

b = bulk
g = gel layer
m = membrane
p = product

Literature Cited

1. Kimura, S; Nakao, S. Desalination, 1975, 17, 267.
2. Nakao, S; Nomura, T; Kimura, S. AICHE J., 1979, 25, 615.
3. Nakao, S; Kimura, S. J. Chem. Eng. Japan, in press.
4. Kedem, O; Katchalsky, A. Biochim. Biophys. Acta, 1958,27,229.
5. Spiegler, K.S; Kedem, O. Desalination, 1966, 1, 311.
6. Jagur-Grodzinski, J; Kedem, O. Desalination, 1966, 1, 327.

RECEIVED December 4, 1980.

Application of Ultra- and Hyperfiltration During Production of Enzymatically Modified Proteins

H. SEJR OLSEN and J. ADLER–NISSEN

Enzyme Applications Research and Development, Novo Industri A/S,
Novo Allé, DK-2880 Bagsvaerd, Denmark

Application of membrane processes during production of purified food proteins is a mild treatment which ensures that the
functional properties of the native proteins are retained. (1)
These properties are mostly found to be superior to those of denatured proteins. However, not all possible needs of the modern
food industry are fulfilled by using native proteins instead of
denatured ones. Therefore, enzymatic modification of proteins has
been demonstrated as a possible means of meeting the needs of the
food industry for high–quality protein ingredients (2), (13),
(14).
Membrane processes have a potential application within many
areas of industrial enzymatic hydrolysis of proteins. Table I
shows how membrane processes can be applied in the different
types of enzymatic modification of protein. Thus membrane processes may be used for pre-treatment of proteins, for the reaction step and as an essential part of the purification or post-
treatment step.
In the following, results from our work with these processes
in Novo's pilot plant for Enzyme Application will be presented.
The results demonstrate that the functional properties of some
of the protein products obtained were improved to such an extent
that the membrane processes may become very important in the modern protein technology. Owing to the interesting preliminary results obtained regarding functional properties, less attention
has been paid to a thorough investigation of the unit operations
as such.

General Characteristics of Enzymatic Hydrolysis. As earlier
reported (2), a limited hydrolysis of a protein product may improve certain functional properties such as whipping and emulsifying capacity.
These improvements are dependent on the enzyme and on the
principle by which the reaction is controlled. The preferable way
of controlling the modification is by application of the pH–stat-
technique, by which the base consumption used for maintaining pH

0097–6156/81/0154–0133$09.25/0

during the proteolytic reaction is directly converted to degree
of hydrolysis (2). Degree of hydrolysis, DH, is the proportion
between the number of peptide bonds cleaved and the total number
of peptide bonds in the intact protein (3).

Proteolytically modified proteins which have been thoroughly
enzyme digested are low molecular protein hydrolysates. Such products have often less pronounced foaming or emulsifying properties than proteins which have been only slightly hydrolyzed (2).
However, a need for this kind of protein products appears in the
beverage industry for enrichment of soft drinks with protein and
in the meat industry for pumping of whole meat cuts with low cost
proteins. Important properties of low molecular protein hydrolysates are a bland taste and a complete solubility over the wide
pH-range used in foods.

The production method for low molecular protein hydrolysates
has been described earlier (4). A controlled batch hydrolysis
using the pH-stat is performed, and the protein hydrolysate is
then recovered by e.g. solids separation. Hyperfiltration may be
used for concentration and/or desalination. Instead of using the
controlled batch hydrolysis and solids separation processes, the
separation of peptides may be performed from an enzyme-substrate
reaction mixture under continuous ultrafiltration in a so-called
membrane reactor.

Highly Functional Soy Proteins

Native soy protein isolate may be produced by ultrafiltration of an aqueous extract of defatted soy bean meal, (1), (5).
The process layout is shown in Fig. 1. A careful selection of
membrane parameters such as flow velocity, pressure drop, temperature, and of the type of membrane and modules is important in
order to obtain a bean protein isolate by a direct ultrafiltration of the clarified extract (5). The protein isolate has a pro-
tein-dry matter ratio higher than 90% (N x 6.25), when using this
process.

Hitherto, enzymatic modification of ultrafiltered soy proteins has not been described. The present investigation shows
that protein products with better properties than enzymatically
modified acid precipitated proteins can be produced by a suitable
combination of the involved unit operations.

Modification of Ultrafiltered versus Acid Precipitated
Soy Protein. When the retentate obtained from the ultrafiltration of soybean extract is subjected to an enzymatic hydrolysis as described earlier (2) for acid precipitated protein, a
hydrolysis curve (DH versus time) may be drawn. A comparison of
such hydrolysis curves is shown in Fig. 2 for acid precipitated
soy protein isolate and ultrafiltered soy protein isolate. The
curves are drawn on the basis of the same hydrolysis parameters.
The enzyme used is the microbial alkaline protease subtilisin
Carlsberg (ALCALASE®).

Table I. Application of Membrane Processes During Enzymatic Modification of Proteins

TYPES OF ENZY-MATIC MODIFIED PROTEINS	PRETREATMENTS	ENZYMATIC REACTION STEP	POSTTREATMENTS
HIGHLY FUNCTIONAL PROTEINS	PRODUCTION OF NATIVE PROTEIN ISOLATE BY UF	-	MOLECULAR SEPARATION BY UF
LOW MOLECULAR PROTEIN HYDRO-LYZATES	-	-	CONCENTRATION AND/OR DESA-LINATION BY HF
	-	MEMBRANE REACTOR BY UF	CONCENTRATION AND/OR DESA-LINATION BY HF

UF ~ ULTRAFILTRATION
HF ~ HYPERFILTRATION

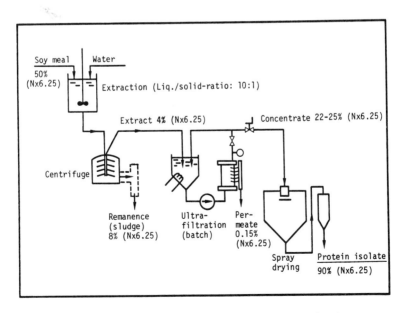

Figure 1.   Production of soy protein isolate by UF in pilot plant

It appears from Fig. 2 that the ultrafiltered soy protein
isolate is hydrolyzed considerably more slowly than the acid precipitated protein. This is due to the compact molecular structure
of the ultrafiltered protein, which is still in the native state.
That the degree of denaturation of a protein substrate has a pro-
found influence on the kinetics of the proteolysis has been known
for long, see Christensen (6). It should be noted that subtilisin
Carlsberg is not inhibited by the protease inhibitors present in
native bean protein (7).

Using the ultrafiltered soy protein isolate described previously (Fig. 1), a series of hydrolysates covering a range of
DH-values (DH = 0 to DH = 6%) was made in the laboratory using
the method outlined in Fig. 3. In all cases the hydrolysis was
terminated by addition of HCl to pH = 4.2 to inactivate the enzyme. After 30 minutes, pH was readjusted to pH = 7.0 by using
NaOH. NaCl was added until the final concentration in a 10% protein (N x 6.25) solution was 0.25 M NaCl (2).

The whipping expansion was determined by 4 minutes whip of
a solution having 3% protein (2). Figure 4 shows whipping expansion versus DH for ultrafiltered and acid-precipitated soy proteins modified by Alcalase. Similar results have also been found
for ultrafiltered and acid-precipitated proteins from faba beans
(Vicia faba) (Sejr Olsen, unpublished results).

It appears from Fig. 4 that in the case of the acid-precipitated protein, higher DH-values cause a distinct reduction of the
whipping expansion. The increasing content of small peptides resulting from a more pronounced degradation of the proteins at the
high DH values is assumed to be responsible for this reduction of
foaming ability. Removal of the small peptides during the processing of the unrefined soy meal to the final whipping agent
might therefore have a positive effect on the foaming ability.

Experimental Details. In order to examine the above hypothesis, the enzymatic hydrolysis was carried out at different
stages during the soy isolate process. Four process combinations
examined in our pilot plant are outlined schematically in Fig. 5.
In all cases the following procedure was used:

Defatted, dehulled white soy meal from Aarhus Oliefabrik A/S
was extracted with water at pH = 8.0 using a liquid : solid
ratio of 10 : 1.

All centrifugations were carried out in a Westfalia SB-7
solids ejecting centrifuge.

All ultrafiltrations were made on a DDS-modul type 35 at
50°C using polysulphone membranes type GR6-P at 3 kp/cm^2.
The module had 2.25 m^2 of membrane area.

Hydrolyses were made by use of ALCALASE 0.6 L at pH = 8.0
in pH-stat.

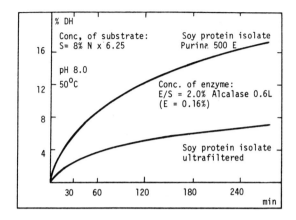

Figure 2.   Hydrolysis curves for soy protein isolates

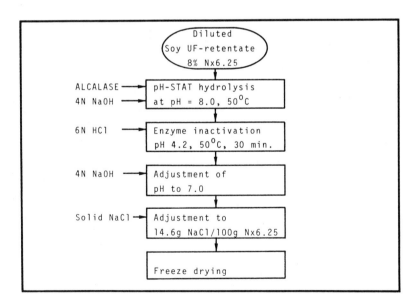

Figure 3.   Laboratory method for proteolytic modification of ultrafiltered soy protein isolate

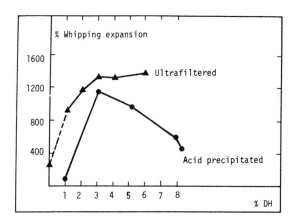

Figure 4.   Whipping expansions vs. DH for soy protein hydrolysates

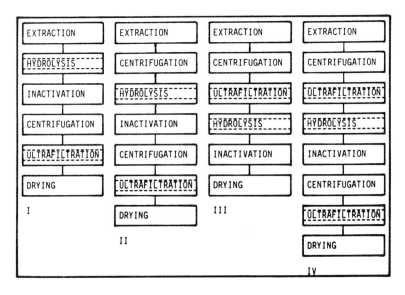

Figure 5.   Process combinations investigated for production of highly functional enzymatically modified soy proteins

In all cases hydrolysis to DH = 3% and DH = 6% was made and inactivation was carried out at pH = 4.0 (50°C) for 30 minutes. The general hydrolysis parameters were:

Substrate concentrations: S = 3 to 8% (N x 6.25)
Enzyme/substrate ratio: E/S = 2% ALCALASE 0.6 L
Temperature: T = 50°C
pH: pH = 8.0

Some of the different ultrafiltration processes within the four process combinations include diafiltration as well. When diafiltration was included at a stage, the sequence, ultrafiltration – diafiltration – ultrafiltration, was used in order to obtain a high separation efficiency and membrane capacity (8).

The final protein products were analysed and evaluated for their whipping expansion, foam stability and in the case of the DH-6%-products for baking performance in a meringue batter as well. The analytical procedures are described below.

Methods of Analysis

Whipping Expansion. Carried out as described previously (2).

Foam Stability. A plastic cylinder (diameter 7 cm, height 9 cm) having a wire net with a mesh size of 1 mm x 1 mm is filled with foam and the amount of foam is found by weighing (A gram). The cylinder is then placed on a funnel on top of a glass cylinder of 100 ml. After 30 minutes the weight (B) of drained liquid in the glass cylinder is determined. The foam stability FS is defined by the equation:

$$FS = \frac{A - B}{A} \times 100\%$$

Baking Performance of Meringue Batter. To 100 ml of a 12% w/w (N x 6.25) solution at pH = 7.0 of the whipping agent, 150 g of saccharose is added. The saccharose is completely dissolved by gentle stirring at room temperature.

The solution is then whipped at speed III (260 rpm) for 10 minutes in a Hobart Mixer (model N – 50) using a wire whisk. Immediately afterwards, ten samples of 10 ml are transferred to an aluminium tray at separate positions by means of a syringe. Baking is then performed at 130°C for 1 hour. After cooling to ambient temperature, the weight, the height (h) and the diameter (d) are determined. The volume is calculated assuming that the meringue is a spherical segment having the volume:

$$V = \frac{1}{6} \times \pi \times (h^2 + \frac{3}{4} \times d^2)$$

The apparent density is then calculated, and the smaller the density, the better the baking performance, provided that the surface is still smooth and the shape is maintained.

Amino-acid Analyses. Carried out by Bioteknisk Institut, Kolding, Denmark.

TCA-soluble Nitrogen. Measured in 0.8 N trichloroacetic acid (TCA) using the method of Becker et al. (9).

Nitrogen Solubility. Carried out as described previously (2).

Free Alpha-amino Groups. Measured by the TNBS-method (10).

Crossed Immunoelectrophoresis. The method is described by Weeke (11).

Results and Discussion

Data from the membrane processing are given in Table IIa and IIb. Average permeate fluxes of the same order of magnitude were seen in all combinations, whether the ultrafiltrations were per-formed on enzyme treated proteins or on raw bean extract. This indicates that protein molecules capable of forming a gel on the membrane surface are still present after the enzymatic modifica-tion. The size of the permeate fluxes obtained is in the interval of about 20-40 $1/h/m^2$, which is in the economically attractive range of the process (5). The protein yields shown in Table IIIa and IIIb are based on 100% recovery of phases. The reason for the rather low yields are low nitrogen solubility of the soy meal used, viz. about 60% at pH = 8. As about 90% of protein may be water extracted from a less denatured soy meal (12), the overall yields would be about 50% higher if such a raw material is used.

If the combinations I, II and IV are compared with respect to the yields and functional properties, it appears that both whipping expansion and foam stability are highest at the high DH-value. However, due to higher content of low molecular peptides at the high DH-value, the overall protein (N x 6.25) yields are lower. The processes have to be evaluated more thoroughly in or-der to find a compromise between the protein yields and the func-tionality wanted.

When comparing the functionality studies with the chemical properties of the DH = 3%-products given in Table IIIa, no signi-ficant correlation is found between TCA-solubility, psi (protein solubility index) at pH = 4.5 or the psi at pH = 7.0. Omitting the III combination which is made by a method which retains some denatured protein (see (2)), only the content of leu-NH_2 equiva-lents significantly correlates with the whipping expansion and the foam stability. Including the results from Table IIIb, the curves shown in Fig. 6 and Fig. 7 clearly show that the higher the content of free NH_2-groups, the higher the whipping expansion and foam stability of the isolated proteins, although the process combinations were different. This confirms the significance of

Table IIa.   Ultrafiltration/Diafiltration Processing Data (DH = 3%)

Process combi- nation	UF or DF	Retentates			Average permeate flux $1/h/m^2$
		Before %(Nx6.25)	Final %(Nx6.25)	Average Prot.re- tention %	
I	UF DF UF	2.9 9.3 9.3	9.3 9.3 18.0	70.7	30.1 26.7 20.0
II	UF DF UF	2.3 10.9 10.1	10.9 10.1 ap20.0	75.5 92.9 93.1	35.6 34.7 -
III	UF	2.8	18.3	93.1	36.0
IV 1st	UF DF	3.2 9.8	9.8 15.7	92.2 98.2	41.9 26.7
IV 2nd	UF	3.3	10.4	84.4	no data

Table IIb.   Ultrafiltration/Diafiltration Processing Data (DH = 6%)

Process combi- nation	UF or DF	Retentates			Average permeate flux $1/h/m^2$
		Before %(Nx6.25)	Final %(Nx6.25)	Average Prot.re- tention %	
I	UF DF	3.1 7.4	7.4 6.7	55.8 83.2	38.5 no data
II	UF	1.8	12.4	69.1	31.1
III	UF	See table 2a		See G-1061a	
IV 1st	UF DF	2.8 9.9	9.9 12.5	95.4 98.5	43.4 21.7
IV 2nd	UF	3.3	6.3	74.2	39.1

**Table IIIa. Protein Yields and Some Properties of the DH 3%
Products Made by Different Process Combinations**

Process combination	I	II	III	IV
% Protein yield (based on soy meal)	39.5	30.9	55.3	28.6
Composition: % PY/HY	96.0	93.1	77.9	95.5
Functionality: % Whipping exp. [1])	667	733	1566	1650
% Foam stability	9	12	no data	42
Chemical prop.: % psi in TCA	10.0	13.2	17.7	13.4
% psi at pH = 4.5	42.7	47.8	42.6	49.7
% psi at pH = 7.0	99.9	94.7	59.9	97.0
leu-NH_2, mol/kg prot.	0.34 ~ DH= -0.2	0.41 ~ DH = 0.8	0.60 ~ DH = 3.1	0.49 ~ DH = 1.8
Immuno precip.	6 archs	6 archs	6 archs	6 archs
[1]) at pH 7.0				

**Table IIIb. Protein Yields and Some Properties of the DH 6%
Products Made by Different Process Combinations**

Process combination	I	II	III	IV
% Protein yield (based on soy meal)	34.3	22.3	55.3	23.8
Composition: % PY/HY	90.1	91.1	77.6	91.2
Methionin (g/16gN)	1.06	1.10	1.36	0.95
Cystin (g/16gN)	1.76	1.93	1.44	1.75
Functionality: % Whipping exp. *	833	1317	1570	2484
% Foam stability	20	50	no data	69
Density of mering. g/m^3 **	0.11 ± 0.01	0.096 ± 0.004	0.21 ± 0.01	0.17 ± 0.02
Chemical prop.: % psi in TCA	20.0	19.0	32.0	30.1
% psi at pH = 4.5	51.0	54.6	53.8	71.7
% psi at pH = 7.0	92.0	100.0	68.9	99.5
leu-NH_2, mol/kg protein	0.42 ~ DH = 0.9	0.49 ~ DH = 1.7	0.87 ~ DH = 6.4	0.67 ~ DH = 4.0
Immuno precip.	3 archs	5 archs	4 archs	2 archs

* at pH 7.0   ** with eggwhites: 0.12 g/cm^3

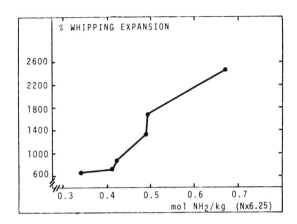

Figure 6.   Whipping expansion vs. the number of free NH₂ groups for highly functional soy protein ultrafiltered after hydrolysis

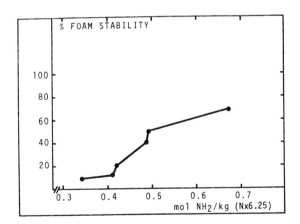

Figure 7.   Foam stability vs. the number of free NH₂ groups for highly functional soy protein ultrafiltered after hydrolysis

using DH as the controlling parameter during protein hydrolysis.
The values of psi in TCA and psi at pH = 4.5 give a rough measure
of the content of low molecular proteins. The presence of arches
determined by crossed immunoelectrophoresis demonstrates that
some high molecular proteins are retained in the modified products. For example IV-DH 6%, which has the best functionality,
consists of only two single high molecular protein fractions compared to the IV-DH 3% which has six fractions. Further studies
are required to elucidate the structural composition of these
high molecular protein fractions in relation to the functionality.

The presence of cystine is important for irreversible gel
formation, but as the content of cystine is practically the same
in the hydrolysate made by I, II and IV as shown in Table IIIb,
it is concluded that the cystine content is not responsible for
the differences seen in whipping properties.

A preliminary organoleptic evaluation of the products did
not show any bitterness, in accordance with the observation that
the bitterness of soy protein hydrolyzed with Alcalase only becomes pronounced at DH-values of 7% and above (2). Therefore, the
present products may be used as nutritious ingredients and highly
functional proteins as well. In many food formulations they may
serve as substitutes for egg-white. This was for example demonstrated in meringue batters (see Table IIIb).

Isoelectric Soluble Protein Hydrolysates

An industrial process has been developed for production of
isoelectric soluble soy protein hydrolysate with no bitterness
and a bland taste (13). The raw material may be acid washed soy
white flakes, soy protein concentrate or soy protein isolate. The
raw material is hydrolyzed by the alkaline protease ALCALASE® to
a specified degree of hydrolysis using the pH-stat at pH = 8.0
(4).

Extensive proteolysis of a protein often results in the formation of bitter peptides (2). Therefore, a compromise between
high protein yield and low bitterness has to be found when
choosing the DH-value at which the hydrolysis reaction should be
terminated. For the present process a DH-value of about 10% seems
to be a reasonable value. The termination is performed by acid
inactivation of the enzyme and the acid used should be chosen in
accordance with the desired organoleptic characteristics of the
final hydrolysate. A totally non-bitter product can be produced
by use of an organic acid like malic or citric acid. Due to the
masking effects of such acids, absolutely no bitterness can be
detected even when the taste evaluation is performed at neutral
pH. Such products are found most suitable for soft drinks. However, when inorganic acids, e.g. hydrochloric or phosphoric acids
are used, a slight bitterness may be detected in the pure hydrolysate. However, when evaluated in for instance a meat product, no
bitterness at all can be tasted even when the hydrolysate is added
up to a proportion of 1 : 3 of hydrolyzed protein to meat protein.

A flow sheet of ISSPH-production is given in Fig. 8. The
carbon treatment removes the last traces of soy off-flavours.

Using the recommended process parameters, the filtered hydrolysate contains about 3% protein. Hyperfiltration is therefore
an attractive process to use for concentration before drying.

In pilot plant experiments we have used a 7 m^2 DDS-module
type 40 with tight cellulose acetate membranes type DDS-990. Concentration has been performed at pH = 4.0-4.5 in a batch system
at ambient temperature using 30 kp/m^2 delivered by a Rannie pis-
ton pump.

In Table IV the composition of retentates and average permeate fluxes are shown for different types of ISSPH. Volumes of
700-900 litres of clear hydrolysates were treated on the 7 m^2 DDS-
module, except for one experiment in which only 60 litres were
treated on a 0.36 m^2 DDS-LAB-module. The protein loss in the permeate was below 3% in all experiments. Figure 9 shows a typical
flux and dry matter curve versus the per cent of water removed as
permeate. Unfortunately the flux decreases rather much during the
process. Both increase in osmotic pressure and concentration polarization are responsible for this dependence. Later studies
have shown that the flux rate can be improved by increasing the
flow velocity over the membrane surface.

Desalination of ISSPH. Specific applications of ISSPH may
require a reduced content of salts, mainly NaCl. The membrane
DDS-865, a cellulose membrane, has been used for both direct hyperfiltration and for diafiltration, and it appears that it has
a high retention of hydrolyzed protein and a low retention of
salt. In Table V results are shown from an experiment in which a
hydrolysate of soy protein isolate containing NaCl-HCl is desalinated.

From a mass balance on nitrogen (N) as well as on non-nitro-
gen material (NNM) the following has been found:

direct hyperfiltration:	11% loss of N,
	74% removing of NNM
hyperfiltration and diafiltration:	23% loss of N,
	93% removing of NNM.

For most applications the product which may be obtained by
the direct hyperfiltration is sufficiently desalinated and the
protein loss of about 11% may be accepted. Preliminary results
also seem to indicate a slight reduction in bitterness and soy
off-flavour due to removal of very small bitter peptides and
other flavour compounds in the permeate when this desalination
membrane is used.

Process for Decoloration of Slaughterhouse Blood. A novel
protein ingredient can be manufactured by a controlled enzymatic

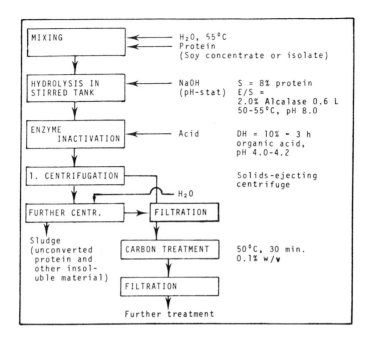

Figure 8. Flow sheet: production of a nonbitter, soluble soy protein hydrolysate suitable for incorporation into soft drinks and other low pH foods.

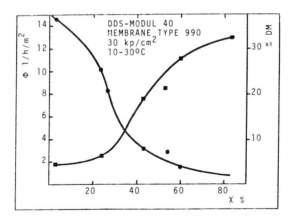

Figure 9. Hyperfiltration of HCl-containing ISSPH: Φ, flux in $1/h/m^2$; X, percentage of water removed; DM, percentage of dry matter (refractometer).

Table IV.   Processing Data Regarding Hyperfiltration of ISSPH

Type of ISSPH		Retentate				Vol. conc. ratio	Av. pres- sure Bar	Average permeate flux l/h/m²
DH(%)	Acid used for inact.	Before %x6.25	%DM	Final %Nx6.25	%DM			
10	malic	2.7	4.5	14.3	22.3	5.1	20	3.80
10	HCl	3.5	4.3	21.1	26.2	6.1	34	4.46
10	HCl	2.0	2.8	14.2	17.6	6.7	34	4.67
15	malic	1.8	3.2	13.0	23.3	7.3	29	4.80
10	malic	3.9	5.6	12.4	19.8	3.4	32	4.03
15	malic	3.5	5.4	16.8	27.5	4.9	32	7.08
10	HCl	-	3.9*	-	30.2*	7.1	30	7.48
10	malic	-	5.8*	-	26.3	5	32	5.96
10	malic	3.9	5.4	14.0	19.7	3.6	43	32.83**

*by refractometer   **60 litres treated on a DDS-LAB-module

Table V.   Desalination of ISSPH by Hyperfiltration on a DDS-865 CA Membrane

Permeate flux l/h/m²	X %water removed	Y %water added	Permeate %Nx6.25	%DM	Retentate %Nx6.25	%DM	% $\frac{Nx6.25}{DM}$
51.7	0	-	-	-	3.44	4.20	81.9
45.0	16.7	-	-	-	-	-	-
38.3	41.7	-	0.25	0.80	6.00	6.89	87.1
25.3	66.6	-	-	-	-	-	-
13.0	83.3	-	1.25	2.52	18.31	19.90	92.0
7.0	87.5	-	(Σ0.44)	(Σ1.08)	-	-	-
8.7	87.5	0	-	-	-	-	-
7.8	33.0	33.0	1.38	2.23	20.38	21.27	95.8
8.3	133.0	133.0					
8.0	233.3	233.3	0.69	0.77	18.50	18.23	101.5
8.7	300.0	300.0	(Σ0.94)	(Σ1.28)			

DDS-LAB-module, average pressure: 29 kp/cm², 20-30°C

hydrolysis and subsequent decoloration of the red blood cell
fraction arising as a by-product in plasma recovery (14). A flow
sheet of this process is shown in Fig. 10. The process is much
similar to that of ISSPH-production.

Hyperfiltration serves the purpose of concentration of both
plasma and hydrolysate separately. Flux data are very similar to
those obtained on soy protein hydrolysates, and also the total
economy of such process seems attractive. The main reason is that
slaughterhouse blood in most cases is regarded as a waste product
having no value, or even a negative value.

Discussion. In the above-mentioned examples membrane processes are found useful for both concentration and desalination.
One reason for recommending hyperfiltration instead of evaporation in this area is the economical factors. Multi-step-evapora-
tors are still more economic than reverse osmosis in very big
plants, but the production of protein hydrolysates will in all
probability be distributed between a number of middle-sized
plants requiring new investments. At a time with increasing costs
of energy, hyperfiltration is recommendable in such plants. Also,
the freedom of choosing membranes which may improve the quality
of the proteins, for example by removing of off-flavours and salt,
speaks for hyperfiltration.

Continuous Protein Hydrolysis in a Membrane Reactor

The membrane reactor is an ultrafiltration system, in which
a high concentration of hydrolytic enzyme is confined. High molecular weight substrate is fed continuously to the reactor, and
the low molecular weight products are removed simultaneously as
permeate. Ideally, a steady state is reached, in which the degradation of the substrate is carried out indefinitely with high efficiency and negligible loss of enzyme.

The membrane reactor concept was demonstrated in laboratory
scale a decade ago by Butterworth et al. (15) and by Ghose and
Kostick (16) in studies on the hydrolysis of starch and cellulose, respectively. Later on several publications have appeared
describing the analogous, continuous conversion of various proteins into peptides intended for human nutrition (17-22). Among
these works only that of Iaccobucci et al. (18) presents a quantitative model of the membrane reactor in continuous protein hydrolysis, and it is also the only demonstration of the practical
feasibility of the concept in pilot plant scale.

Iaccobucci et al. (18) applied an acid, thermostable fungal
protease from Penicillium duponti in their work. The choice of
this enzyme had two advantages: The hydrolysis conditions ensured
virtual sterility (pH = 3.7, 60°C) and the peptides were quite
palatable (23). A major disadvantage of working in the acid range
is that soy protein isolate, which was used as substrate, is insoluble. In practice this causes mechanical problems if the substrate concentration is not kept sufficiently low (18).

As described previously in the present publication, we have developed a batch process for producing isoelectric soluble soy protein hydrolysate (ISSPH) with a bland taste. From studies of the kinetics of the hydrolysis reaction, which takes place in this process, we have come to the conclusion that the reaction is adequately controlled by keeping pH constant and monitoring DH. Termination of the reaction at a preset value of DH ensures a reproducible, optimal organoleptic quality of the product.

In the following the possibilities are discussed of producing ISSPH with a fixed DH-value during a continuous hydrolysis reaction in a membrane reactor using similar hydrolysis conditions as in the batch process. The slightly alkaline conditions are advantageous from a mechanical point of view, because the substrate is dispersible/soluble, but may also imply a greater risk of infection. The change from an insoluble to a soluble substrate, and in particular the application of the DH concept, immediately led to the conclusion that the quantitative model described by Iaccobucci et al. (18) would in our case have to be substituted by an independently derived and more complete model, which only on certain points is inspired by the former. The full derivation of the model is described in the Appendix of the present publication. Based on the kinetics of the batch hydrolysis it is demonstrated in this model that it is possible to run the membrane reactor in steady state, i.e. DH can be kept constant in the reactor. The steady state is intrinsically stable and can be achieved immediately by carrying out the hydrolysis as a batch reaction with zero membrane flux until the desired DH-value is reached, cf. Fig. 11. At this point, the flux is increased to a preset value, and if the various parameters in the system have been chosen correctly, DH will be maintained constant.

A few experiments have been carried out in the laboratory scale with a one litre hydrolysis vessel, connected to a small impeller pump and a Sartorius laboratory module fitted with DDS GR6-P membranes (0.2 m^2). However, the flow resistance in this module was too large, and it was soon concluded that a resonably constant flux was unattainable. Despite these difficulties, the qualitative behaviour of the reactor variables could be predicted from the model and verified experimentally. For example, with decreasing flux DH increased, but the rate of the base consumption decreased, while the protein concentration in the permeate remained quite stable as predicted. The hydrolysate was evaluated and found comparable in quality to ISSPH produced in the batch process. These results have encouraged us to continue the work in pilot plant with the DDS-35 module, where we can expect considerably more favourable flow conditions. The first experiments carried out so far indicate that a reasonable flux in the order of 50 1/m^2/h (approx. 1 1/m^2/min.) can be attained but that foaming problems necessitate the construction of pressurized air free reactor. Future studies will therefore be needed to produce a complete experimental verification of the derived model.

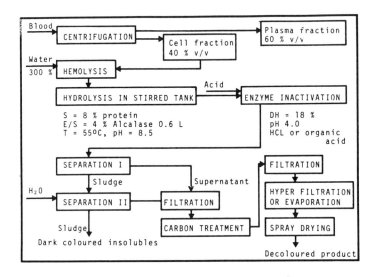

Figure 10.   Enzymatic decoloration of blood

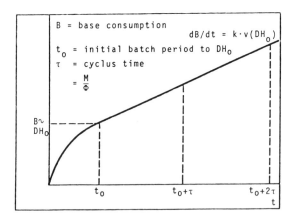

Figure 11.   Base Consumption—ideal steady-state protein concentration at $t_o = P_o$

An overview of the variables in the membrane reactor process is given in Fig. 12, and those equations, which are most relevant from an engineering point of view, are summarized in Box 1. The significance of most of the variables should appear from Fig. 13 and Box 1 immediately, – for a full explanation, the reader is referred to the appendix.

The main rationale behind the membrane reactor generally appears to be savings of enzyme and the high conversion yield, compared with a batch hydrolysis process, It should perhaps be mentioned that the emphasis on enzyme costs is not particularly relevant in the present case, as the major cost factors for the existing batch process are the raw materials and the capital costs (13). In any case the rationale is based on the assumption that the reaction can be carried on for many cycles with no or only a slight purging. However, if a substantial fraction of the substrate is non-degradable, inert material will rapidly build up in the reactor causing mechanical problems. A considerable purge is necessary if the concentration of this material shall be kept at a reasonably low level. This has a drastic, negative influence on the instantaneous yield, as demonstrated in Fig. 14 and Table VI. Also the enzyme loss during purging will be considerable unless the fraction (y) of degradable protein in the substrate is close to 100%. For soy protein isolate Iaccobucci et al. (18) found that 6.2% of the protein in the substrate accumulated as inert material – in other words, when comparing the membrane process with the batch process, it seems most relevant to use y = 94%.

If a short cycle time is chosen (e.g. 10 min.) Table VI shows that the enzyme consumption will be much higher than in the batch process, as soon as purging starts (1.8 hours from start). The enzyme consumption can be decreased by enlarging the reactor size, as enzyme concentration and reactor size are inversely proportional (eq. I, Box 1), but it will still be of the same order of magnitude as in the batch process. The increase in reactor size has, however, the disadvantage that more protein substrate is confined and lost in the end (Table VI). The concomitant loss of confined enzyme is found to be the same in both cases, which is obvious from eq. I.

If we look at Table VII, the figures for a total run of twelve hours are given, and it appears that the short cycle time will give a 1% higher protein yield than the long cycle time, but at the expense of a much higher enzyme consumption. A yield above 80% appears at the first glance favourable compared with the batch process where the hydrolysis process yields a little above 60% (13). However, the yields must be compared with respect to the original raw material: soy white flakes. It is, of course, necessary to feed the reactor with soy isolate and this is produced from white flakes in a yield of 60–65%. Based on white flakes the protein yield of the membrane process as well as the batch process will be approximately 50%.

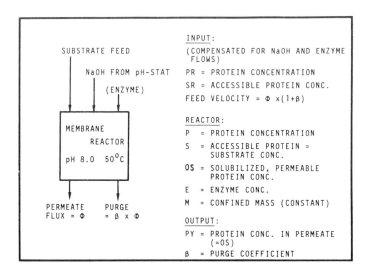

Figure 12.   Variables in reactor model

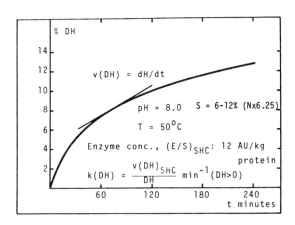

Figure 13.   SHC for soy isolate & alcalase

Table VI. Some Key Figures for the Production of ISSPH on the Membrane Reactor

M/Φ	y %	β %	$n_o \cdot M/\Phi$ hours	η %	a AU/kg	b	Substrate processed at n_o, kg
10 min.	98	2.7	6	94.1	9.9	150 AU	15.0
	96	5.6	2.8	88.3	19.9	&	7.4
	94	8.7	1.8	82.7	30.0	0.6 kg	5.0
40 min.	98	2.7	24^c	94.1	2.5		58.2^c
	96	5.6	11.3	88.3	5.0	150 AU	27.8
	94	8.7	7.3	82.7	7.5	&	18.2
	92	11.9	5.3	77.3	10.0	2.4 kg	13.4
	90	15.4	4.0	72.0	12.5		10.2

a) Enzyme consumption per kg substrate
b) Enzyme and substrate present at start in reactor
c) Unrealistic in practice because of microbial deterioration

Table VII. Total-Yield Calculations on the Membrane Reactor

M/Φ cycle time	y %	n_t	n_o	E AU/l	pr m² membrane Subst. used kg	Enz. used AU	Enz./subst. ratio AU/kg	Total yield %
10 min.	98	72	36	15	29.8	296	9.9	94.0
	96		17		30.6	612	20.0	88.0
	94		11		31.5	946	30.0	82.3
40 min.	98	18	36	3.75	31.2	150	4.8	89.7
	96		17		31.3	158	5.0	87.2
	94		11		32.2	241	7.5	81.3

I: $E \simeq \dfrac{\Phi}{M} \times PR \times (E/S)_{SHC} \times \dfrac{1}{k(DH)}$

II: $P_o = \dfrac{PR}{f(DH)}$ $(f(DH) < 1)$

III: $\beta = \left[\dfrac{Z_m}{PR \times (1-y)} - 1 \right]^{-1}$

IV: $\eta = y \times \left[1 - \dfrac{P_o}{Z_m} \times (1-y) \right]$

V: $n = (t-t_o) \times \dfrac{\Phi}{M}$ (number of cycles)

VI: $n_o = \dfrac{Z_m}{PR \times (1-y)} - \dfrac{P_o}{PR}$

Substrate used: $M \times [P_o + PR \times (n_t + \beta \times (n_t-n_o))]$

Enzyme used: $M \times E \times [1 + n_t \times C + \beta \times (n_t-n_o)]$

Total yield: $\sim$ $\dfrac{n_o \times y + (n_t-n_o) \times \eta - P_o/PR}{n_t}$

Box 1. Equations used in engineering calculations of the membra-
        ne reactor

The derivation of the equations is given in the appendix.

I   is used for calculating the enzyme concentration from the
        kinetic data of the batch hydrolysis.

II   gives P_o (protein conc. at start in reactor)

III   gives β, the purge coefficient from acceptable level of
        inert matter = Z_m

IV   gives η, the instantaneous yield

V   gives the number of cycles for a given period

VI   gives the number of cycles before purging must be started.

If we briefly consider the main investments in the two processes for a production of 1000 tons of ISSPH per year and include in the membrane process equipment for producing soy isolate, the membrane process appears to require slightly higher total investments.

The results given above indicate that there is no obvious advantage of substituting the existing batch process for production of ISSPH by a membrane reactor process. However, this does not in general mean that continuous protein hydrolysis in a membrane reactor will be uneconomical. For example if the substrate is more completely degradable than soy protein (casein might be such a substrate), it is expected that in a small scale plant (where the capital costs would favour the membrane reactor) the membrane reactor process could be very attractive. The production of protein hydrolysates for dietetic and medical use, could well be considered in this context.

APPENDIX

Development of a Kinetic Model for Protein Hydrolysis in a Membrane Reactor

General considerations

Basis for the kinetic model is a standard batch hydrolysis experiment (2). Fig. 14 shows the standard hydrolysis curve for soy protein isolate - Alcalase. The reaction constant (pseudo first order rate constant) is calculated from the standard curve by fitting the inverse curve in a small DH-range (ΔDH $\sim$ 1.3%) to a second order Newton-Gregory polynomium (24), and finding v(DH) by differentiation. This procedure has in our experience proved to be the simplest and most reliable way of obtaining values of the reaction rate. k(DH) is shown in fig. 15. - it varies strongly with DH.

As demonstrated previously (25) there is substrate saturation throughout the reaction which means that for a constant E/S v(DH) and therefore k(DH) is independent of S. Also, E/S and v(DH) are proportional to each other as usual (ibid).

Fig. 12 gives an overview of the variables in the reactor model. In accordance with what was demonstrated by Iacobucci et al. (18) it is assumed that the concentration of solubilized, permeable protein is equal on both sides of the membrane. This assumption is substantiated by the fact that the protein hydrolyzate consists mainly of smaller, soluble peptides and unconverted protein (2). The concentration of accessible protein in the feed stream, SR, will be smaller than PR, as it is likely that a small, constant percentage of the protein is undegradable, in accordance with what was found by Iacobucci et al. (18). This fraction counts as protein in a Kjeldahl analysis, but is otherwise consi-

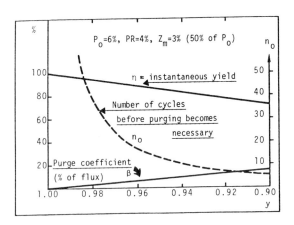

Figure 14. Relationship between certain important variables in the membrane reactor

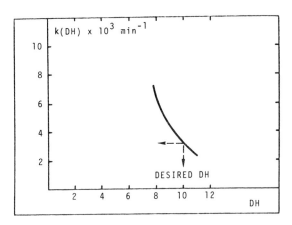

Figure 15. The reaction constant, k(DH), from the standard hydrolysis curve

dered inert, i.e. it is assumed that its accumulation in the retentate does not influence the hydrolysis kinetics appreciably.
This assumption will be substantiated later.

It has been found in batch hydrolysis experiments that the
proportion of soluble nitrogen to total nitrogen is gradually increasing with DH (2). For a constant DH this proportion is independent of S (26) in accordance with the fact that v(DH) is independent of S. It thus seems reasonable to assume that OS/S will
be a monotonously increasing function of DH and independent of S.
The relative increase of OS/S will always be equal to or smaller
than the corresponding relative increase in DH – this is a mathematical consequence of the fact that the average peptide chain
length in the soluble fraction of a hydrolyzate will be constant
or decreasing with DH (26).

In batch hydrolysis experiments we have generally not distinguished between S and P, but have assumed S = P for the standard hydrolysis curve. However, the distinction between S and P
is crucial in the present case where inert protein (N×6.25) accumulates. P_o denotes the protein concentration in the beginning
of the experiment.

Fig. 11 shows the principles in an ideal, steady state experiment. At t=0 the hydrolysis is started as a batch hydrolysis
($\Phi = 0$). When the desired DH-value has been reached (DH=DH_o at
t=t_o) the membrane reactor is started, i.e. peptides are permeating through the membrane with the volume flux, Φ, and fresh substrate is added continuously to replace the degraded protein.
In the following it will be proved that if the values of the independent variables (i.e. PR, P_o, E, M, Φ and β) have been chosen
correctly, the reactor will immediately be in steady state, most
generally defined as DH remaining constantly equal to DH_o. The
equations which describe the relationship between the variables
will be derived in the following sections.

The above general considerations are summarized in Box 2.

The steady-state equations

The most general definition of steady state was given previously
namely that DH should remain constant. However, this definition
is too general to be of practical use, and it is therefore necessary in the following to assume that the following parameters also remain constant throughout the experiment:

$$\text{PR, M, E, } \Phi \text{ (and } \beta) \quad \text{all constant} \qquad (9)$$

Convenience dictates that PR and M should remain constant.
E is kept constant by replacing the loss of enzyme through inactivation, permeation and purging. Φ can be regulated by the
pressure drop and can be maintained reasonable constant in a
well built system in which high flow rates are obtained.

Quasi-stationary conditions, i.e. slow changes in the above
parameters will be dealt with later.

Mass balance considerations in the time period t_0 to (t_0+dt) lead to the following:

$$v(DH) = \frac{E/P_0}{(E/S)_{SHC}} \times v(DH)_{SHC}, \text{ which can be written as}$$

$$\frac{d(DH)}{dt} = \frac{E}{P_0} \times \frac{1}{(E/S)_{SHC}} \times DH \times k(DH) \tag{1}$$

$$PY = OS \tag{2}$$

$$y = \frac{SR}{PR} = \frac{S}{P_0} < 1 \quad (y \text{ is constant}) \tag{3}$$

Accumulated inert material:

$$Z = P - S = P - P_0 \times (\frac{SR}{PR}) \tag{4}$$

$$\frac{OS}{S} = f(DH) \qquad (\text{indep. of } S) \tag{5}$$

$$0 < \left|\frac{d(OS/S)}{OS/S}\right| \leq \left|\frac{d(DH)}{DH}\right| \tag{6}$$

which in combination with (3) leads to:

$$0 < \left|\frac{d(OS/S)}{OS/S}\right| = \left|\frac{d(OS/P_0)}{OS/P_0}\right| \leq \left|\frac{d(DH)}{DH}\right| \tag{7}$$

Base consumption in batch experiment:

$$B = \alpha \times h_{tot} \times (\frac{DH}{100}) \times M \times S \tag{8}$$

where: α is the dissociation factor for the amino group. In the present case, where pH = 8.0 and pK = 7.1, α = 0.88

h_{tot} is the total content of peptide bonds in the protein. In the present case, h_{tot} = 7.8 meqv./g (N×6.25) (soy protein)

Box 2. Summary of fundamental relationships which are generally valid

Substrate-product balance:

$$SR \times \Phi \times (1+\beta) \times dt = PY \times \Phi \times dt + S \times \Phi \times \beta \times dt + M \times dS$$
$$\text{(input)} \qquad\qquad\qquad \text{(output)} \qquad\qquad\qquad \text{(accum.)}$$
$$\tag{10}$$

or:

$$\frac{dS}{dt} = \frac{\Phi}{M} \times [SR \times (1+\beta) - PY - \beta \times S] \tag{11}$$

Note that S denotes hydrolyzed as well as unhydrolyzed protein.

Base balance: The added substrate from the feed is the left side of eq. (10), this substrate shall be hydrolyzed to DH_o, cfr. eq. (8):

$$dB = \alpha \times h_{tot} \times \left(\frac{DH_o}{100}\right) \times SR \times \Phi \times (1+\beta) \times dt \tag{12}$$

Base consumption thus takes place at a rate given by this equation:

$$\frac{dB}{dt} = \alpha \times h_{tot} \times \left(\frac{DH_o}{100}\right) \times SR \times \Phi \times (1+\beta) \tag{13}$$

Now, if the hydrolysis were continued as a batch hydrolysis in the period t_o to (t_o+dt), DH would increase from DH_o to $(DH_o + d(DH))$. This increase in DH would of course be accompanied by a consumption of base. From eq. (8) we know that dB and d(DH) are proportional in the batch hydrolysis, where S is constant (and equal to P_o). Thus

$$\frac{dB}{dt} = \alpha \times h_{tot} \times M \times P_o \times \frac{1}{100} \times \frac{d(DH)}{dt} \tag{14}$$

Inserting eq. (1) in eq. (14) for DH = DH_o gives:

$$\frac{dB}{dt} = \alpha \times h_{tot} \times M \times E \times \frac{1}{(E/S)_{SHC}} \times \left(\frac{DH_o}{100}\right) \times k(DH_o) \tag{15}$$

Neither eq. (13) nor eq. (15) depend on the actual substrate concentration in the reactor. In both equations it can be seen that the steady state criteria in eq. (9) result in dB/dt being constant with time, cfr. fig. 12. Eq. (13) and eq. (15) can therefore be equalized, whereby α, h_{tot} and $(DH_o/100)$ cancel out:

$$SR \times \Phi \times (1+\beta) = M \times E \times \frac{1}{(E/S)_{SHC}} \times k(DH_o) \tag{16}$$

or; as

$$SR = y \times PR \qquad \text{(eq. (3)):}$$

$$E = \frac{\Phi}{M} \times y \times PR \times (1+\beta) \times (E/S)_{SHC} \times \frac{1}{k(DH_o)} \qquad (17)$$

Eq. (17) is the desired relationship between the variables in steady state.

   Substrate product balance in steady state: For DH=DH$_o$ (constant) eq. (7) leads to that (OS/P_o) must be constant with time. As OS/S is a function of DH and independent of S, cfr. eq. (5) we can see that S must be constant in steady state. Eq. (11) therefore leads to:

$$0 = \frac{\Phi}{M} \times [SR \times (1+\beta) - PY - \beta \times S] \qquad (18)$$

or:

$$PY = SR \times (1+\beta) - \beta \times S \qquad (19)$$

As PY=OS, eq. (19) can be rearranged to give

$$\left(\frac{OS}{S}\right) = f(DH_o) = \frac{SR}{S} \times (1+\beta) - \beta \qquad (20)$$

From (3) it is seen that $SR/S = PR/P_o$; inserting this in (20) gives:

$$f(DH_o) = \frac{PR}{P_o} \times (1+\beta) - \beta \qquad (21)$$

(21) is used to calculate P_o (assuming f(DH) is known for DH = DH$_o$).

(3) inserted in (19) gives:

$$PY = y \times [PR \times (1+\beta) - \beta \times P_o] \qquad (22)$$

In case $\beta = 0$, PY = y × PR. y can thus be measured easily by Kjeldahl analyses on the permeate in steady state with no purge.

Stability of the steady state

In the following it will be proved that the steady state, as it is defined by eq. (17) is intrinsically stable. In other words when the independent variables, E, Φ, M, SR and β are kept constant, the system should stabilize itself around the predicted values of DH = DH$_o$ and S = S$_o$.

   Mass balance considerations on the definition of DH, i.e. the percentage of peptide bonds cleaved, immediately lead to the result that an instantaneous change in S leads to an inversely proportional change in DH.

$$\left(\frac{dS}{S}\right)_t = - \left(\frac{d(DH)}{DH}\right)_t \qquad \text{(t constant)} \qquad (23)$$

The addition of fresh, unhydrolysed substrate does not per se change the reaction rate, expressed as dB/dt, because we have substrate saturation in the system. This is also indirectly expressed in equations (13) and (15) which do not contain any term in S. However, dB/dt does change because of the change in DH, and it is now postulated that this change is adequately described by eq. (15):

$$\frac{dB}{dt} = \alpha \times h_{tot} \times M \times E \times \frac{1}{(E/S)_{SHC}} \times \left(\frac{DH}{100}\right) \times k(DH) \qquad (15a)$$

The validity of eq. (15a) rests on the assumption that the addition of fresh substrate to a hydrolyzate with $DH = DH_o$ will result in a new substrate composition which is kinetically identical to a hydrolyzate with a correspondingly lower DH-value as given by eq. (23). This is only approximately true in reality, but it has been demonstrated that dB/dt does increase considerably when fresh substrate is added to a batch hydrolysis experiment (26). This observation is in qualitative accordance with eq. (15a) and this is sufficient for the following line of arguments.

Differentiation of eq. (8) leads to

$$\frac{dB}{dt} \times dt = \alpha \times h_{tot} \times \left[M \times S \times \frac{d(DH)}{100} + M \times dS \times \frac{DH}{100}\right] \qquad (24)$$

The period t to (t+dt) is now considered. After the change in S from S_o to $(S_o+\Delta S)$ $(\Delta S>0)$, we know from eq. (23) that DH is lowered and that dB/dt in eq. (24) increases compared with equations (13) and (15). The increase in fresh substrate which shall be hydrolyzed to the new, lower value of DH, is as in eq. (13) equal to the amount supplied by the feed. Thus the second term in the bracket in eq. (24) is equal to:

$$SR \times \Phi \times (1+\beta) \times \frac{DH}{100} \times dt < SR \times \Phi \times (1+\beta) \times \frac{DH_o}{100} \times dt \qquad (25)$$

The right side is equal to $\frac{dB}{dt} \times \frac{1}{\alpha} \times \frac{1}{h_{tot}}$

before the instantaneous change in S from S_o til $S_o + \Delta S$ (see 13)). As dB/dt increases after this change, (25) proves that the first term in the bracket in (24) must be positive:

$$M \times (S_o + \Delta S) \times \frac{d(DH)}{100} > 0 \qquad (26)$$

and consequently: $d(DH) > 0$.

If $\Delta S < 0$ a similar line of arguments will lead to the conclusion that DH will immediately assume a new higher value and thereafter decrease. We have thus demonstrated that there is negative feed-back in the system with respect to DH.

The <u>instantaneous</u> change in S ($\Delta S > 0$) will, of course, not change OS as it is assumed that the fresh substrate does not contribute to OS. However, it can be shown that immediately after, OS will begin to rise because the inequality (6) will always be valid. In the present case where OS is not changed immediately the equality sign will hold approximately:

From eq. (5) we get:

$$OS_o = f(DH_o) \times S_o \qquad (5a)$$

$$OS = f(DH) \times (S_o + \Delta S) \qquad (5b)$$

Which gives:

$$\frac{OS}{OS_o} = \frac{f(DH)}{f(DH)_o} \times \frac{S_o + \Delta S}{S_o} \qquad (27$$

or:

$$\frac{OS}{OS_o} > \frac{DH}{DH_o} \times \frac{S_o + \Delta S}{S_o}$$

The lowest possible value of DH/DH_o is according to eq. (23) equal to S_o/S, in the present case: $S_o/(S_o + \Delta S)$. Thus the inequality below must hold, as soon as DH reincreases towards DH_o.

$$\frac{DH}{DH_o} > \frac{S_o}{S_o + \Delta S} \qquad (29)$$

Combining eq. (29) and eq. (28) leads to:

$$\frac{OS}{OS_o} > 1$$

The rise in OS means that PY will rise, because OS = PY. From eq. (11):

$$\frac{dS}{dt} = \frac{\Phi}{M} \times [SR \times (1+\beta) - PY - \beta \times S] \qquad (11)$$

we can then conclude that because both PY and S are larger than previously, dS/dt (which is zero in steady state) must be negative.

A similar line of arguments leads to the conclusion that if $\Delta S < 0$, dS/dt will be positive. There is therefore negative feed-back in the system with respect to S.

The demonstration of negative feed-back for the two dependent variables, DH and S, is proof of the intrinsic stability of the steady state.

Quasi-stationary conditions

If the changes in the independent parameters are slow, we have quasi-stationary conditions and the steady state equations will hold. By slow changes is meant that the rate of change in DH caused thereby is slow compared to the reaction rate, d(DH)/dt, as given by eq. (1).

$$\left| \frac{\Delta DH}{\Delta t} \right| << \frac{E}{P_o} \times \frac{1}{(E/S)_{SHC}} \times DH \times k(DH) \qquad (30)$$

The relevant steady state equations are:

$$E = \frac{\Phi}{M} \times SR \times (1+\beta) \times (E/S)_{SHC} \times \frac{1}{k(DH)} \qquad (17a)$$

$$PY = SR \times (1+\beta) - \beta \times S \qquad (19a)$$

$$f(DH) = \frac{SR}{S} \times (1+\beta) - \beta \qquad (20a)$$

From fig. 15 is obtained that:

$$DH = 8 \Rightarrow k(DH)^{-1} = 160 \text{ min}$$
$$DH = 9 \Rightarrow \text{do.} = 230 \text{ min}$$
$$DH = 10 \Rightarrow \text{do.} = 310 \text{ min}$$
$$DH = 11 \Rightarrow \text{do.} = 420 \text{ min}$$

Consequently, even rather large changes in the independent variables will only lead to comparatively small changes in DH. For example, a 20% relative change in E, Φ, M, SR og $(1+\beta)$ will only change DH approximately 0.6 units (e.g. from 10 to 10.6%).

The corresponding relative change in f(DH) is less than 6% and
this leads again to a change in S of less than 6%, eq.(20a), provided $\beta \ll 1$. This is of considerable importance in practice, as
it is difficult to avoid some decrease in the values of E and Φ
during continuous operation of the membrane reactor due to fouling and enzyme losses. Fortunately, according to eq. (17a) E and
Φ will partially counteract each other in their effect on DH.

The above has the practical consequence that because
$y \times (1+\beta) \simeq 1$ in most cases, E is adequately given by the simplified equation:

$$E \simeq \frac{\Phi}{M} \times PR \times (E/S)_{SHC} \times \frac{1}{k(DH)}$$ (17b)

At any time the DH-value can be calculated quite simply from the
base consumption in the period, Δt (13)

$$\frac{\Delta B/\Delta t}{\Phi} = \alpha \times h_{tot} \times \left(\frac{DH}{100}\right) \times SR \times (1+\beta)$$ (31)

As the relative change in DH is less than the relative de-
crease in Φ it appears from eq.(31) that $\Delta B/\Delta t$ will decrease with
decreasing Φ, although DH actually increases!

The change in PY as a result of changes in the independent
parameters is negligible. This is evident from eq. (19a) because
S changes only slightly and $\beta \ll 1$. It will therefore be observed in practice that PY remains very stable during the operation
of the reactor.

The question of accumulated, inert matter. The data of Iacobucci et al. (18) indicate that even considerable amounts of
accumulated inert matter (half of total solids content in the reactor) did not disturb the steady state. How the case will be in
the present system, where Alcalase is used instead of P.duponti
protease has not yet been investigated, but as it will be shown
in the following it seems plausible that a similar result could
be obtained.
It seams reasonable to assume that the most likely kinetic
effect, if any at all, of the inert residual matter from the degradation of soy protein will be that of a competitive enzyme in-
hibitor. As demonstrated previously (25), V decreases but K_m remains fairly constant with increasing DH. No non-competitive inhibition of Alcalase takes place in the system at least at DH =
0 (fig. 3, ibid.). If these observations are extrapolated V
drops to zero, but K_m can be expected to remain constant (or at
least not decrease) for the undegradable residue.
The standard Michaelis-Menten equation for competitive inhibition is:

$$v = \frac{V}{1 + K_m/S \times (1+I/K_i)} \tag{32}$$

From the above we can expect that $K_i \sim K_m \sim 0.7\%$ (average of K_m values in fig. 4, ibid.). If $S = 6\%$ and I changes from 0 to 1%, the decrease in v will be 15%. This will correspond to a decrease in E of 15%. The possible inhibitory effect of the accumulated inert matter could thus be counteracted by gradually increasing E.

Future experiments will be needed to elucidate the kinetic effects of the inert matter. However, the above considerations indicate that the problems encountered in practice will be small.

The concentration of inert material, Z, in the reactor can be found from the protein mass balance:

$$PR \times \Phi \times (1+\beta) \times dt = PY \times \Phi \times dt + P \times \Phi \times \beta \times dt + M \times dP \tag{33}$$

By applying the expression for PY in steady state as given by eq. (22), eq. (33) is reduced to:

$$PR \times (1+\beta) \times (1-y) = \beta \times (P - y \times P_o) + \frac{M}{\Phi} \times \frac{dP}{dt} \tag{34}$$

From eq. (4) we know: $Z = P - y \times P_o$ and $dZ = dP$. Thus

$$\frac{M}{\Phi} \times \frac{dZ}{dt} + \beta \times Z = PR \times (1+\beta) \times (1-y) \tag{35}$$

Eq. (35) is a linear, first order differential equation ($\beta > 0$). The boundary condition is that $Z = P_o \times (1-y)$ for $t = t_o$, independently of β. The solution to eq. (35) is then:

$$Z = PR \times \frac{(1+\beta)}{\beta} \times (1-y) \times \left[1 - \left(1 - \frac{P_o}{PR} \times \frac{\beta}{(1+\beta)} \right) \right.$$
$$\left. \times e^{-\beta \times \frac{\Phi}{M} \times (t-t_o)} \right] \tag{36}$$

For $t \Rightarrow \infty$ $Z_{lim} = PR \times \frac{(1+\beta)}{\beta} \times (1-y)$ \tag{37}

In case $\beta = 0$, (35) is immediately solved:

$$Z = \left[\frac{\Phi}{M} \times PR \times (t - t_o) + P_o \right] \times (1-y) \tag{38}$$

As expected, Z increases linearly with time, when there is no purge.

Compensation for Enzyme Losses

Enzyme is lost through purging, inactivation and permeation. All three are proportional to E. The mass balance on the enzyme gives:

$$M \times dE = \Phi \times \beta \times E \times dt + C_1 \times E \times dt$$
$$\text{(purge)} \qquad \text{(inactiv.)}$$

$$+ C_2 \times \Phi \times E \times dt$$
$$\text{(permeation)} \qquad\qquad\qquad (39)$$

or:

$$\frac{dE}{E} = \left[\frac{\Phi}{M} \times (\beta + C_2) + C_1 \right] \times dt \qquad (40)$$

If the inactivation losses are small, eq. (40) can be simplified to

$$\frac{dE}{E} \simeq \frac{\Phi}{M} \times (\beta + C) \times dt \qquad (41)$$

or on finite form:

$$\frac{\Delta E}{E} \simeq \frac{\Phi}{M} \times (\beta + C) \times \Delta t \qquad (42)$$

Yield Calculations

The instantaneous yield, η is defined as the proportion between the substrate flux and the permeate flux (protein basis). From the protein mass balance (33), η is immediately obtained:

$$\eta = y \times \left[1 - \frac{P_o}{PR} \times \frac{\beta}{(1+\beta)} \right] \qquad (43)$$

The total yield is the yield based on a complete run, including the starting up. The protein present in the reactor at $t = t_o$ cannot be recovered in the end, because if the substrate feed is interrupted (PR = 0), DH cannot be maintained constant, but will increase rapidly.

The most economical way of running the reactor is to keep $\beta = 0$ until Z reaches a preset limit, Z_m. The number of cycles, i.e.: $n \equiv (t-t_o) \times \frac{\Phi}{M}$, which corresponds to Z_m is found by solving (38):

$$n_o = \frac{Z_m}{PR \times (1-y)} - \frac{P_o}{PR} \qquad (44)$$

Following the period given by n_o, purging is established and is found solving (37):

$$\beta = \left[\frac{Z_m}{PR \times (1-y)} \; 1 \right]^{-1} \tag{45}$$

Combining eq. (45) with eq. (43) gives:

$$\eta = y \times \left[1 - \frac{P_o}{Z_m} \times (1-y) \right] \tag{46}$$

In one cycle the mass of substrate fed is $PR \times M \times (1+\beta)$.
In n_t cycles $(n_t > n_o)$ the total yield (including the loss of protein confined at the end), can be calculated from the instaneous yields:

Product formed:

$$n_o \times y \times PR \times M + (n_t - n_o) \times \eta \times PR \times M \times (1+\beta)$$

Substrate used:

$$M \times P_o + n_o \times PR \times M + (n_t - n_o) \times PR \times M \times (1+\beta)$$

The last can be simplified slightly to:

$$M \times [P_o + PR \times (n_t + \beta(n_t - n_o))]$$

$$\text{Total yield} = \frac{n_o \times y + (n_t - n_o) \times (1+\beta) \times \eta}{\dfrac{P_o}{PR} + n_t + \beta(n_t - n_o)} \tag{47}$$

In most practical cases, where β is small and the number of cycles is 10-100, eq. (47) can be simplified to:

$$\text{Total yield} \simeq \frac{n_o \times y + (n_t - n_o) \times \eta - P_o/PR}{n_t} \tag{48}$$

The amount of enzyme consumed is $M \times E \times (\beta+C)$ per cycle.
Total amount of enzyme in n_t cycles is then (including inital enzyme):

Enzyme used: $M \times E + n_o \times C \times M \times E + (n_t - n_o) \times (\beta+C) \times M \times E$

or: $\tag{49}$

Enzyme used: $M \times E \times [1 + n_t \times C + \beta \times (n_t - n_o)] \tag{50}$

Acknowledgement

We wish to thank the staff at Enzyme Application Technology Pilot
Plant and at Enzyme Application Technology I for their skillful
assistance in all the practical work carried out in connection
with this paper. Also we want to thank Mr. Peer N. Jørgensen at
Pharmacological Laboratory - Novo Industri A/S, Bagsvaerd for the
immunochemical examinations. Finally we thank our colleague,
Mr. Finn Jacobsen for drawing our attention to the possibilities
of using hyperfiltration for desalination of ISSPH.

Literature cited

1. Manak, L.J., Lawhon, J.T., and Lusas, E.W., J. Food Sci.
    (1980) 45, 236-245.

2. Adler-Nissen, J., and Sejr Olsen, H., ACS Symp. Ser.
    (1979) 92, 125-146.

3. Adler-Nissen, J., J. Agric. Food Chem. (1976) 24, 1090-93

4. Adler-Nissen, J., Process Biochem. (1977) 12 (6), 18-23,32.

5. Sejr Olsen, H., Lebensm.-Wiss. u.-Technol., (1978) 11,57-64.

6. Christensen, L.K., Compt.-rend. Lab Carlsberg, Sér. chim.,
    (1952) 28 (1), 39-169.

7. Novo Industri A/S, "Proteolytic Enzymes for the Modification
    of Food Proteins", IB 163, Bagsvaerd 1978.

8. Sejr Olsen, H., Isolation of Bean Protein by Ultrafiltration
    In: Proceedings of the International symp. on Sep. proc. by
    Membranes, Ion-exchange and Freeze-concentration in Food In-
    dustry. IUFOST and FEEC, Paris (1975), p. A 6-1, A6-21.

9. Becker, H.C., Milner, R.T., and Nagel, R.H., Cereal Chem.
    (1940) 17, 447-457.

10. Adler-Nissen, J., J. Agric. Food Chem., (1979) 27, 1256-62.

11. Weeke, B., 3. Crossed Immunoelectrophoresis, p. 47-56. In:
    N.H. Axelsen, J. Krøll and B. Weeke: A Manual of Quantita-
    tive Immunoelectrophoresis - Methods and Applications. Uni-
    versitetsforlaget, Oslo, 1973.

12. Smith, A.K., and Circle, S.J., Ind. Eng. Chem. (1938) 30,
    1414-1418.

13. Sejr Olsen, H., Adler-Nissen, J., Process Biochem. (1979) 14 (7) 6-8, 10-11.

14. Novo Industri A/S, "Decoloration of Slaughter House Blood by Enzymatic Modification". IB 225, Bagsvaerd 1980.

15. Butterworth, T.A., Wang, D.I.C., Sinskey, A.J., Biotechnol. Bioengin. (1970), 12, 615-631.

16. Ghose, T.K., Kostick, J.A., Biotechnol. Bioengin. (1970), 12, 921-946.

17. Roozen, J.P, Pilnik, W., Process Biochem. (1973), 8, 24-25

18. Iacobucci, G.A., Myers, M.J., Emi, S., Myers, D.V., Proc. IV Int. Cong. Food Sci. Technol., Madrid 1974, 5, 83-95.

19. Bhumiratana, S., Hill Jr., C.G., Amundson, C.H., J. Food Sci. (1978), 42, 1016-1021.

20. Payne, R.E., Hill Jr., C.G., Amundson, C.H., J. Food Sci. (1978), 43, 385-389.

21. Cunningham, S.D., Cater, C.M., Mattil, K.F., J. Food Sci. (1978), 43, 1477-1480.

22. Roozen, J.P., Pilnik, W., Enzyme Microb. Technol. (1979), 1, 122-124.

23. Myers, D.V., Ricks, E., Myers, M.J., Wilkinson, M., Iacobucci, G.A., Proc. IV Int. Congr. Food Sci. Technol., Madrid 1974, 5, 96-102.

24. Bennet, A.A., Milne, W.E., Bateman, H.,"Numerical Integration of Differential Equations", Dover Publ., Inc., N.Y. 1956, p. 27.

25. Adler-Nissen, J., Ann. Nutr. Alim. (1978), 32, 205-216

26. Adler-Nissen, J., Unpublished experiments.

RECEIVED December 4, 1980.

Separation of Biopolymer from Fermentation Broths

W. L. GRIFFITH, A. L. COMPERE, C. G. WESTMORELAND,
and J. S. JOHNSON, JR.

Chemistry Division, Oak Ridge National Laboratory, Oak Ridge, TN 37830

The separations feasible by filtration have expanded enor-
mously over the last generation. The developments this symposium
has commemorated, and the individuals it has honored, have been
largely responsible. The removal of dissolved solutes or other
low-molecular-weight substances from water by hyperfiltration or
reverse osmosis, which the Loeb-Souririjan membrane made technically and economically feasible, has become an industrial-scale
operation. Ultrafiltration of colloids and filtration of coarser
materials from liquids have become much more efficient with the
use of cross flow of liquid to slow the buildup of filtercake;
appreciation of the benefits from shear at the interface has
become much more general from the necessity of controlling concentration polarization and fouling in salt filtration.

This paper is an account of our attempts to apply these
developments to a class which still poses formidable problems:
separation from each other of two substances, both dispersed in a
liquid as aggregates of different but large size. Even though
filters are now likely to be available of pore dimensions which
should discriminate, the filter cake or dynamic membrane that
builds up soon dominates, and the pore size of the filter becomes
irrelevant. One more than likely ends up concentrating both substances, rather than passing one with the liquid through the
filter.

In research aimed at lower chemical costs for enhanced oil
recovery, we are attempting a separation of this type, biopolymer
from fermentation broth. The motivation is to eliminate the conventional precipitation of polymer by alcohol addition, a step
which contributes a substantial fraction of production cost,
perhaps as much as 40%, with the necessity to recover alcohol for
recycle (Figure 1). Precipitation is necessary to prepare a dry
product, economical to ship. (Concentrated broth, prepared at a
central facility, is also proposed, at a penalty in transportation costs.)

Biopolymers are needed in petroleum production to increase
viscosities of fluids injected into formation, to improve sweep

0097-6156/81/0154-0171$05.50/0

in water floods, and to prevent viscous fingering in surfactant,
or micellar, floods. If one attempts to drive surfactant or
banked oil with water, which is of lower viscosity than the
driven banks, an unstable front develops, and eventually water
breaks through prematurely to the production well. A path of low
resistance to flow between injection and production wells is
established, and much of the oil and expensive chemicals are thus
not forced toward the production well. Raising viscosity of the
drive water, and perhaps of the surfactant bank, by polymer
addition tends to counteract this difficulty.

A wet separation of biopolymer from broth would be particularly advantageous if biopolymer were produced near the site of
use. Not only would the expense of alcohol precipitation be
bypassed, but also the difficult redispersion of dry biopolymer
into aqueous solutions and removal of cell debris and poorly
dispersed polymer fragments, etc., which would plug the pores of
the formation.

Large quantities would be used in a micellar flood program.
In a recent field pilot, for example, involving nine injection
and 16 production wells, about 770,000 pounds of polyacrylamide
were used (1). (Approximately the same amount of biopolymer
would have been required.) In a full-scale project, much more
would be needed, a rough rule of thumb being one to two pounds
of polymer per barrel of projected enhanced oil. An on-site
production facility is therefore an option. Biopolymers have
certain advantages over partially hydrolyzed polyacrylamides, the
other leading candidate; they are less sensitive to salinity and
hardness ions and are less degraded by shear, among other aspects.
They are more expensive, however. Lowering cost through field
production would lessen this disadvantage.

The criterion of a good separation is production of a solu--
tion of the desired viscosity which does not unacceptably plug
formations, without loss of substantial fractions of the polymer
in the process. Diatomaceous earth filtrations have customarily
been used to remove plugging constituents. In filtration of
fermentation broths, particularly in the field, it is desirable
to minimize use of these filteraids. If the biomass is heavily
contaminated with them, possible beneficial use as a cattle-feed
supplement may be inhibited, and an expensive waste disposal
problem may be incurred: a cost adding 20¢ to 40¢/lb of polymer
is conceivable.

In our evaluation of possibilities of lowering biopolymer
costs in oil recovery, we concluded that scleroglucans probably
were a better choice for field production than the more usually
considered xanthan gums (2). Viscosity properties of solutions
of the two are similar, but the organisms (*Sclerotium rolfsii*,
et al.) producing scleroglucans are more genetically stable than
those producing xanthan gums (*Xanthanomas campestris*), are less
pathogenic to plants, and because they produce acid during fermentation, their broths, which may reach pH values as low as 1.5,

are less liable to contamination by unwanted species. We have
previously reported results of fermentation with this class, both
with conventional glucose as carbon source (3) and with waste or
low-value carbohydrates (4). Other scleroglucan-producing organisms (mushrooms) have also been investigated (5). Some preliminary studies of separation of biopolymers from broth have been
reported earlier (6, 7), as well as of treatment with enzymes
which reduce plugging by degrading poorly dispersed polymeric
aggregates (8). Here we summarize the present status, from these
and other results. Further details can be found in periodic
reports (9).

Experimental

    Fermentation and broth treatment. Only an outline will be
given here; details may be found in references 3 and 4. Bench-
scale fermentations were carried out in approximately 10-liter
batches in a 14-liter Chemapec fermenter, type GF0014, sparged
by air at a rate of one volume per volume of broth/minute.
Mechanical agitation was at 300 rpm, and at ambient temperature.
The organisms used were *Sclerotium rolfsii* 15206 or a production
culture provided by Ceca, S.A. The medium contained per liter,
3 g $NaNO_3$, 1 g KH_2PO_4, 0.5 g $MgSO_4$, 0.7 H_2O, 0.5 g KCl, 30 g
glucose, 0.05 g $FeSO_4$, and 1 g Ambrex 1003 yeast extract, plus
small amounts of anti-foam agents. Fermentations were allowed to
proceed until polymer production was maximal, a condition usually
reached when reducing sugar level was about 0.5%. Biopolymer
for microscreen tests was produced in the ORNL Biology Division
400-liter fermenter.
    Assay of polymer was by precipitation with isopropyl alcohol.
Procedures varied in detail from time to time, but in general,
biomass was removed by centrifugation before precipitation. Biomass was taken to be "volatile suspended solids," the weight loss
of the washed centrifugate between 102°C and 550°C.
    Broth is usually heated to stop fermentation, neutralized,
and subjected to shear to release polymer attached to cell walls.
Figure 2 summarizes effects of various orders of carrying out
these treatments on viscosity. It is clear that the first blending to which the sample is subjected has the greatest effect on
the viscosity.
    These treatments have some effect on mycelial microstructure,
as the photomicrographs of Figure 3 illustrate. The neutralized
and blended (NB) broth had relatively small amounts of particles
other than mycellium. The fibrils were highly branched and
aggregated in loose tangles. After autoclaving (NBA), the
tangles were more closely packed, and the fibrils shorter. Further blending (NBAB) broke up the tight aggregates and produced
some small particulates. Additional autoclaving (NBABA) increased
breakdown of cell fibrils and resulted in a relatively large
number of fine particles. Even the fine particles, however, are

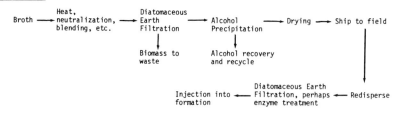

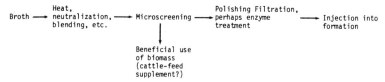

Figure 1.   Separation of biopolymer from fermentation broth.   (Application: mobility control for enhanced oil recovery.)

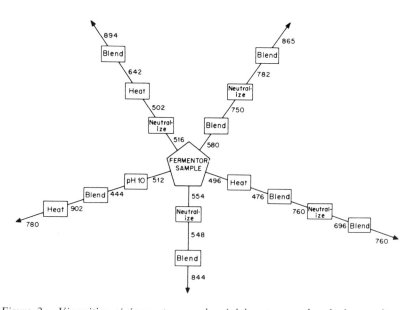

Figure 2.   Viscosities of fermenter sample of laboratory-produced glucan after various treatments: blend, 60 s at low speed of blender; heat, to 90°C for ∼ 30 min; neutralize, to pH 6.5–7.0. Numbers refer to viscosities in centipoise, measured at 60 rpm Brookfield LVT, spindle No. 3, T = 25° ± 1°C.

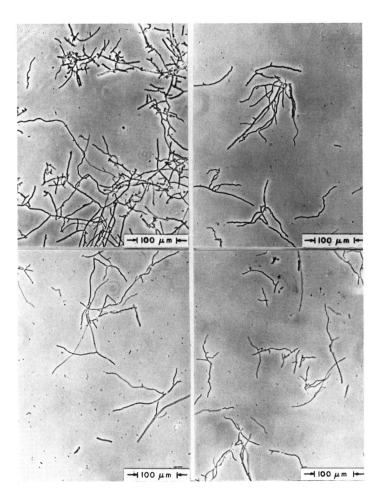

Figure 3. Photomicrographs of culture broth after treatment: upper left, *NB;* upper right, *NBA;* lower left, *NBAB;* lower right, *NBABA.*

several orders of magnitude larger than the expected size of
biopolymer species.

    Axial filtration. In most of our bench-scale filtrations
cross flow was effected by use of axial filters (10). In this
configuration (Figure 4), a membrane is wrapped around a rotor,
which is spun in a chamber, into which feed is introduced under
pressure. The rotor is perforated, and passages are provided for
filtrate (e.g., by an intervening screen) from the membrane to
these holes. Filtrate exits through the axis. Rotation speeds
providing velocities of up to about 15 ft/sec at the membrane-
feed interface can be attained in available equipment.

    Pleated ultrafiltration module. The axial filter is conven-
ient for experiments, in that volumes small relative to ordinary
ultrafiltration systems can be studied and in that pumping of
viscous solutions is limited to that necessary to replace filtrate or concentrate bled from the chamber, rather than that
necessary to maintain desired cross flow velocities. There is no
obvious reason it could not be scaled up to moderate sizes for
practical separations, but so far as we know, no large-volume
axial filters are available. For the operations of interest,
any of the commercial ultrafiltration systems would be candidates.
We have tested one module, recently developed by Gelman, which
incorporates a pleated membrane (Figure 5), with somewhat more
open feed passages than those of spiral-wound membranes, and
which allows backwashing. Other applications of the module were
discussed at this symposium by A. Korin in a paper coauthored
by G. B. Tanny, and a written account is presumably in these
proceedings.

    Microscreens. In the course of this research, we came to
the opinion that a preliminary screening to remove most of the
biomass was desirable. We shall report evaluations of microscreens, or microstrainers, for this purpose. These devices have
been available for several decades for waste water treatment (11).
They are low-hydraulic-head filters, comprised of a screen
mounted on a rotating drum. Apertures of available screens range
down to micron sizes. Feed is introduced into the drum. Filtercake control is by backwash with air or a portion of the filtrate,
once each rotation, the backwash being caught in a tray. A
schematic is shown in Figure 6.
    In pilot-scale tests, we used a mobile unit provided by the
Envirex division of the Rexnord Company. The drum was four feet
in diameter by two feet long. To aid in planning pilot tests, we
also carried out some preliminary one-cycle short-time (less than
30 sec) tests of screens in bench-scale apparatuses, designed
by manufacturers to evaluate the potential of microscreens.

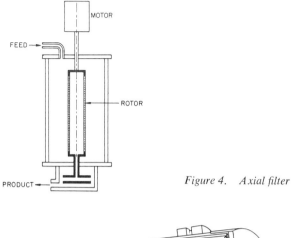

Figure 4.   Axial filter

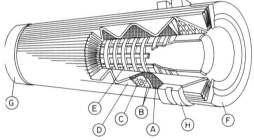

Figure 5.   Gelman pleated crossflow filter cartridge. Cartridge components: (A) a porous pleated support screen to provide mechanical support under applied pressure; (B) the pleated microporous filtration element; (C) the pleated spacer which creates the thin flow channel and promotes turbulent flow; (D) the impermeable film which creates the flow channel; (E) a porous support tube to provide an exit for permeate; (F) open-end cap which provides for exit of product flow; (G) closed-end cap completely which seals one end of module; (H) outer seal ring which creates the seal between the impermeable film in the module and the interior of the housing. The back pressure support tube is not pictured. The ends of the cartridge are potted and sealed. A space between the ends of Film D and the end seals is provided to allow the entrance and exit of the flow-channel fluid.

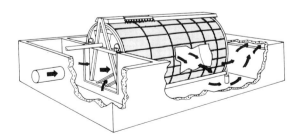

Figure 6.   Microscreen flow pattern

Results

Laboratory tests. A preliminary test of axial filtration on broth from a scleroglucan fermentation, diluted to give a solution within the range of viscosities used in oil recovery, was encouraging. In passage through 1.2 μm Acropor (Gelman) membranes there was no significant loss of viscosity, measured under the same shear rate, either of the broth or of resuspended dry glucan or xanthan polymer (range from 20 to 25 cp). The filtration was carried out at 20 psig and at 2000 rpm, corresponding to about 11 ft/sec at the membrane surface. Axial filtration appeared to lower greatly the level of plugging constituents. Figure 7 compares the flux decline in passage through 1.2 μm filters, without crossflow, of the three polymer solutions before and after axial filtration (axial filtration fluxes at the time of collection of the samples for the plugging tests are listed in the figure legend.) It can be seen that the decline is much less rapid for the filtrates. The fermenter broth, for which the decline rate was greatest before axial filtration, had the lowest plugging rate subsequently.

These results were obtained with a diluted broth, without neutralization, autoclaving, and blending steps. Although they indicate a potential of cross flow in these separations, it is not surprising that results of subsequent tests were not always reproducible. Without going into detail, later results implied that a two-step separation, involving a coarse screening to remove most of the biomass, followed by a polishing filtration to reduce plugging constituents to a tolerable level, would be advantageous. The bulk of the biomass would be uncontaminated by diatomaceous earth and might therefore be suitable as a cattle-feed additive. Polishing the effluent from screening with filteraid would pose much less of a waste disposal problem than treating the diluted broth directly. However, the possibility of eliminating filteraid use altogether by ultrafiltration should be improved with lower biomass content.

Some bench-scale tests indicating the potential of this scheme were described in reference 6. Here we summarize some later results of experiments designed in the light of our experience in the earlier runs. In these, broth was heated, neutralized, and blended, and diluted to about one gram of biopolymer per liter. It was then stored under refrigeration until use. Part was subjected to screening with a metal screen of about 125 μm apertures, mounted on an axial filter. Most of the biomass was removed in this step, with no significant loss of viscosity. Fluxes in the coarse screening were several hundred gallons per square foot per day.

The screened broth was then compared with unscreened broth in polishing by the axial filter wrapped with 5 μm Nuclepore membranes. Figure 8 compares the fluxes. Neither are as high as one might hope, though the screened feed values appear

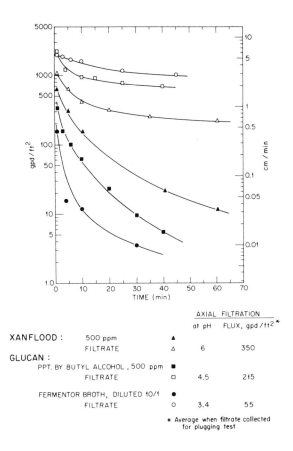

XANFLOOD :	500 ppm	▲	AXIAL FILTRATION	
			at pH	FLUX, gpd/ft² *
	FILTRATE	△	6	350
GLUCAN :				
PPT. BY BUTYL ALCOHOL , 500 ppm		■		
	FILTRATE	□	4.5	215
FERMENTOR BROTH, DILUTED 10/1		●		
	FILTRATE	○	3.4	55

* Average when filtrate collected for plugging test

Figure 7.   Plugging of 1.2-μm Millipore filter by polymer solutions under 15 psig pressure; before and after axial filtration through 1.2-μm Acropor filter (20 psig, 2000 rpm or ~ 11 ft/s). Viscosities of all solutions are 20 to 25 cps.

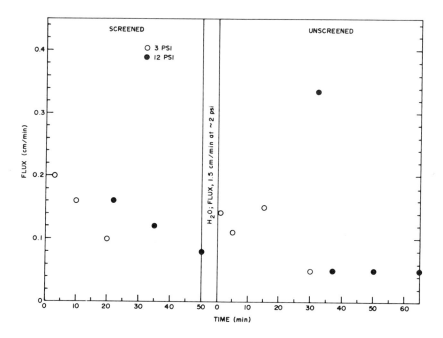

*Figure 8.   Fluxes in axial filtration of diluted glucan fermenter broth through 5-μm
Nuclepore filters (2000 rpm ~ 11 ft/s)*

somewhat higher. Figures 9 and 10 compare plugging by the filtrates from the polishing axial filtration with the respective feeds, diluted broth and screened diluted broth. It can be seen that the flux decline with both the filtrates is much less than for the feeds. The slopes of the flux declines are not markedly different for polished filtrates from screened and unscreened feeds. However, the fluxes in plugging tests with the filtrate from the screened feed appear significantly higher than with the filtrate from the unscreened feed.

Figures 11 and 12 compare the viscosities of the axial filtration effluents and feeds for the screened and unscreened broths. Here there is a clear advantage of the screening step. There is little decrease of viscosity between feed and filtrate for the screened material, but about a 25% decrease for the unscreened. There are sometimes decreases in viscosity incurred from diatomaceous earth filtration.

The results in Figures 8-12 are somewhat more favorable than results in reference 6. One might infer that the reason is the use here of Nuclepore filters, which have cylindrical pores normal to the surface in a narrow size range, rather than the Acropor membranes in reference 6, whose pores are more tortuous. We do not have sufficient information for a definitive conclusion on this point. However, a later comparison of fluxes in axial filtration by the two types (Figure 13) does not indicate any great difference. Comparisons of viscosity of feeds and filtrate and of plugging rates of filtrates also did not support a significant difference between Nuclepore and Acropor.

Removal of biomass by microscreens. Laboratory tests: Preliminary evaluation of microscreens, or microstrainers, as a commercially available device for the initial removal of the bulk of the biomass from broth was carried out by means of bench once-through tests of filtration with small areas of screens of plastic and of stainless steel having different apertures, on broths subjected to different preliminary treatments. These procedures have been designed by the manufacturers to simulate the performance for times comparable to backwash intervals and to give information allowing projection of the size of a treatment system necessary for a given application. Although the results were useful in planning the subsequent tests with the mobile pilot unit, they were not closely predictive of performance. The reason is not clear, but it is possible that backwash in the pilot unit was not complete with these feeds, and there was some contribution of cake to the filtration.

The results did indicate that under the proper conditions biomass could be separated from broth without appreciable filtration of biopolymer and that performance varied widely with the history of the broth. Figure 14 illustrates effects of broth treatment. Large differences in the fractional removals of biomass are apparent for different screen apertures and treatments

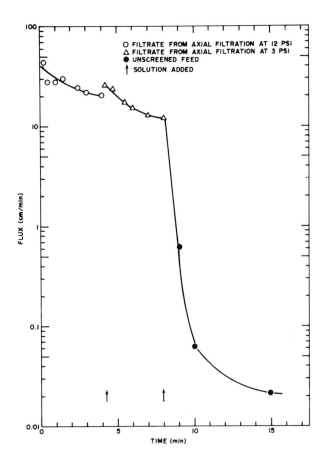

Figure 9. Unscreened feed for axial filtration: plugging of 1.2-μm Nuclepore filters by filtrate from 5-μm Nuclepore filter mounted on axial filter (plugging test pressure = 12 psi).

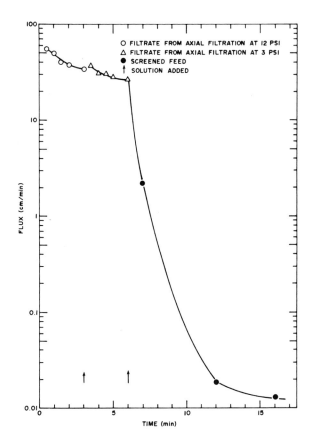

Figure 10. Screened feed for axial filtration: plugging of 1.2-μm Millipore filter by filtrate from 5-μm Nuclepore filter mounted on axial filter (plugging test pressure, 12 psi).

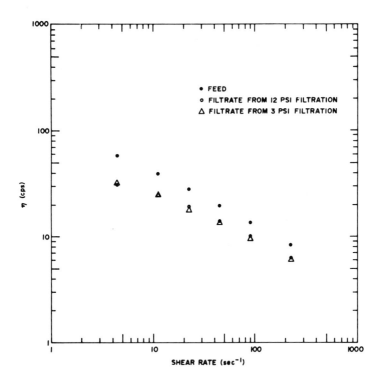

Figure 11.   Unscreened feed: comparison of viscosities of feed and filtrates from axial filtration (25°C; axial filtration through 5-μm Nuclepore filter)

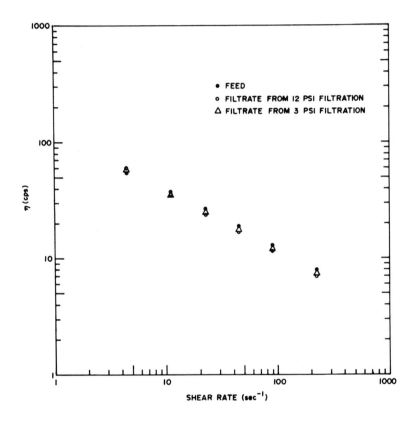

Figure 12.   Screened feed: comparison of viscosities of feed and filtrates from axial filtration (25°C; axial filtration through 5-μm Nuclepore filter).

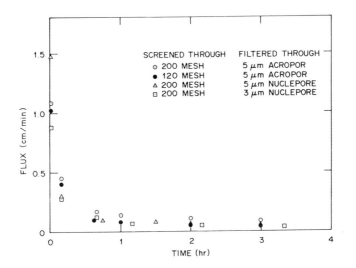

Figure 13. Axial filtration at a rotational speed of 2,000 rpm (~ 11 ft/s) of screened fermenter broth at 7.5:1 dilution and 7 psi

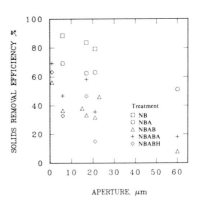

Figure 14. Biomass removal. Effect of media aperture and broth treatment at 11-in. hydraulic head.

(the treatment symbols were identified in the discussion of Figure 3, except for H, which signifies filtered while hot). However, within scatter, there appeared to be no differences in the viscosities of feeds and filtrates.

Pilot tests: Even with 350-liter fermentations, diluted to viscosities in the injection range, the volume of feed was less than ideal for the Rexnord mobile pilot unit. To make runs over the times and under the conditions we wished, it was necessary to recycle effluent and material collected in backwashing to the feed tank. For these tests, feed was neutralized with NaOH and pasteurized in the fermenter; it is believed that adequate blending was accomplished by shear from stirring during dilution and from pumps, along with passage through other elements of the system.

Figure 15 presents fractional biomass removal in runs with polyester screens of several different aperture sizes. Except for 21 μm filter media, removals by single-stage runs were mostly above 80%. For some reason, treatment by a second-stage 1-μm screen of 21 μm effluent gave little improvement although single-stage removal by 1 μm screens were good.

Figure 16a compares biomass concentration at various points in the system for the run with 21 μm screen. Although biomass removal in this run was the lowest of the tests in Figure 14, it can be seen that biomass is over a factor of ten higher in back-wash than in filtrate. Figure 16b indicates that polymer concentration is similar at all points and is not being removed by the filter. This behavior was general in all single-stage micro-screen runs and was confirmed by the fact that viscosities of samples at different points were not statistically different. The effluent from the two-stage (21 μm followed by 1 μm) screening had a lower viscosity than the feed.

The possibility that microscreening alone might be adequate without polishing filtration was evaluated in the plugging tests summarized in Figure 17a. It appears that further treatment is necessary.

Polishing of microscreen effluents: Diatomaceous earth treatment should be much easier and less costly after micro-screening, but alternatives are still desirable. Figure 17b compares plugging of microscreen effluent before and after further filtration through 1.2 μm Gelman Acropor AN filters in an axial configuration and in the pleated cartridge of Figure 5. Plugging rates are greatly decreased, the Gelman cartridge (loop) giving solution of the highest fluxes. However, the filtrates from it were somewhat lower in viscosity than the feeds. The results with the axial filter appear less favorable than in earlier tests with prescreened feeds, and it is suspected that there may have been leakage around seals in this case.

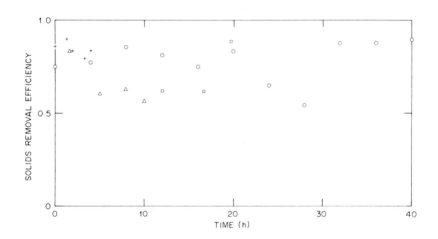

Figure 15. *Volatile suspended solids removal efficiencies for various media:* +, *6 μm; ○, 1 μm; △, 21 μm; and □, 1 μm following 21 μm.*

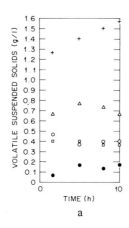

a

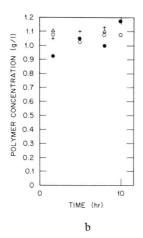

b

Figure 16. Concentrations at various points in the microscreen system equipped with 21-μm screens: a, volatile suspended solids; b, polymer. □, *feed tank;* ○, *influent;* ●, *effluent;* +, *backwash.*

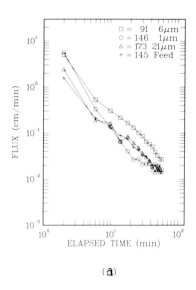

(a)

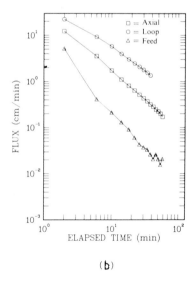

Figure 17. Plugging test results: a, pilot microscreen effluents; b, filtrates from polishing by crossflow filtration through 1.2-μm Acropor filter in axial filter (1.5 psi, 1000 rpm) and in pleated cartridge (loop).

(b)

Discussion

Although there are a considerable number of questions yet
needing answers, the results so far are promising with respect to
filtration without filteraid, or with much less than is customary,
for separation of biopolymer from fermentation broth. Table 1
summarizes estimates of capital costs and power requirements for
a ton of biopolymer per day separation plant by diatomaceous
earth filtration, centrifugation, and microscreening. The microscreening is lowest, but a polishing step would have to be added.

With respect to microscreening of scleroglucan broths, tests
should be carried out on broth neutralized by lime. Because some
of the acid produced in the fermentation is oxalic, its removal
is probably necessary before injection, to avoid precipitation
as calcium oxalate in the formation. Lime precipitation should
effect this. It is probable that filtration with calcium oxalate
in the feed will proceed somewhat differently than without, but
it is difficult to predict whether performance will be better or
worse.

Further optimization of the polishing step is clearly necessary. The mediocre fluxes in cross-flow and axial filtration
suggest that systems allowing backwash at frequent intervals may
be necessary. Many commercial ultrafiltration systems, including
the one used here, have this capability.

The biomass concentration in the microscreen backwash is low.
We have established however that centrifugation at 2800 g appears
to allow concentration up to 2 or 3% dry solids, or by about a
factor of ten. The pasty cake obtained could be used directly as
an animal-feed additive if there were a market nearby, or could
be dried for shipment. Centrifugation of microscreen backwash is
a relatively low cost operation; we estimate that it would add
$10,000 to the capital cost and 2 hp to the power requirement of
the estimates in Table 1.

Table 1

Cost and energy of processes for a 10^3 kg/day
(10^6 liters/day) installation

Process	Capital Cost, 10^3 $	Power, hp
DE filter	155	180
Centrifuge[1]	107	40
Microscreen[2]	80	8

[1]Maxium power demands up to 60 hp.

[2]Polishing step required.

Moderate decreases in viscosity in polishing filtration do not necessarily imply biopolymer loss. So long as polymer is not incorporated in filtercake as it would be in diatomaceous earth filtration (or if it can be backwashed off, even if it is), it should be possible to operate with a feed of higher viscosity than necessary for injection, and to recycle feed through the filtration apparatus, perhaps after dilution. Another possibility would be to recycle polishing filtration blowdown into the microscreening system.

Acknowledgments

Research was sponsored by the Division of Chemical Sciences, Office of Basic Energy Sciences, U. S. Department of Energy, under contract W-7405-eng-26 with Union Carbide Corporation.
We are indebted to J. B. Cravens of Rexnord for collaboration on bench-scale and pilot microscreen tests. E. F. Phares and M. V. Long of the ORNL Biology Division carried out the 350-ℓ fermentations for these tests. S. V. Greene and J. M. Crenshaw provided technical assistance in many aspects of the research.

Literature Cited

1. Kleinschmidt, R. F. "North Burbank Unit Tertiary Recovery Pilot Test," Final Report, Phillips Petroleum Co. to U. S. Dept. of Energy DOE/ET/13067-60 (1980).
2. Baldwin, W. H., et al., "Chemicals for Enhanced Oil Recovery," Annual Report, April 1977-April 1978, U. S. Dept. of Energy BETC/W-26-4.
3. Griffith, W. L.; Compere, A. L. Developments Industrial Microbiology, 1978, 19, 609.
4. Compere, A. L.; Griffith, W. L. Developments Industrial Microbiology, 1978, 19, 601.
5. Compere, A. L.; Griffith, W. L.; Greene, S. V. Developments Industrial Microbiology, 1980, 21, 461
6. Griffith, W. L.; Tanny, G. B.; Compere, A. L. Developments Industrial Microbiology, 1979, 20, 743.
7. Griffith, W. L.; Compere, A. L.; Cravens, J. B.; Erickson, P. R. Developments Industrial Microbiology, submitted.
8. Griffith, W. L.; Compere, A. L.; Crenshaw, J. M. Developments Industrial Microbiology, 1980, 21, 451.
9. Compere, A. L., et al., "Chemicals for Enhanced Oil Recovery," Quarterly reports for Winter, Summer, and Fall 1979, Department of Energy BETC/W26-5, BETC/W26-10, BETC/W26-15.
10. Kraus, K. A., Proceedings 29th Industrial Waste Conference, Purdue Research Foundation, 1974, 1059.
11. Cravens, J. B.; Kormanik, R. A. J. Water Pollution Control Federation, in press.

RECEIVED February 18, 1981.

Externally Wound Tubular Membrane Elements in Modular Assemblies: Production and Application

S. MANJIKIAN
ARAMCO, Dhahran, Saudi Arabia

C. K. WOJCIK
University of Petroleum & Minerals, Dhahran, Saudi Arabia

Tubular R.O. systems have been slow to develop especially when compared with the successful mass marketing of spiral and hollow fine fiber type R.O. systems. In the water desalination field, the high membrane packing density of spiral and hollow fine fiber systems has given them an overwhelming economic advantage over tubular systems. However, the advantageous design feature of spiral and hollow fine fiber units also serves to limit their application to relatively clear fluids free of colloidal and par- ticulate matter. This effectively curtails their practical application in areas such as the separation and concentration of fluid foods, pharmaceutical mixtures and the treatment of indus- trial wastes. Tubular system can and should effectively fill this gap.

The externally wound tubular membrane system and conventional tubular designs have the necessary design, production and func- tional features to meet more demanding task of processing fluids of high particulate content and, in rotary assemblies, treatment of delicate and structurally sensitive fluids and chemical mixtures.

System Description

The externally wound membranes were developed by Universal Water Corp., San Diego, California. In this design, the membrane element consists of a porous supporting tube on which are simul- taneously wound, in helical fashion, a strip of permeable fabric overlaid with a helical wound strip of semipermeable membrane film. Adjacent turns of the membrane overlap in winding, and these over- laps are sealed by a bonding solvent so that, the membrane itself

0097–6156/81/0154–0193$05.00/0

forms a unitary tube enclosing the fabric and the porous supporting tube. A diagram of such helically wound membrane element is
shown in Fig. 1.

Modular assemblies designed to house a number of helical elements are constructed by arranging individual membrane elements,
in spaced relationships, within flow guide tubes inside a suitable
pressure vessel. Various diameter flow tubes are used to provide
the desired annular spacing between membrane surfaces and brine
flow channel walls. By this means the cross sectional area of
brine flow channels around each element can be selected to provide
best conditions for specific processing applications. For example,
a relatively wide spacing may be required for fluids that are viscous or have a high content of particulate or colloidal matter as
in food processing applications. On the other hand, close spacing
may be required in water desalination applications to prevent concentration polarization by producing a turbulent flow and to
reduce pumping rates. The diagram of a typical module is shown in
Fig. 2.

A module just described is a fixed module in which the membrane elements are stationary. A radical departure from the conventional mode of R.O. systems operations is the rotary system
wherein externally wound membrane elements clustered around a
central shaft are rotated in a stationary pressure vessel filled
with pressurized feed stock. Here the separated permeate is
replaced by an equivalent volume of fresh feed stock under a constant head. The basic rotary concept is depicted in Fig. 3.

The most important features of the externally wound membranes
are:

- Low cost. No advanced technology or sophisticated equipment is involved in making of such membrane elements. They
  can be manufactured on site.
- Serviceability and maintenance. Being on the outer surface
  of tubular elements, the membranes are readily accessible
  to inspection and cleaning. Assembly and disassembly of
  modules can be accomplished easily and quickly in the fluid.
- Good mechanical reliability of the system. The membrane
  elements are subjected to compressive stresses only, therefore, non-corrosive materials of lower tensile strength
  may be used.

Membranes

Membranes for externally wound elements were either obtained
as finished product from commercial sources, or produced in-house
from raw materials.

Purchased membranes were initially tested for compliance with
the specifications designed to assure their suitability for winding operations (thickness, tensile strength and elongation) and
for their performance characteristics (flux and salt rejection)

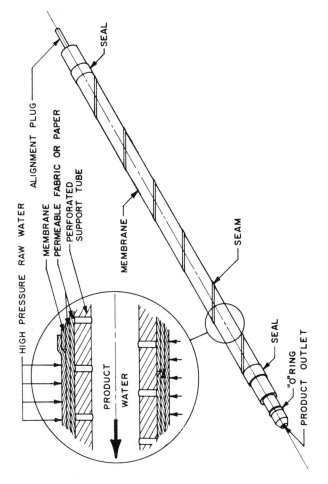

Figure 1.   Helical membrane element

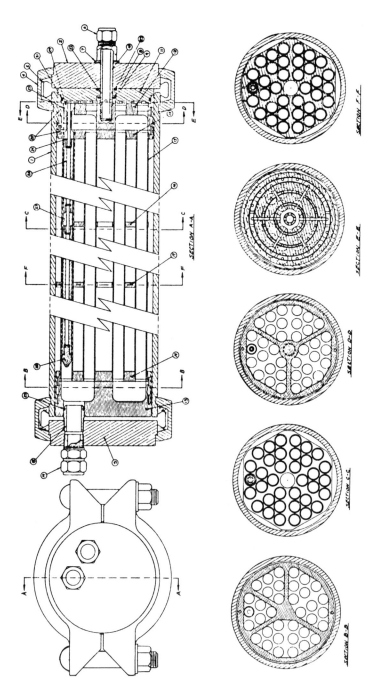

Figure 2.   Module layout

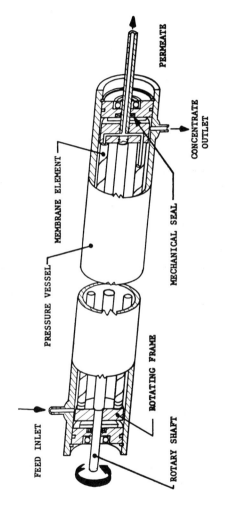

Figure 3. Rotary module

within the prescribed range of operation. After meeting successfully these specifications, they were evaluated in terms of their
applicability to helical winding and compatibility with overlap
sealants. Most of the commercial membranes were found to be suitable for helical winding application.

The in-house membranes were fabricated, with minor modifications, along well established procedures which included: formulation, casting or forming, gellation and curing at elevated temperatures. Various casting solutions were tried first for their performance as flat test membranes before their suitability for winding operations was considered. The preferred casting formulation
for membranes used in the helically wound elements comprises:
     24% Cellulose acetate E-398-6 or -10
     29% Formamide
     35% Acetone
     12% Pyridine
Addition of pyridine to the cellulosic casting formulations results
in membranes having superior mechanical properties in terms of
their strength and ductility.

Prior to casting, the mixed formulations were filtered for
removal of particulate and insoluable matter and transferred to
special canisters. Casting was done at ambient temperatures and
water curing at $1^{o}C$ for a period of 45 minutes. Prior to use, the
membranes were first annealed and then slit into strips, say
1.065 ± 0.005 inch wide for a 7/16 inch diameter element, and
rolled on special capsules for insertion into winding feeders. The
curing temperatures required for given performance specifications
for the externally would membranes were found to be 2 to $5^{o}C$
higher than those for flat membranes. For brackish water applications, the membrane elements were cured at $84^{o}C ± 0.2^{o}C$ for the
period of 10 ± 0.5 minutes.

Support Structures

In the construction and assembly of externally wound tubular
membrane systems, the support structure is generally a rigid non-
compressible tubular body of sufficient mechanical strength to
withstand required operating pressures and of adequate porosity to
freely transmit the separated permeate. Materials having uniform
porosity would be the most desirable, however, cellular porosity
is often (at least in the cases tested) associated with low
mechanical strength, lack of uniformity and long term reliability
and a relatively high cost of production. In absence of such
materials, porosity in supporting tubes was achieved by drilling
holes at spaced intervals using a specially designed multi-spindle
drilling fixture. It was established experimentally that the most
satisfactory passage of water was achieved through 0.028 inch
diameter perforations spaced at three inch intervals along two
straight lines 180 degrees apart.

Desirable properties for supporting tubes are: corrosion resistance, thermal stability, dimensional stability under wet conditions, compatibility with other components of the module, mechanical strength, and good machineability.

A highly practical material is ABS (acrylonitrite-butadiene-styrene). Membrane elements, fabricated with 7/16 nominal diameters extruded ABS tubing as support structures, were successfully operated at pressure up to 1500 psig.

Backing Materials

Backing materials are used in the construction and assembly of externally wound tubular membrane elements to provide for lateral transfer of permeate to spaced perforation sites in the support structure. Principal characteristics desirable in membrane backing materials include high porosity for adequate liquid permeation at minimum pressures, high density combined with a smooth surface texture to minimize embossing or otherwise deforming of membrane surfaces and mechanical strength to bridge over perforations in the support tube.

Dacron pressed paper was found to be highly adequate for permeate transport while possessing the wet strength plastic properties needed in winding operations. Dacron paper was also used in casting membranes directly on support structures.

Sealants

In the fabrication of externally wound tubular membrane elements and modular assemblies solvent bonding fluids and O-rings are commonly used as sealants. In winding operations, strips of membranes are wound in an overlapping manner to form a unitary tube where helical winding overlaps are solvent bonded during winding while the ends of the windings are sealed to the support tube. Commercially available glues and bonding mixtures were found to be impractical in the continuous and immediate sealing requirements of the winding process. Most of the epoxy formulations were rejected because of their setting and curing time requirements. Commonly known cellulose acetate solvents were tested individually and in combination. In general, pure solvents were found to be too strong for that purpose, as they tended to penetrate membrane surfaces rather than spread over the overlap interface, thus, resulting in an imperfectly bonded seams, with physically weak and brittle areas at the joint. Experimentally, weak solvents in combination with diluents and plasticizers were found to be highly acceptable. A composition, found to be the most effective, consisted of a mixture of triacetin and alcohol. Cellulose acetate was added to the mixture to increase its viscosity and a dye to color it for the quality control purposes. This mixture, a weak solvent by itself, produced an extremely strong and reliable bond of the membrane overlaps. The composition of this sealant mixture was:

Triacetin   94 parts by volume
1-Propanol   6' parts by volume
Cellulose acetate
(E 398 - 10)   3 g per 100 ml of triacetin
Red commercial dye 1 g per liter of mix.

The bond obtained using this sealant was found to be effective
with both wet and dry membranes. Further, tensile tests showed
that the bond was at least as strong as the membrane itself. Most
important, the bonding took place instantaneously at ambient temperatures. No curing or setting time is required. Hence, this
bonding method was found to be ideally suited for the automatic
and continuous winding of membrane elements. Pressure adhesive
tape was used for sealing membrane winding edges and affixing same
to the supporting tube.

Structural Materials

As noted above, externally wound tubular membrane elements
are fabricated primarily of extruded ABS tubing (natural), cellulosic or blend membranes and dacron paper. The cartridge assembly
designed to house the membrane elements and provide for the uniform distribution/flow of feed stock is fabricated of extruded
thin walled polystyrene headers. Pressure vessels were fabricated
either by using epoxy coated steel pipe or fiberglass vessels.

Helical Winding Process

Fabrication/assembly of externally wound tubular membrane
elements is accomplished by specially designed equipment that
simultaneously and continuously winds, in helical fashion, infinite
lengths of membrane and backing material strips onto prefabricated
tubular support structures. Membrane strip winding overlaps are
solvent bonded during the winding process.
A successful method for achieving this motion is based on the
use of three driving rollers equally spaced on the circumference
of the support tube. In operation such rollers are in compressive
contact with the surface of the supporting tube and positioned at
an angle to its axis. The rollers are driven by a single motor
and thus rotate at identical speeds. This arrangement imparts a
precise helical motion to the element support tubing with respect
to the stationary feeding spools.
To maintain a constant helix angle, synchronization of rotary
and linear motions is essential. Also, the determination and use
of backing materials and membrane strips of proper width is
important in optimizing the effective membrane surface area for a
given support tubing nominal diameter. The geometrical relationships between these widths and the helix angle are given in Fig. 4.
Here, the helix angle is denoted by α, d is the diameter of the

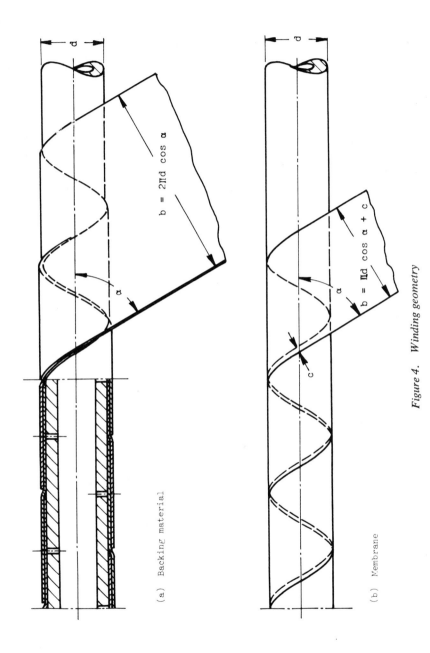

(a) Backing material

$b = 2\Pi d \cos \alpha$

α

(b) Membrane

$b = \Pi d \cos \alpha + c$

α

c

Figure 4.   Winding geometry

supporting tube (it is also the nominal diameter of the element),
and c is the amount of membrane overlap (usually 0.062 to 0.125
in.). In practice, the helix angle was set in the range of 35° –
45°.

Another important factor in the winding operation is tension
applied to the backing material and to the membrane strip. Tension
is needed to insure smooth wrinkle-free wound surfaces and to provide the necessary pressure between membrane overlaps to obtain
proper bonding. A minimum tension of about 3 lb/in is required for
winding the backing material, while the optimal tension for membrane strips amounted to 1 lb/in.

Winding machinery comprises: (1) a drive mechanism to provide
means for imparting simultaneous rotary and linear motion to support structures in a continuous manner, (2) membrane and backing
material feeder cartridges, (3) a sealant applicator assembly, (4)
electromechanical controls, (5) cut off/separation tooling, and
(6) completed element handling equipment.

Modular Assemblies

A modular assembly housing externally wound tubular membrane
elements may be defined as a pressure vessel within which are
assembled a multiplicity of individual elements, means for connec-
ting and sealing said elements to common headers and a feed stock
distribution system that provides for adequate feed flow across
membrane surfaces.

In the development and design of modular assemblies, housing
a multiplicity of externally wound tubular membrane elements, the
following factors were considered: effectiveness of element packing arrangements and density, feed stock distribution patterns for
controlled and uniform feed flow across membrane surfaces, sealing
reliability of modular sub-assemblies, overall system reliability,
module serviceability and ease of maintenance, system productibil-
ity, and economic viability.

In utilization of externally wound tubular membrane elements
in modular assemblies for conventional systems operations, that is,
selective separation via the circulation of pressurized feed across
membrane surfaces, flow guide tubes were found to be essential for
the proper distribution and control of feed flow. This was
achieved singularly by the use of individual element shrouds or
flow tubes creating an annular gap through which feed stock was
circulated across membrane surfaces.

A representative multi-element modular assembly is depicted
in Fig. 2. In this design the module comprises three major components:
  ● 36 membrane element assemblies
  ● flow guide tube cartridge assembly
  ● 5 in. diameter 12 ft. long pressure vessel.

Rotary Modules

Conventional reverse osmosis systems are generally designed
to operate by pressurizing raw feed fluids to required operating
pressures and circulating said fluids across membrane surfaces.
To meet the operating requirements of the reverse osmosis process,
a pumping system is commonly used to pressurize and circulate feed
fluids at sufficient velocities to maintain the desired turbulence
and to provide pressurized make-up fluid to replace withdrawn permeate and concentrate fluids.

The above approach is often uneconomical and energy consuming
since in most cases substantial amounts of pressurized fluid are
required to maintain the desired turbulent flow. Additionally, in
treatment of certain fluids containing colloidal and particulate
matter, turbulent flow of the raw fluid does not always accomplish
the cleaning action necessary to keep the membrane active surface
free of fouling deposits.

A unique and improved method which substantially reduces the
required amount of pressurized fluid flow has been developed by
Universal Water Corporation. In this approach the pumping system
is primarily employed to pressurize the raw fluid and a rotable
assembly carrying membrane elements is used to provide turbulence
over the membrane surfaces. This approach separates the functions
of pressurization and feed fluid recirculation. Thus, the pumping
system needs to pressurize and pump only the volume of feed stock
necessary to make up for the separated permeate while rotation of
the membrane element assembly provides the desired turbulence.
Additionally, and more specifically in batch processing systems,
pressurization can be achieved by means other than a pump.

In essence, a rotary system comprises a pressure vessel containing a rotable assembly carrying membrane elements, means for
pressurizing the fluid feed, and means for rotating the membrane-
element assembly. A conceptual rendition of a rotary module is
shown in Fig. 3, and a flow schematic of a rotary system is shown
in Fig. 5.

Main advantages of the rotary approach include:
- reduced energy consumption
- continuous by-batch operation convenient for food processing
- minimal exposure of treated fluids to pumping system,
  pressure fluctuations and contamination
- reduced cleaning and maintenance costs
- high suitability for maximum recoveries and efficient
  concentration of treated fluid
- relatively uniform concentration of feed fluids within
  modules
- suitability for use with fluids containing particulate and
  colloidal matter.
- limited exposure of treated fluids to contamination.

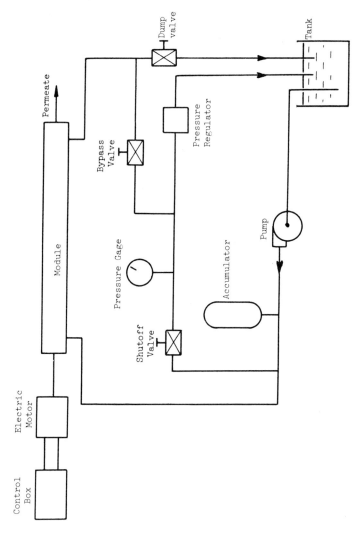

Figure 5.   Flow diagram for rotary module

The rotary concept makes possible the design of modular assemblies which would truly permit the insitu cleaning of membranes during operation by simply changing the direction and rate of rotations.

Areas of Application

R.O. systems utilizing externally wound tubular membrane element in modular assemblies have been used in the desalination of brackish and sea waters, the treatment and/or concentration of industrial waste waters, the separation/concentration of fluid food, pharmaceuticals and chemical solutions, and the manufacture of water purifiers for domestic use. Generally, externally wound tubular membrane systems have been found to be highly suitable for ultrafiltration applications in the processing industry and in water pollution control applications.

More specifically, these systems, whether operated in the conventional mode or as rotary units have been successfully utilized in applications such as the recovery of protein and lactose from cheese whey, separation of fermentation products, concentration of fluids foods and juices, manually operable sea water desalinators, recovery of starch from potato processing fluids, and processing/separation of pharmaceutical and chemical mixtures.

RECEIVED December 4, 1980.

Membrane Development, Production, and Use in Hyperfiltration Systems

W. KOFOD NIELSEN

A/S De Danske Sukkerfabrikker, Driftteknisk Laboratorium, 4900 Nakskov, Denmark

At an anniversary like this, it is usual to look back through the period in question, in this case the past 20 years.

The great discovery by Loeb and Sourirajan made it possible to consider reverse osmosis as an industrial process.

The core of membrane filtration is the membrane, but the core in itself must be surrounded or supported, and this leads to the system or module in which the membrane is mounted.

During these 20 years, a large number of module systems has been made. The first idea was to use the conventional filter press, the plate-and-frame system, as done by Aerojet General Corp. However, this system never proved to be very successful in the U.S.A., and consequently new configurations, such as tubes, hollow fibers, and spiral-wound systems were invented.

The red thread through the whole period was desalination of sea and brackish water, and grants sponsored by the Office of Saline Water directed the development into this field.

In Europe, and especially by our company, The Danish Sugar Corporation, DDS, in Denmark, we attacked the problem in a different way. Primarily, we saw a great number of advantages in the plate-and-frame system, and by solving some of the problems, such as sealings, manufacturing of plates and frames by injection moulding, etc., in 1970 we came up with a system which at that time we considered to be a competitive product.

At that time, we saw the most accessible market in the pharmaceutical and food and dairy industries, because within these industries membrane filtration was so advantageous that the relatively high investment and operating costs were no impediment.

Later, our system proved to work successfully also for desalination of water, but the development through the pharmaceutical to the food and dairy industries and pulp and paper industry did give a great deal of experience which has been extremely valuable for our design of water desalination plants as constructed today.

The Plate-and-Frame Membrane-Filtration System

The DDS plate-and-frame system and the principle of it are
shown in Figures 1, 2, and 3.

I shall not go into details on the principle, as it has been
published at several occasions (1, 2), but some consideration
ought to be given to the reasons why this system has proved to be
successful within such a wide range of applications, and below we
state some factors which in our opinion play an important role in
this respect.

The System

(1) Injection moulding of support and spacer plates makes a
low-cost, large-scale production method possible.

(2) The specially developed sealing system in our plastic
plates, where the very membrane is used as a seal between two
plates, gives a system which is simple and easy to handle because
no O-ring sealings are necessary.

(3) The flow-channel design can be optimized, dead spots
avoided, and the dead volume minimized.

(4) Very high flexibility in series and parallel arrangements
within one module.

(5) Flow velocity and flow distribution are easily controlled.

(6) The permeate side is liquid-filled and kept at a low internal volume, and there is flow in all parts of the permeate
system, securing safe bacteriological conditions.

(7) Each membrane pair is easily inspected, securing product-
quality control, and in case of membrane rupture, the membrane can
be detected and easily exchanged.

The Membrane

(1) Any membrane cast in sheet form of sufficient dimensions
can be mounted into the system.

(2) The distance between membrane development and membrane
production, utilization, and application is the smallest possible.

(3) During production, a very effective quality control is
possible, since each piece of membrane is inspected, and membranes
with faults are discharged.

I think, these ten factors explain some of the obvious advantages obtained by a plate-and-frame system. However, I would like
to add that without the great work carried out by Dr. R.F. Madsen
in our company who started a research programme within this field
some 15 years ago, there would be no DDS plate-and-frame system
today (3).

Review of Membrane Development

The development of reverse-osmosis membranes began with investigations made by Reid and Breton (4) in 1959 on dense films of

Internal Flow, UF

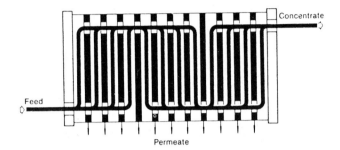

Internal Flow, HF

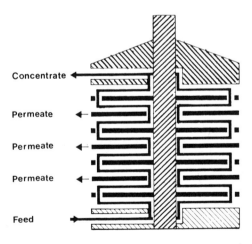

Figure 1.   The principal configuration of DDS plate-and-frame systems

Figure 2. The 30-cm module containing 19-m² membrane area

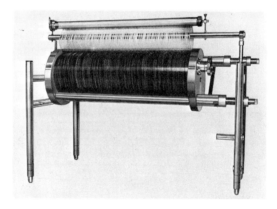

Figure 3. The 35-cm module containing 27-m² membrane area

cellulose acetate (CA). This led to the development by Loeb and
Sourirajan (5) of the manufacture of an asymmetric, skinned CA
membrane with a flux of up to 500 times higher than seen before.
CA was dissolved in acetone, and water and magnesium perchlorate
were added as swelling agent. The casting was performed at $-11^{\circ}C$.
A later development was made by Manjikian et al. (6), in which
formamide was substituted for magnesium perchlorate/water.
    A considerable step forward was the cellulose triacetate
blend membrane (CA CTA) of Saltonstall (7). Later, membranes produced from CTA alone have been manufactured with properties
superior to those of CA and CA/CTA membranes.
    A special development was the work carried out by Kesting (8)
who invented the "dry process" for producing dry/wet reversible
asymmetric membranes by complete evaporation.
    Parallel to the development of sheet membranes based on CA
and CTA, the development of hollow fine fibers spun from nylon was
made. With the development by Du Pont of the B-9 and B-10 permeators based on aromatic polyamides, the hollow fine fibers were a
realistic alternative to CA membranes.
    Later, hollow fibers made from CTA were spun by Dow Chemical
(9, 10).
    The thin-film composite membrane developed by Riley et al.
(11) led to the PA-300 membrane produced by UOP. Within the thin-
film composite membrane development, a remarkable work was done
at the North Star Research Institute by Cadotte et al. (12, 13, 14)
leading to the NS-100, NS-200, and NS-300 membranes.
    Later, a group of people from the North Star Research Insti-
tute founded the company FilmTec, and in 1979 the FT-30 membrane
was introduced (15), and this membrane seems to be the best of
thin-film composite membranes till now.
    At the same time, a number of Japanese companies introduced
new membranes, of which the membrane from Toray (16) should be
mentioned.
    Also membranes from other polymers, such as sulphonated poly-
sulphone and polyphenylene oxide, were reported, but apparently
they were not put into production. This also counts for the polybenzimidazole (PBI) introduced by the Celanese Research Company
(17).
    The company Teijin in Japan introduced a polybenzimidazolone
membrane which was claimed to be on the market.
    Besides this development of reverse-osmosis membranes, there
was a simultaneous development of ultrafiltration membranes, which
began with Michaels (18). For UF, membranes from cellulose acetate,
polyamides, polysulphone, polyvinylidenfluoride, polytetrafluoride,
and polyacrylic acid are produced and commercialized by various
companies.
    Finally, the development of inorganic membranes ought to be
mentioned. To our knowledge, the only commercialization is the
carbon tubes developed by Union Carbide for ultrafiltration.
    The membrane-development review is indicated in Figure 4.

Membrane Development

When looking at the membrane development carried out throughout the world, there is a large number of literature describing
several new membranes. However, when looking at the practical results of this development, they are rather poor.

Since the first cellulose-acetate membrane was made, and the
hollow fine fiber was introduced, very few new membranes for reverse osmosis have been brought on the market.

Why is that so? Primarily, the way from casting a membrane
in the laboratory and to have it running in production is long and
difficult and requires facilities and machinery which are often
not available for people doing research at for instance universi-
ties. In our company, the membrane research and development is not
finished until a final formula and procedure for casting the membrane in industrial scale has been made.

Previously, our membranes were cast separately from the support paper, but today we usually cast the membranes on the support
paper. This gives a reinforcement of the membrane, and generally
it prolonges the lifetime.

The various steps in membrane development can be summarized
as follows:

Selection of New Polymers. This is a field where most efforts
have been made to produce better membranes. However, when looking
for polymers, one must realize that even with a considerable
growth of RO/UF, the quantities of polymers necessary to cover the
demand are limited.

Consequently, manufacturers of polymers show only a small
interest in developing special polymers for membrane filtration.

On the other hand, it might still be worthwhile for the polymer industry to take a closer look at the subject since the price
for polymers for this use is less important than usually because
the raw-material cost of polymers is only a small part of the
total production costs for membranes.

Modification of Polymers. One way to solve the problem of
finding good polymers for membranes is to make modifications of
the chemical structure of the polymer. Sulphonation for instance
of polysulphone (19) is a well known example of how a hydrophobic
polymer can be modified to a hydrophilic polymer with charged
groups. Other attemps have been made, for instance to modify cellulose acetate by putting charged positive groups in the form of
quaternary ammonium into the polymer (20).

Production of New Polymers. The polybenzimidazole developed
as a raw material for specially thermal-stable textile fibers by
the Celanese Research Company proved to be a potential membrane
polymer due to the exceptionally high water absorption (17).

Formulation of Casting Solutions. Once a polymer has been
selected, the next step is formulation of the casting dope. This
includes finding solvents, swelling agents, and non solvents, and
making a formula for the proportion of the different substances.
The solubility parameters are of a certain help, but still it is
mainly trial and error through lots of experiments which leads to
the result.

Casting on Glass Plates. When the casting dope is ready for
trial, the first step is usually to cast it on a glass plate under
controlled conditions.

Casting on Machine. When tests of the membranes from the
glass plates prove to be satisfactory, the next step will be preparation of larger quantities of casting dope for casting experiments on the membrane-casting machine. This is usually the most
difficult step which is also rather time consuming. In this respect, the reproducibility of the membrane is a decisive factor
for going on with the project.

Heat Treatment and Various Other Modifications. Heat treatment and other modifications, such as chemical treatment of the
membrane, are well known as a last step to modify or "tailor" the
membrane for its final use.

Support Paper. The selection of support paper is a very important part of the membrane development. This is often done in
cooperation with the manufacturer of support paper. However, also
here it must be realized that despite an extremely high growth of
membrane filtration, the amount of support paper is very small
compared to the usual manufacturing of paper.
    We have found that non-wowens of polyester or polypropylene
and possibly polyethylene provide the best material for RO and UF
membranes.

    The membrane-development procedure is shown in Figure 5.
    As to membrane development, it should finally be remarked
that usually the requirements to new membranes will be properties
corresponding to those for desalination of sea or brackish water.
    We found that a membrane being able to reject sugar up to
100 percent is a very interesting membrane for concentration of
waste waters or industrial process streams. For cellulose acetate,
this corresponds to 85-90% salt rejection which is usually considered being too low for desalination. I think that several membranes of polymers alternative to CA could fulfil these requirements and that such membranes have been lost in the hunt for a
high degree of desalination.
    UF membranes are usually characterized as asymmetric barriers
where the support layer gives an insignificant contribution to
flow resistance, and where the skin layer gives the membrane its

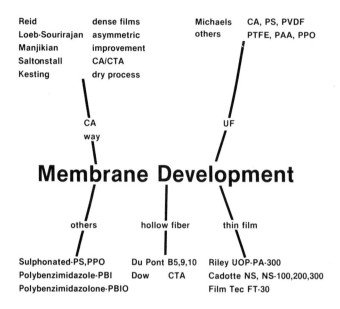

Figure 4.   Membrane-development review

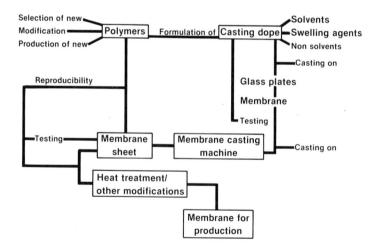

Figure 5.   Membrane-development procedure

rejection/separation characteristics. In our system, we operate in a wide pressure range for UF from 1 to 10 bars. In order to give the membrane an optimum performance rate and to create conditions for being able to clean and sanitarize large continuous plants at high temperatures, we found it relevant to limit the resistance to flow in the membrane, and this is done by increasing the flow resistance in the support layer.

Membrane Production

The membrane production steps are shown in Figure 6. Since many of the steps are similar to those mentioned in the previous section, I shall not go through all of them, but draw the attention to some special issues connected to membrane production.

The exchange of experience between membrane producers is very limited, and this fact is easily explained through the very decisive role the membrane plays in membrane filtration and the great amount of know-how contained in the ability to produce membranes.

Some membrane producers consider membrane production more as an art, and in some respects this might well be true.

The machinery used for the production is not something you can buy, but it must be developed and produced by the manufacturer himself.

The storage and handling of solvents need special care, and the security regulations in our country are very strict today. This also involves the casting machine and associated machinery, where high security regulations are required.

The ventilation and air-conditioning system is an important part of the machinery and requires great care to operate satisfactorily.

In order to obtain a good membrane quality and a high degree of utilization, a careful operation is necessary. This requires skilled people who know their job.

Quality control is involved in several steps in the manufacturing process, as shown in Figure 6. The advantage in our system of cutting the roll into the required sizes of membranes for our various sizes of modules is that we can have a visual or similar inspection in the very last step of manufacturing, and membranes with casting faults can be taken out. This ensures the customer the best possible quality of membrane.

The environmental protection also requires attention to the waste water which has to be carefully considered.

Membrane Utilization

From a customer's point of view, membrane utilization is extremely important. Having invested in a membrane filtration plant, he must consider the following points carefully:

Membrane lifetime
Membrane-exchange costs

Security in delivery
Shut-down period for exchange
Possibility of membrane inspection
Product control.

In order to secure the customer, the membrane manufacturer usually gives some kind of guarantee. When comparing guarantee data, it must be done carefully, and as a common guideline, the overall cost per product unit for exchange where all the above mentioned subjects are converted into cash should be used.

However, this is not very easy. Membrane guarantees of 2-3 years for water desalination is not unusual, even when the membranes have to be exchanged each year. The membrane manufacturer could, of course, compensate for this by adjusting the membrane-exchange price.

When comparing different systems as the customer has to do, it is worthwhile to look at the basic principle of the system and the way in which the membranes are exchanged.

1. Hollow Fibers. The whole membrane-filtration system is exchanged, including membrane, support, flow channel, and high-pressure vessel.

2. Spiral-Wound Systems. The package consisting of membrane support material and flow channels are exchanged from the high-pressure tube.

3. Tubular Systems. The membrane is generally cast on the inside of a porous glass-fiber tube or inserted loosely into a stainless-steel tube.

4. Plate-and-Frame Systems. The membrane cast on support paper is exchanged and replaced by membranes cut out in the proper size.

In respect to manufacturing costs, transport costs, and handling, the plate-and-frame system should have the most economical exchange procedure. The drawback is the necessary work in making the exchange which is usually made by the customer, but for desalination plants this is less important since they are often situated in areas where labour costs are low.

This does not mean that plate-and-frame systems do have the lowest operating costs in respect to membrane exchange, but we believe that the basic principle of reducing the exchange costs counts in favour of plate-and-frame systems. The control of product quality from membrane-filtration plants has also been improved in the plate-and-frame systems, because very small membrane areas can be inspected, and in case of membrane leakage, the membrane in question can be exchanged in a short time. Figure 7 shows the membrane-exchange procedure.

In the food and dairy industries, the sanitation and cleaning of the plant are extremely important. Here, the easy access to each membrane is very valuable for the inspection as well as an immediate exchange of broken membranes, securing optimum bacteriological conditions.

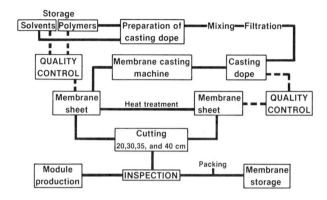

Figure 6.   Membrane-production scheme

Figure 7.   Membrane exchange in a 35-cm module

Security in delivery is most likely best obtained by dealing with companies of a reasonable size and well introduced in the field of membrane filtration. But also here, the plate-and-frame system has an additional advantage, because membranes from other manufacturers who can cast membranes in sheet form can be used direct in our modules, though this is not something DDS is very much in favour of.

Thin-Film Composite Membranes

Finally, I shall briefly mention the thin-film composite membrane. In our description of membrane development and production, this was not included because the conditions involved are rather different, both in respect to development and to production.

When the thin-film composite membrane was introduced, many people considered it to be too difficult to handle in practical life. However, recent publications seem to indicate that these problems have been overcome and that we can expect to have thin-film composite membranes on the market. We are here thinking of the PA-300 from UOP and the recent publication from FilmTec (15).

Membranes in the Future

Twenty years have passed since the first membrane for desalination was made. Today, membrane filtration is an established process which has been integrated in a number of industrial applications.

What can be expected in the next twenty years?

We believe that for reverse osmosis new membranes with high chemical stability, high temperature resistance, and improved performance rates in respect to rejection characteristics and flux rates are coming on the market very soon in the form of improved thin-film composite membranes.

Besides boosting the market for desalination by RO, this means new applications in a large number of processes within the food, dairy, and pharmaceutical industries and for waste-water treatment. Especially the oil shortage and increasing energy prices tend to reinforce the search for energy-saving methods of which RO is a very good example.

The breakthrough for UF was made when we could replace the cellulose-acetate membranes by more resistant materials. We expect the same breakthrough for RO in the years to come.

The development of the membrane production to real large-scale production will increase the realiability of membrane-filtration plants and increase the competitive power of the membrane-filtration process.

Also in the field of UF, new solvent-resistant membranes will increase the application range, e.g. to the oil industry.

Literature

1. Nielsen, W.K., Madsen, R.F., Olsen, O.J., Desalination, 1980,
    32, 309-326.
2. Madsen, R.F., Nielsen, W.K., ACS, Washington D.C., Sept. 1979.
3. Madsen, R.F., Ed. "Hyperfiltration and Ultrafiltration in
    Plate-and-Frame Systems", Elsevier, Amsterdam, 1977.
4. Reid, C.E., Breton, E.J., J. Appl. Polymer Sci., 1959, 1, 133.
5. Loeb, S., Sourirajan, S., Advan. Chem. Ser., 1962, 38, 117.
6. Manjikian, S., Loeb, S., McCutchan, J.W., Proc. First Int.
    Symp., Paper SWD/12, Washington D.C., Oct. 3-9, 1965.
7. Saltonstall, C.W., OSW R&D Progress Report No. 434, June 1969.
8. Kesting, R., U.S. Patent 3,884,801, May 20, 1975.
9. Dow Chemical Company, U.S. Patent 3,423,491, 1966.
10. Anon. Membrane Digest, U.S. Dept. of the Interior, OSW, 1972,
    1, 23.
11. Riley, R.L., Lonsdale, H.K., Lyons, C.R., Merten, U., J. Appl.
    Polymer Sci., 1967, 11, 2143.
12. Rozelle, L.T., Cadotte, J.E., Cobian, K.E., Kopp, C.V., in
    Sourirajan, S., Ed. "Reverse Osmosis and Synthetic Membranes",
    National Research Council Canada, Ottawa, 1977, Ch. 12, p. 249.
13. Cadotte, J.E., Kopp, C.V., Cobian, K.E., Rozelle, L.T., In
    Situ-Formed Condensation Polymers for Reverse Osmosis Mem-
    branes: Second Phase, Report No. PB-234198, National Technical
    Information Service, Springfield, VA, June 1974.
14. Cadotte, J.E., Steuck, M.J., Petersen, R.J., Research on In
    Situ-Formed Condensation Polymer for Reverse Osmosis Membranes,
    National Technical Information Service, Springfield, VA,
    March 1978.
15. Cadotte, J.E., Petersen, R.J., Larson, R.E., Erickson, E.E.,
    Desalination, 1980, 32, 25-31.
16. Kurihara, M., Kanamaru, N., Harumiya, N., Yoshimura, K.,
    Hagiwara, S., Desalination, 1980, 32, 13-23.
17. Model, F.S., Davis, H.J., Poist, J.E., in Sourirajan, S. Ed.
    "Reverse Osmosis and Synthetic Membranes", National Research
    Council Canada, Ottawa, 1977, Ch. 11, p. 231.
18. Michaels, A.S., in Perry E.S., Ed. "Advances in Separations
    and Purifications", Interscience Publ., New York, 1968.
19. Chapurlat, R., Proc. of the 4th Int. Symp. on Fresh Water
    from the Sea, Vol. 4, 1973, 83-93.
20. Kesting, R.E., Jackson, K.F., Newman, J.M., Proc. of the 5th
    Int. Symp. on Fresh Water from the Sea, Vol. 4, 1976, 73-78.

RECEIVED December 4, 1980.

Multiyear Experience with Oily and Organic Chemical Waste Treatment Using Reverse Osmosis

D. DEAN SPATZ

Osmonics, Inc., 15404 Industrial Road, Hopkins, MN 55343

I appreciate this opportunity to speak at the same time on the last day of this symposium just as my close friend and mentor, Dr. Sourirajan spoke on the first day of this symposium. In concluding his talk, Dr. Sourirajan said, "The inherent potential of reverse osmosis processes and reverse osmosis membrane to contribute significantly to the health and welfare of all being and also to the progress of many fields of science, engineering, biology and medicine is far more than what one can comprehend at any time."

Whether we call the process we have talked about during this week reverse osmosis or hyperfiltration or ultrafiltration is of little importance. The important thing is that the membrane invented by Loeb and Sourirajan slightly over 20 years ago is a marketable product and has a fantastic future. Too often we allow semantics to act as a barrier to our mutual understanding of this technology.

After listening to these other fine papers, I guess I should feel lucky to be able to attend this symposium and even luckier to present a paper. My paper has no fancy equations. Yes, I studied Mass Transport by Byrd, Stewart and Lightfoot, but it has been a few years since I could understand the equations which have been projected on the screen in the last three days. I do not consider myself a scientist -- perhaps a technologist and most definitely an entrepreneur of reasonable success.

Dr. Sourirajan has had much to do with my success and to the success of our technology. I feel that a short history of one of those successes would be a fitting tribute to this man who has lived "reverse osmosis" for the last 24 years of his life.

In 1964, while studying at Dartmouth College and considering what would be the best method of removing salt from brackish water, I had the great opportunity to meet with Dr. Loeb and later on with Dr. Sourirajan. This was in 1964, and at that time my colleagues and I decided that reverse osmosis had to be the

0097–6156/81/0154–0221$05.00/0

most economical way to remove the salts from brackish water.
Certainly the commitment to this technology that Dr. Sourirajan
had was instrumental in making me decide to work in this field.
With the help of Dr. Sourirajan and Dr. Myron Tribus, we obtained
a contract from the Office of Saline Water which carried through
1968.

In 1969, I founded Osmonics, Inc. to carry the technology of
reverse osmosis and ultrafiltration to the marketplace. We
originally purchased membrane from Eastman Kodak Company and
made our own spiral elements. We continued purchasing membrane
until Kodak decided not to remain in the membrane business and
we decided to begin the manufacture of membrane. By 1973, we
were in full production manufacturing cellulose acetate membrane
using the Loeb-Sourirajan approach. One year later, we were
manufacturing polysulfone membrane for ultrafiltration. Last
year, 1979, Osmonics manufactured over one million square feet
of RO/UF membrane.

Osmonics became a public corporation in 1971, and since becoming public we have grown at an average rate in excess of 33%
per year. This is equivalent to increasing in size twenty times
over a ten year period. Osmonics has been profitable in every
year since 1973, the year we first started to produce membrane.
Since 1973, our sales and profits have increased in each succes-
sive year. We now occupy 46,000 square feet of manufacturing
space and we are in the process of building a new 85,000 square
foot manufacturing facility to consolidate our business.

ALL OF THIS SUCCESS I OFFER TO THIS MEETING AS A TRIBUTE TO
THE PIONEER OF OUR TECHNOLOGY, MY ESTEEMED MENTOR---DR. S.
SOURIRAJAN.

Discussion

Now that the most important part of my talk is finished, I
would like to tell you about two case histories where RO/UF was
used to satisfy a water pollution control problem. But before we
get into the case history, let us review some of the basic
criteria we use in an RO/UF system.

Figure 1 will give you an idea of RO/UF equipment. This is
a photograph we call the "largest to the smallest". It will give
you an idea of one of the smallest RO units on the market being
held in the engineer's hand and next to the engineer one of the
largest RO units put onto a single skid. There are larger RO
units than the one shown but most of these occupy two skids or
are fabricated on the job site. In addition to the smallest and
largest machine is a medium sized cabinet RO unit for the
production of medical pure water.

Figure 2 shows a generalized view of reverse osmosis/ultra-
filtration. You will note that the artist has purposely shown
the membrane having an isotropic nature, i.e., a dense topskin
with small pores with a very porous support layer. The feed

Figure 1. RO/UF equipment. This photograph contains one of the smallest RO units on the market and one of the largest RO units. There are larger RO units than the one shown but most of these occupy two skids or are fabricated on the job site. In addition to the smallest and largest machines, there is a medium-sized cabinet RO unit for the production of medical pure water.

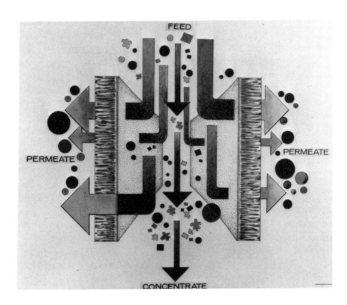

Figure 2. A generalized view of RO/UF. Note that the artist purposely has shown the membrane having an isotropic nature, i.e., a dense topskin with small pores with a very porous support layer. The feed solution flows between the two membranes and as the pressurized feed solution passes over the membranes, permeate passes through the membranes and concentrate exits from between the membranes. The artist has made an effort to show that the impurities in the water are being concentrated as the permeate is being removed.

solution flows between the two membranes and as the pressurized
feed solution passes over the membranes, permeate passes through
the membranes and concentrate exits from between the membranes.
You will also note that the artist has made an effort to show
that the impurities in the water are being concentrated as the
permeate is being removed.

Stepping from the generalized concept of RO/UF to the more
specific mechanism we have Figure 3. Figure 3 shows the mechanism of ultrafiltration. This is ultrafiltration as defined in
the marketplace. Note that this membrane has pores which are too
large to effect desalting but are small enough to remove practically all of the organic molecules larger than 1000 molecular
weight.

Figure 4 shows the mechanism of what is generally referred
to as reverse osmosis in the marketplace. As you can see, the
pore size is approximately equal to twice the thickness of the
pure water layer over the membrane which is void of any ions.
This membrane, when constructed of cellulose acetate, will
typically remove over 99% of the organics in excess of 200
molecular weight and removes over 98% of monosaccharides such
as dextrose and glucose.

But look---aren't these membranes really the same with the
exception of the fact that the pores are smaller for the one we
consider an RO membrane and larger for the one we consider a UF
membrane? Yes, they are basically the same membrane and they
are made in practically the same manner. However, most users
feel uncomfortable in calling both of these membranes by one name
and those of us in the marketplace have therefore, informally
agreed to call a membrane which rejects salts a reverse osmosis
membrane and a membrane which does not reject salts but is of a
pore size smaller than 0.05 microns an ultrafiltration membrane.

I purposely picked two applications to discuss where an RO
membrane is being used for what is considered a UF application.
In other words, a membrane with very small pores is being used
to remove organic matter generally larger than 500-1000 molecular
weight. Do we call it reverse osmosis or do we call it ultrafiltration? Let's compromise and call it RO/UF.

These two applications were also purposely chosen because
too many researchers are overly concerned about the RO/UF membrane used for water purification. At this meeting others have
talked some about RO/UF used in food processing and my discussion
should help you see the diversity of our technology.

The key to the successful use of the RO/UF membrane is in
the packaging of the membrane. Until economical, easily fabricated and stable packages were developed, membranes were of
little commercial value. We use the spiral wound type of membrane element for all of our equipment. Other packages such as
the tube, the hollow fiber with bore flow and the hollow fiber
with outside flow are all valuable and useful packages. However,
the spiral package is by far the most universal in its ability to

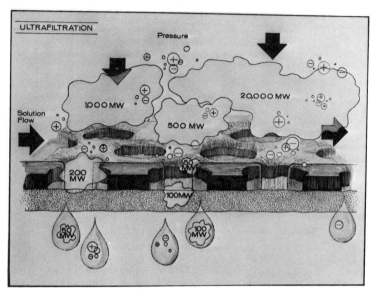

Figure 3.   Mechanism of UF as defined in the marketplace. This membrane has pores that are too large to effect desalting but are small enough to remove practically all of the organic molecules larger than 1000 mol wt.

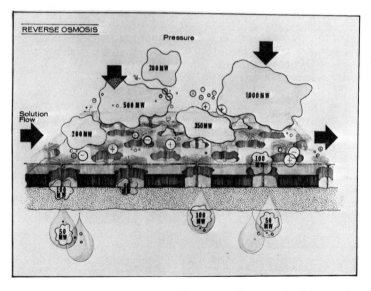

Figure 4.   Mechanism of RO in the marketplace. The pore size is approximately equal to twice the thickness of the pure water layer over the membrane which is void of any ions. This membrane, when constructed of CA, typically will remove over 99% of the organics in excess of 200 mol wt and removes over 98% of monosaccharides such as dextrose and glucose.

treat all types of water, waste water, and industrial solutions.
We have handled many solutions which are normally not considered
appropriate for spiral wound membrane elements simply by applying
good chemical engineering practice.

   Let's take a quick look at the spiral membrane element so
that all of us have the opportunity to understand its makeup.
This is a figure of a partially unrolled spiral membrane element
which we call a sepralator (Figure 5). The sepralator has a
permeate tube for collecting the permeate, the membrane is laid
onto a permeate carrier material and the edges of the membrane
and the permeate carrier are glued together. The membrane is
integrally cast onto a backing material as shown in the figure.
Figure 6 is an enlargement of cross sections of the sepralator.
You can see the two layers of membrane which are similar to the
idealized RO/UF drawing in Figure 1. In order to construct the
sepralator, a mesh spacer is used to keep the membranes from
touching each other. This mesh spacer is also used as a turbulence promoter. The mesh spacer is typically 30 mils (0.762 mm)
in thickness but can be either thinner or thicker as required.
It is not unusual to go as thin as 20 mils (0.508 mm) nor as
thick as 60 mils (1.53 mm) or even 120 mils (3.05 mm). We have
found that a 30 mil thickness allows us to optimize turbulence,
maintain relatively low flows and reduce the pumping energy required to have minimal fouling of the membrane. Once the
permeate goes through the membrane it enters the permeate carrier
which is a relatively porous synthetic material. The permeate
carrier is connected to the permeate tube and small holes carry
the permeate from the permeate carrier to the permeate tube and
finally to the permeate collection manifold. The end cross
section shows how the permeate proceeds through the permeate
carrier spirally to the permeate tube.

   Spiral wound elements have been used by a number of companies in the water purification area since 1968. Osmonics has
been unique in that we have used spirals on a very large number
of non-water purification applications, including oil concentration, latex concentration and of course, the concentration and
fractionation of cheese whey. In fact, our installed capacity on
cheese whey is approximately 324,000 sq. ft. (29,160 m2) of membrane or 20 miles (32 km) of membrane as it comes off of our
machinery 3 ft. (1 meter) wide. Or, if you prefer the installed
capacity is capable of handling 800,000 lbs (360,000 kg) of
cheese whey per hour.

Case History - Whitestone Chemical Co.

   The first case history we will discuss is a medium sized
chemical company, Whitestone Chemical Co. which is a department
of BASF Wyandotte Corporation. They manufacture specialty
organic chemicals and are located in Spartanburg, South Carolina.
Whitestone manufactures primarily alkoxylates; surfactants from

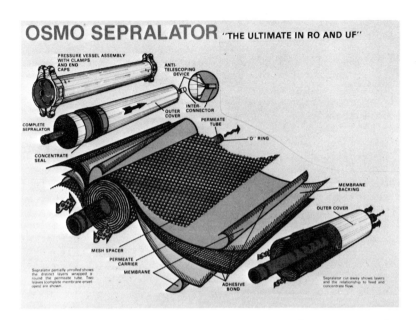

Figure 5. A partially unrolled spiral membrane element known as a sepralator. The sepralator has a permeate tube for collecting the permeate; the membrane is laid onto a permeate carrier material and the edges of the membrane and the permeate carrier are glued together. The membrane is integrally cast onto a backing material as shown in the figure.

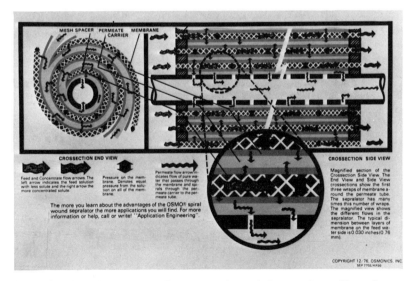

Figure 6. An enlargement of the cross-sections of the sepralator. Note the two layers of membrane which are similar to the idealized RO/UF drawing in Figure 1. In order to construct the sepralator, a mesh spacer is used to keep the membranes from touching each other and is used also as a turbulence promoter.

propylene and ethylene oxide, and esters for the textile industry.
The plant has the capacity to manufacture 35 million pounds
(15.8 million kg) of product per year and generates approximately
30,000 gallons (114 m3) of waste water per day. Because Whitestone is a manufacturer of specialty organic chemicals the waste
water is composed primarily of organics. The primary sources of
pollution are reactor and equipment washouts and some spillage.
These pollutants cause problems in meeting the biochemical oxygen
demand (BOD), total suspended solids (TSS), ammonia, phenol, and
petroleum hydrocarbon standards. From 1971 through 1977, Whitestone Chemical had relied on biological digestion of the organics
in its waste water in order to meet the EPA guidelines.

     However, with more stringent guidelines and since Whitestone
was discharging its waste after treatment directly to a stream,
it was decided to install an RO system on the final aeration
pond. A pilot test of approximately 1000 hours showed the use-
fulness of reverse osmosis and allowed Osmonics to specify the
membrane elements and system layout with sufficient certainty to
guarantee a reasonable life and operating characteristics to
Whitestone.

     Whitestone did evaluate many alternatives prior to choosing
RO. They decided to use RO because the initial cost was low,
maintenance requirements were low and operator attention was
minimal compared to the alternatives. Whitestone also calculated
that the operating costs, both in manpower needs and in actual
chemicals and membrane replacement, was less than other alternatives. Since the RO system would be operating on biologically
active materials it was decided that cleaning every 8 hours would
be appropriate. Therefore, an automatic Clean-In-Place (CIP)
system was developed and installed with the RO unit. There is
typically a 40% reduction in permeate rate due to fouling prior
to the time that Whitestone cleans the RO unit.

     The basic waste treatment system at Whitestone includes:
          Feed pumps from the collection area
          Bag filters
          The RO unit
          Permeate storage tank
          Mixing pit
          Discharge pumps
          CIP system.
The system is housed in a pre-engineered metal building of
sufficient size to add additional treatment capacity if and when
the need arises. The entire system was built and installed for
less than $100,000 and has been in operation since June of 1977.

     The RO machine consists of 78 sepralators using SEPA®-97
membrane. A 50 Hp motor is the only energy required and it runs
a pump supplying pressure to the membranes at 450 to 480 psig
(3041-3243 kPa). The most common feed water temperature to the
RO is 80-85°F (27-30°C) but the temperature will fluctuate depending on the specific time of the year. The machine is running

at 95% recovery of the feed as permeate. In other words, 95% of the water that enters the machine comes out as permeate and 5% is concentrate. The permeate is meeting all of the EPA requirements for discharge to the stream.

The system does get dirty and requires CIP cleaning about every 8 hours. Algae blooms have periodically caused a problem but chlorine feed coupled with additional cleaning using a proprietary cleaner has always restored the permeate rate. Sepralator life appears to be about 24 months and Whitestone has changed their sepralators once in the last 3 years. Even though cleaning every 8 hours may appear to be excessive to some of you who have spent most of your time in the brackish or sea water purification area, it is economical for Whitestone to clean that often rather than spending excessive time trying to develop some type of unique method for pretreatment that would reduce the cleaning frequency. At this time the system is performing well, membrane life is reasonable and the pollution control requirements are being met.

Case History #2 - Cummins Engine Company, Charleston, South Carolina

Another installation in South Carolina but of much larger physical size is the Cummins Charleston Division of Cummins Engine Company. This location has over 900,000 square feet (81,000 sq. m.) of manufacturing facility. The manufacturing operations are centered around manufacture, assembly and testing of diesel engines. Various unit operations include grinding, machining, parts washing, parts cleaning, assembly, painting, testing and storage. The nature of the operations is such that considerable volumes of oil or oily compounds are used. The major contributor to the waste water at Cummins is the testing facility where the engines are tested prior to shipment. All of the waste water production at Cummins amounts to approximately 180,000 gal/day (681 m^3/day).

The waste water is composed of coolants, cutting oils, diesel fuel, lubrication oils, hydraulic oils, wash tank solutions, degreasers, and phosphate rinse from the painting operation. A typical analysis of the waste water shows:

pH = 8
Total dissolved solids = 1106 mg/l
Total suspended solids = 76 mg/l
BOD = 325 mg/l
Total phosphate = 15 mg/l
Iron = 3.7 mg/l
Aluminum = 4.0 mg/l
Lead = Less than 0.01 mg/l
Oil and Grease = 700 mg/l

230

After a minimal amount of testing, an OSMO® dual RO system was installed and started up in early 1975. Each of the two RO machines contains 120 sepralators. Each machine is designed for 60 gpm (13.6 m³/hr) permeate rate at 400-500 psig (2702-3041 kPa) and 95 to 97% recovery of the feed as permeate. Figure 7 shows the system at Cummins. The waste water is collected in different holding containers, pumped through the bag filters and cartridge filters prior to the RO machine and then to the RO machine.

On start-up it was recognized that this system should have had more extensive pilot testing. Unfortunately, the engine manufacturing was not even in partial operation when the pilot tests were run and synthesized waste had to be used. By the time the machine was started up the lagoons used by Cummins for waste water storage had developed a substantial algae bloom that was never anticipated. However, this problem did allow us to learn how to remove algae when it has fouled the RO system. We also learned how to remove oil fouling. The addition of 100-200 mg/l of chlorine is about the only way to remove substantial amounts of algae from the RO machines. Once the first bloom of algae was taken care of the machines stabilized, requiring cleaning every 24-36 hours. As long as the Cummins operator practiced good cleaning techniques and took reasonable care with the RO unit, the system performed very well. If cleaning was missed or done incompletely the resultant fouling took two to three days to overcome.

The engineers at Cummins had heard that it was unusual for RO equipment to be cleaned as often as every 24 to 36 hours. They decided to investigate the possibility of pretreating the waste water prior to the RO or possibly replacing the RO with some other device which would require less operator attention. It is interesting at this point to compare the attitude of the operators at Whitestone Chemical, who were prepared to clean the RO unit based on the pilot tests, to the operators at Cummins who were unprepared to clean the RO unit and therefore, were upset by a cleaning frequency which was 1/3 as often as the cleaning frequency at Whitestone.

Cummins did extensive testing which is summarized as follows:
1. Diatomaceous earth filtration was used with many types of diatomaceous earth (DE) of both the oil absorbing and standard types. The DE filtration produced good quality water removing as much as 95% of the total suspended solids and 50% of the oil. However, rapid blinding of the DE required frequent changes on the precoat and caused concern about the disposal of the contaminated DE.

The DE did reduce the fouling on the RO unit and would have extended the cleaning cycle for the RO. However, in order to obtain an economical filtration run with the DE, prefiltration prior to the DE would be required. Since the objective was to pretreat the RO and not to have two pretreatments, Cummins decided to drop consideration of the DE filters as pretreatment.

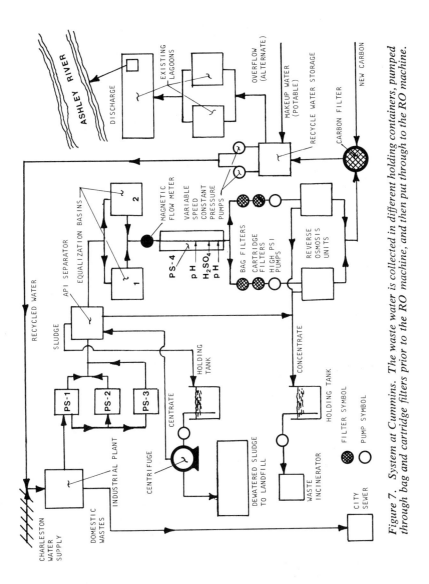

Figure 7. System at Cummins. The waste water is collected in different holding containers, pumped through bag and cartridge filters prior to the RO machine, and then put through to the RO machine.

Figure 8. A typical RO system with a clean-in-place (CIP) unit adjacent to the RO. The CIP unit is plumbed into the RO unit so that the operator can CIP the RO system by simply changing three valves and making certain that the cleaning chemicals are used.

Figure 9. A bag filter system used for pretreatment prior to an oily waste application. We are using 5-μ-rated bags which we feel are approximately equal to 15-μ cartridge filters. Bags are valuable because the waste that is collected can be thrown away.

Figure 10. The actual operating installation of a system that uses both spiral-wound UF and spiral-wound RO to handle oily waste which also is contaminated with phosphates

Figure 11. A beaker containing the concentrate from an RO unit on oily waste and a second beaker showing the permeate from oily waste processing. Normally the oily wastes can be concentrated until the oil "breaks" due to concentration and separate phases are apparent to the naked eye.

2. The next method of pretreatment which was tried was
    ultrafiltration. Pilot size UF units using the hollow
    fiber bore flow type cartridge and the 1" tube module
    were tested. As would be expected, the permeate from
    the UF unit was quite clear and when used as feed for
    the RO, absolutely no fouling was apparent.

    However, the UF fouled at about the same rate as
    the RO had fouled. The UF could be cleaned just as the
    RO could be cleaned.

    The Cummins engineers decided that UF as a pre-
    treatment to RO in this case was not economical because
    of excessive capital and operating costs and should not
    be pursued. As an aside, Osmonics does have some instal-
    lations where UF prior to RO is a viable pretreatment
    and can be economically justified. It just did not fit
    this application.

3. A new process called eclectic treatment was tried. This
    uses a conventional belt skimmer for removing free oil
    and then the addition of electricity to aid in forming a
    floc of the suspended or emulsed oils. On-site pilot
    data could not be collected within a reasonable time and
    Cummins decided not to pursue the eclectic system.

4. Chemical treatment and settling is the most commonly
    used method of treating waste water. Alum and polymer
    flocculating agents were used and were found to be
    successful in pretreating the waste water prior to the
    RO unit. One of the big advantages of a chemical system
    is that it can be tailored on a daily basis to meet
    changing requirements. The operator can consider the
    differing water coming to the waste treatment plant.
    However, the process is operator intensive.

    Cummins has not totally decided to go with chemical
    treatment since the cost of disposing of the sludge
    could be excessive.

5. A fairly new technology which many people in the waste
    treatment of oils firmly believe in is dissolved air
    flotation (DAF). DAF was originally tried at Cummins
    but either the oil at Cummins was too soluble or the
    concentration was too low to hold together the floc for
    a long enough period to have reasonable flotation. After
    the first review, the air flotation process was consid-
    ered not appropriate.

    Subsequent to the general testing and continued
    operation of the system as originally installed, Cummins
    did additional testing with DAF. They found that the
    DAF worked fine if the oil concentration in the waste
    solution was sufficiently high. After a program of
    water conservation gave a reduced total effluent flow
    and an increased oil concentration, additional tests were
    run with DAF. Again, alum and polymer were added. At

this stage the DAF proved to be a reasonable and attractive method of removing a good share of the heavier oils
and other contaminants which were probably fouling the
RO unit.

At the present time, Cummins has decided to install a pretreatment system using dissolved air flotation as the primary
treatment followed by an anthracite/sand backwashable filter and
an activated carbon polishing filter. The effluent from the
filters then goes to the RO unit. The RO will remove the last
traces of the most soluble oils and organics. It is Cummins'
intention to have the effluent from the filters at a turbidity of
less than 45 JTU's. This should keep the RO units from fouling
and will allow the RO to be used with minimal cleaning.

Like all unit chemical processes, the RO is usually not
capable of standing entirely by itself. The important thing to
remember is that a system must be developed to give a complete
product. In the case of Cummins, the complete system includes
dissolved air flotation, anthracite/sand filtration, activated
carbon filtration and RO. In the case of Whitestone Chemical, the
complete system includes RO and a cleaning regimen to maintain
the RO at the required permeate flow rate. Time will tell which
of these alternatives has the best economics. The economics and
the proper system using RO are both dependent on the problem that
requires a solution.

Conclusion

In conclusion, I would like to leave you with two thoughts:
First, I am often asked by investment bankers and those
who follow our technology, why this technology has not grown
as fast as everyone said it would. At first my inclination
was somewhat defensive, but then I did some research into the
growth of other new technologies. I looked at:
- Semiconductors which were invented at the turn of the
  century and have only seen growth in the last decade.
- Colored television which was around in 1925 but never
  became a viable product until 1960 -- 35 years later.
- Nuclear reactions, would we say 1933 for the invention?
  Is the business really that big even now?

My fellow membrane technologists, do not become defensive when someone asks the growth question, instead ask them
to tell you one other technology which 10 years after its
invention had more than 10 active companies selling products
using this technology and now only 20 years later has probably 30 active manufacturing companies and as many more who
are researching the possibility of entering the field.
Secondly, I want to remind all of you that the only true
test of the worth of any research is the ultimate effect of
that research on society in general and in the marketplace in
particular. Twenty years after the beginning of reverse

osmosis and ultrafiltration, the marketplace has proclaimed that this membrane technology is a success. We all look forward to the next twenty years which will see this technology emerge as one of the greatest basic inventions of the 20th Century.

Acknowledgements

I wish to extend my deepest appreciation to Dr. S. Sourirajan who for over 16 years has helped me to gain a better understanding of this unique field of reverse osmosis and ultrafiltration and to the following four individuals whose personal attention to my requests for information on the case studies helped me in preparing this talk.

Beal, Thomas W., Operations Manager, Whitestone Chemical Div., BASF Wyandotte Corp., Spartanburg, SC

Franklin, Patricia V., P.E., Cummins Charleston, Inc., Charleston, SC

Karasiewicz, W. Richard, P.E., McNair, Gordon, Johnson and Karasiewicz Company, Columbia, SC

Davis, William, Sepratech Inc., Rock Hill, SC

RECEIVED February 18, 1981.

A Novel Membrane System for the Ultrafiltration of Oil Emulsions

G. B. TANNY and A. KORIN

Gelman Sciences, Inc., 600 S. Wagner Rd., Ann Arbor, MI 48106

The concentration of emulsions is a subject of considerable importance, encompassing the treatment of industrial wastewater cooling or cutting fluids[1], the processing of foods, and certain pharmaceutical preparations. When one takes into consideration the increased use of microemulsions[2], further growth in this area may be anticipated. Ultrafiltration has quickly become the method of choice for carrying out this process[1], and in the past a report has been made on the use of a new conventional thin-film composite UF membrane[3] to accomplish this goal.

The present contribution describes a novel low pressure, high flux system which utilizes an "in situ" dynamically formed silica membrane particularly suited for the ultrafiltration of emulsions. The support for this selective layer of silica was a pleated, thin channel crossflow module[4] (tradename "Acroflux", Gelman Sciences, Inc.) containing 0.1 m^2 of 0.2 um pore size acrylonitrile copolymer membrane.

This design configuration for flat sheet microporous membrane is relatively new and therefore bears description. Through the pleating process one creates a pleat pack of flow channels consisting of: (1) a cover channel material; (2) a turbulent flow promoting spacer; and (3) the microporous membrane support. A cross section of one of these pleated channels is shown in Figure 1a. The pleat pack is then arranged about a central drain tube, glue seamed down the longitudinal axis, and a seal ring is added to prevent fluid bypass. A schematic of the cartridge in its housing is shown in Figure 1b. Since the cover channel material does not extend into the glue seals at each end of the cartridge, and is somewhat free to move, it facilitates backwashing and is thus especially suited to the membrane regeneration aspect of dynamically formed membrane applications.

In the sections which follow, we shall examine (a) the hydrodynamics of this new module, (b) the formation and properties

0097–6156/81/0154–0237$05.50/0

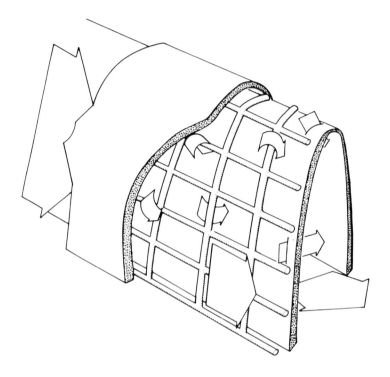

Figure 1a.   Cross-section of a pleated channel

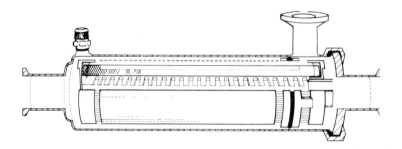

Figure 1b.   Schematic of an Acroflux cartridge in a housing

of the silica dynamic membrane, and (c) its performance in the
module with oil/water emulsions under various conditions.

A. Theory: Operation and Hydrodynamic Analysis of the Acroflux
Module. The schematic cross section of a single pleated
channel of a unit mounted in its housing is shown in Figure
2. In the case under consideration, the flexible channel
cover wall material is impermeable to flow and all the space
between it and the wall of the housing becomes pressurized
to P_F, the feed entrance pressure. Thus, at any point
within the length of the channel, a pressure drop,
$P_F-P(x)$, exists both along the channel and across the
channel cover wall. This pressure drop helps to seat the
channel cover wall on the spacer and maintain channel dimensions. (On the other hand, during the backflush operation,
the channel cover wall is somewhat free to move away from
the spacer to facilitate cleaning.)

Let us consider the mass and force balance in an element dx along the channel. Assuming unitary width, the
change in the flow rate, dQ, is given by:

$$-dQ = \frac{P(x) - P_P}{R_m}\, dx \qquad (1)$$

The change in pressure down the channel over the same
element dx is given by the equation[5]:

$$-dP = aQ^n\, dx \qquad (2)$$

where "a" is the constant reflecting the friction and height
of the spacer (identical to that of the channel) and "n" is
a constant, with the values

n = 1, for laminar flow, and
n = 2, for turbulent flow.

Combining equations (1) and (2) yields:

$$\frac{dQ}{dP} = \frac{1}{aR_m}\frac{(P-P_P)}{Q^n} \qquad (3)$$

Rearranging and integrating to the appropriate boundary
conditions, one obtains:

$$\int_{Q_R}^{Q_f} Q^n\, dQ = \frac{1}{aR_m}\int_{P_R}^{P_F} (P-P_P)\, dP \qquad (4)$$

This equation can now be used to obtain the following relationships between the experimentally relevant factors, ΔP_C, the total trans-channel pressure drop, $\overline{\Delta P}_m$, the average operating pressure, Q, the permeation rate, and $X = \dfrac{Q_R}{Q_P}$: (see Appendix No. 1).

1. For the turbulent flow condition:

$$\Delta P_C = \left(\frac{2Z}{K}\right)^{1/2} \gamma \, Q_P^{3/2} \qquad (5)$$

where

$$Z = 1/3 \left[(1+X)^3 - X^3\right] \qquad (6)$$

$$k = \frac{1}{aR_m} \qquad (7)$$

$$\gamma = 1 - \frac{\Delta P_R}{2\overline{\Delta P}_m} \qquad (8)$$

and

$$\overline{\Delta P}_m = R_m Q_P \qquad (9)$$

These relations can be used to generate the diagram in Figure 3, which defines the anticipated range of pressure drop and average pressure necessary to achieve any desired permeation rate at some desired ratio of retentate to permeation flow rate.

2. For laminar flow conditions

$$\Delta P_C = \left(\frac{\beta}{2k}\right)^{1/2} Q_P \, \gamma \qquad 1/2 < \gamma < 1 \quad (10)$$

where

$$\beta = [(1+X)^2 - X^2]/2 \qquad (11)$$

B. Dynamic Membrane Formation. Colloidal oxides filtered through microporous supports typically give rise to "Class II" dynamically formed membranes, whose formation mechanism characteristics and properties have been reviewed[6]. The most important relations are:

$$Q_P = \frac{1}{2} (K/t)^{1/2} \qquad (12)$$

where

$$K = \frac{2A^2 \overline{\Delta P}_m}{\eta \, C \, R_C} \qquad (13)$$

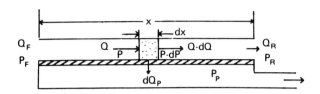

Figure 2.   Schematic of a flow in a thin channel

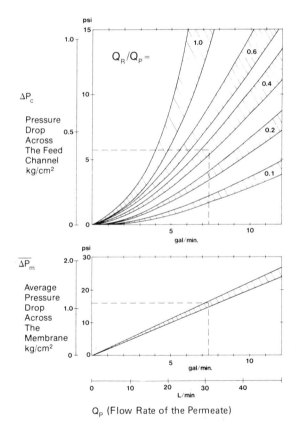

Figure 3.   Experimental results of hydrodynamic test of 10-in. Acroflux cartridges. The shadowed area covers the ranges of the experimental points.

t is time, A is membrane area, η is the liquid viscosity, C is the concentration of the cake forming particulate and R_C is the hydrodynamic resistance of the cake formed. Thus, we also anticipate $Q_p \propto (\Delta P_m)^{1/2}$. It should be noted that the above relations are only really valid for the initial stages of dynamic membrane formation, in which the convective forces bringing colloidal material up to the membrane surface are far larger than any "lift" effects which are present due to the turbulent flow regime[7].

Experimental

A. Testing of Acroflux Cartridge Hydrodynamics. The apparatus used for flow experiments was otherwise identical to that described in Reference (4), except that the crossflow cartridge housing used was polypropylene (model #12806). In order to avoid false pressure readings due to pressure drops in plumbing, the gauges shown in Figure 3 of Reference (4) were attached directly to the housing. All experiments were carried out using 0.2 um filtered well water, maintained by a heat exchanger at a constant temperature of 20 $\pm$ 0.5°C.

Six points ranging from 2-10 gpm for the product flow rate were tested at reject/product flow ratios between 0.1 and 1.0. At each setting, the pressure drops were allowed to reach equilibrium (usually within 2 minutes) and then recorded.

B. SiO_2 Dynamically Formed Membranes. The procedures and equipment used to create the dynamically formed membrane have already been described in an earlier work (4), but will be discussed briefly.

A 500 ppm dispersion of silica (Cab-O-Sil, EH-5, Calbot Corp.), 8 liters in volume, was prepared by dilution of a 2 g/l dispersion which had been sonicated for 40 min. in a Bransonic ultrasonic bath. The turbidity of the final solution was 24 NTU. With the permeate valve closed, the crossflow velocity and formation pressure were set. Timing for a total of 30 min. was begun when the permeate was opened, and readings of permeate flow rate and turbidity were taken at periodic intervals. After formation, and without allowing system shut-down, the silica solution was flushed out with DI water and replaced with the Pazomus B oil emulsion. (Emulsion concentrations are % vol/vol, e.g., 3% represents 30 cc/l of the commercial mixture.)

C. Analytic Procedures

1. Total Organic Carbon Analysis (TOC). TOC analysis was carried out on a Beckman 915A Total Organic Carbon analyzer according to the standard procedures used with this instrument.

2. Hydrocarbon Extractables with Freon Measured by IR.
    Extractable oil was measured by a modified Standard
    Methods tentative procedure[8]:
    a. To 200 cc of sample, 20 cc of 2N HCl is added plus
        4 cc of saturated NaCl.
    b. The above solution is placed in a separating fun-
        nel to which 30 cc of Freon TF is added and shaken
        for 3-5 min. The mixture is then allowed to sep-
        arate and the lower fraction (Freon) is removed
        and added to a 100 ml volumetric flask by dripping
        through a filter funnel containing Na_2SO_4 on a
        paper filter. This procedure is repeated five
        times and the volume is made up of 100 cc (part of
        the Freon evaporates).
    c. Half an hour to one hour prior to IR analysis, 1g
        of Na_2SO_4 is added to the volumetric flask.
    d. IR analysis is carried out in matched 1 cm quartz
        cells and the Freon vs. Freon baseline is gener-
        ated in the range of 3100-2700 cm^{-1}. The spec-
        trum of the sample vs. Freon blank is then gener-
        ated and the absorbance, A, at 2960 cm^{-1} is calcu-
        lated from $A = -\ln\frac{T}{T_o}$.   Sample CH_2 content is ob-
        tained from a calibration curve.
3. Conductivity. Measurements were made with a Radiometer
    Type CDM-2d conductivity meter.

Results and Discussion

A. Hydrodynamics of the Acroflux Module   The experimentally ob-
    tained relationships for a 10" long Acroflux cartridge, op-
    erating on pure water at various ratios of $X = Q_R/Q_p$, is
    shown in Figure 3. As anticipated, a straightline relation
    is obtained between ΔP_m and Q_p.

        For different values of X, ΔP_C shows a clearly non-
    linear behaviour, which is anticipated for turbulent flow
    conditions (c.f., Equation 5). In Figures 4 and 5, log-log
    plots of theoretical values of ΔP_C vs Q_p at a given val-
    ue of X are shown with experimental results. The slope of
    3/2, predicted by Equation 5, seems to fit the results quite
    well.

        Similar plots are shown in Figure 6 for the 20" module.
    In this case, at lower values of X, one also finds that a
    portion of the results fit the laminar flow model, and the
    slope of log ΔP_C vs log Q_p is unity.

        Aside from facilitating the design and initial choice
    of operating conditions, the results in Figures 4-6 make it
    possible to know the state of hydrodynamic flow for any

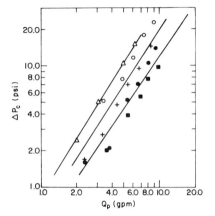

Figure 4. Log–log plot of thin channel pressure drop of 10-in. Acroflux vs. permeate rate at various $X = Q_R/Q_P$ *values:* △, *1.2;* ○, *1.0;* +, *1.0;* ●, *0.6;* ■, *0.6.*

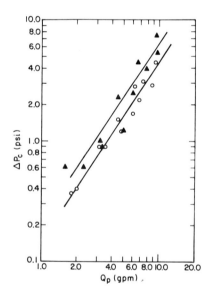

Figure 5. Log–log plot of thin channel pressure drop of 10-in. Acroflux vs. permeate rate at various $X = Q_R/Q_P$ *values:* ▲, *0.4;* ○, *0.2.*

given unit and set of operating conditions. Since ultrafiltration flow rates are very sensitive to boundary layer phenomena, one strives to achieve well developed turbulence at the lowest value of Q_r possible, in order to minimize the pumping energy required. Figure 6 shows that the 20" Acroflux unit is quite efficient. Examining the curve for X = 0.2, one finds that a retentate flow of only 1.5-2 gpm is sufficient to create turbulent flow under conditions in which one is removing 7-10 gpm of product. i.e., the recovery ratio, R.R. is:

$$R.R. = \frac{Q_P}{Q_r + Q_P} \times 100\% = \underline{83.3\%}$$

Of course, these results are for pure water and when the unit is used with a dynamically formed membrane, the increased membrane resistance does not allow us to draw such high absolute values of Q_P. However, the important point is that the ratio of flows required to achieve turbulence in the channel will not change significantly and thus the overall module efficiency can be expected to remain at a high value.

B. Dynamically Formed SiO_2 Membranes

1. Membrane Formation. In earlier work[9] it was found that fumed silica particles could be dispersed in aqueous suspension with the aid of ultrasonic sound. Observations under the electron microscope showed that the dispersion contained disc-like particles, approximately 150-200 Å in diameter and 70-80 Å in height. Filtration experiments carried out in the "dead-end" mode (i.e., zero crossflow velocity) on 0.2 um membrane support showed typical Class II cake formation kinetics, i.e., the permeation rate decreased according to equation (12). However, as may be seen from Figure 7, the decrease in the permeation rate observed during formation in the crossflow module is only $t^{-0.1}$, considerably slower than the $t^{-0.5}$ dependence predicted and observed earlier. This difference may be expected due to the presence of lift forces created by turbulence in the crossflow device, and models for the hydrodynamics in such cases have been proposed.[7]

    After formation, we utilized pure water to measure the hydraulic permeability, L_p (cm/atm-min) of the dynamic layer. For a constant crossflow velocity, L_p is seen to decrease with an increase in the pressure of formation, as seen from Trials 1-4 in Table 1. This could be interpreted either as due to an increase in the thickness of the dynamic layer or a "tightening" of

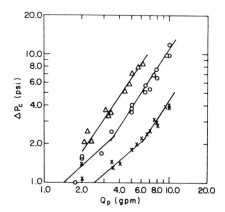

Figure 6. Channel pressure drop of 20-in. Acroflux vs. permeate rate at various X = Q_R/Q_P values: △, 1.0; ○, 0.6; ×, 0.2.

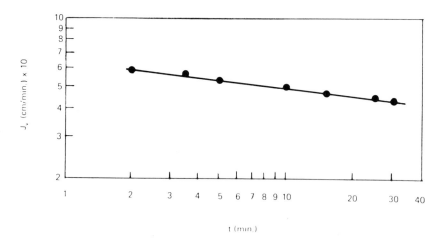

Figure 7. Permeate rate vs. circulation time of 500-ppm dispersion of silica using 6-in. Acroflux capsule

its structure due to the applied pressure on the colloidal cake. Since the membranes show some salt rejection toward dilute solutions ($10^{-3}M$) of sodium sulfate (Na_2SO_4), one would also expect this rejection to increase if the matrix undergoes compaction at higher formation pressures, even at the low pressures involved. (This concentration of Na_2SO_4 solution was chosen because it has roughly the same conductance as the oil emulsion.)

The true measure of the dynamic layer's selectivity, is the intrinsic salt rejection, $\overline{R}_{int}$. However, due to concentration polarization effects caused by the large volume flow through the membrane, one actually measures R_{obs}, the apparent salt rejection, given by the relation

$$R_{obs} = 1 - \frac{C_p}{C_f} \qquad (15)$$

where C_p and C_f are the product and feed salt concentrations respectively. From studies on concentration polarization and membrane performance, it has been found possible to account for these effects by the relation[10]

$$\ln \frac{1-R_{obs}}{R_{obs}} = \frac{kJ_v}{U^{0.75}} + \ln \frac{1-\overline{R}_{int}}{\overline{R}_{int}} \qquad (16)$$

where k is a constant influenced by the hydrodynamic conditions in the system and U is the crossflow velocity which, for the module, is taken as the pumping rate. Thus, if the salt rejection is measured at a number of pressures and/or crossflow velocities, the intrinsic salt rejection, $\overline{R}_{int}$ can be obtained from intercept of a plot of

$$\ln \frac{1-R_{obs}}{R_{obs}} \quad \text{vs.} \quad \frac{J_v}{U^{0.75}}$$

Examples of such plots can be found in Figure 8, for three different dynamic membrane formation conditions. As predicted by equation (16), the data yields good straight line plots, and the values of $\overline{R}_{int}$ calculated from the intercepts are given in Table 1. One sees that the salt rejection increases from 28% to 33% when the formation pressure is increased from 10 to 15 psi. Thus the corresponding decrease in L_p (c.f.

Table 1) is due, at least in part, to a tighter colloid layer structure. Membranes formed at the same
pressure but different crossflow velocities show similar values of $\bar{R}_{int}$ (Trials 5-8 in Table 1), although at
the higher velocities there is some decrease, which
may be due to imperfections in the thinner dynamically
formed layer.

2.   Performance with Oil Emulsions

a.   Flow Rate. In Figure 9, plots are shown for the
flow rate versus applied pressure for an oil
emulsion containing 2.5-3.0% oil (vol/vol). The
dotted straight line represents the pure water
flow rate, while the curves obtained for the oil
emulsion at different crossflow velocities are
typical of situations in which formation of a
boundary layer restricts the flow of water. In
this case, oil droplets are packing together at
the membrane boundary and restricting the flow of
water by their presence. At higher pressures, the
layer thickness and the packing density increases
so that the water flow remains constant. Such behaviour has been observed previously, with oil
emulsions, blood and proteinaceous solutions and
has been classified as "Class I" dynamic membrane
formation[6]. Since the phenomenon involves
boundary layer hydrodynamics, the stirring conditions should clearly affect the performance. Thus
we see that at higher crossflow velocities, the
early data remain closer to the pure water performance line, and the plateau assumes a higher
constant flow rate.

The value of the exponential dependence of
the product flow rate on the crossflow velocity
is indicative of the hydrodynamic conditions
which prevail. The plateau values, or near plateau values of the product flow are shown in Figure 10, plotted versus the crossflow velocity,
and the slope is found to have a value of 0.86.
For a turbulent flow situation in a tube, the
mass transfer coefficient is given by[11].

$$\overline{Sh} = 0.023 \ R_e^{7/8} \ S_c^{1/4} \qquad (17)$$

$$\overline{Sh} = 0.023 \left(\frac{Ud}{\nu}\right)^{7/8} \left(\frac{\nu}{D}\right)^{1/4} \qquad (18)$$

i.e., $\overline{Sh} \propto U^{7/8}$

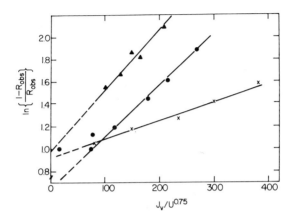

Figure 8. The dependence of the membrane rejection on the flow condition. R_{int} can be calculated from the intercept: ▲, *Trial 1;* ●, *Trial 2;* ✕, *Trial 3.*

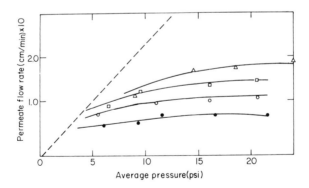

Figure 9. UF of a 3% oil emulsion with a dynamically formed SiO_2 membrane in a pleated crossflow module. Q_R (gpm): ●, *0.67;* ○, *1.0;* □, *1.33;* △, *1.67.*

where U is the crossflow velocity, d is the tube
diameter, ν is the kinematic viscosity and D is
the diffusion coefficient. Thus the dependence
of product flow on the crossflow velocity is
clearly consistent with turbulent flow conditions.

b.   Quality of the Product. Results for the rejection of TOC, extractables and conductivity, are
quite dependent on the type of surfactants in the
cutting oil emulsion tested. Tests on oil used
in the present study, "Pazomus B", showed that it
contains an anionic surfactant, which is probably
a sulphonic acid, since chemical analysis showed
that it contained sulfur. Other neutral polar
molecules, such as alcohols, may also be present.
For 3% "Paz" solutions, the average values of the
product TOC are shown in Table 2. They range
from 160-500 ppm, which is similar to the results
obtained with the 10K ultrafiltration membrane[3]. The results of extraction experiments
are lower than TOC because TOC also measures the
presence of small, polar, water soluble species.
These are only partially extracted by the Freon
in the course of these analysis.

An examination of the data for dynamic membranes formed under various conditions suggests
that a combination of higher pressure and crossflow rate yields both the highest product flux
and lowest oil extraction values. However, the
overall impression is that the TOC or extractables level of the product is far less sensitive
to formation conditions than the hydraulic permeability or even the intrinsic salt rejection toward 10^{-3}M Na_2SO_4 solutions. Further evidence of this lack of sensitivity can be seen in
Table 2. At a later stage in the work, it was
realized that conductance measurements of the
feed and product could be used to examine the
distribution of surfactant between the larger oil
drops retained by the dynamic membrane, and small
conductive surfactant micelles (approximately
100-200Å) which pass through. As the results in
Table 2 demonstrate, about 50-60% of the conductive species are retained by the membrane. Since
the membrane has some intrinsic rejection for
dilute salts, it is possible that part of the
smaller charged species are also rejected.

c.   Effects of Concentration and Time. Since real
systems will have to concentrate the oil emulsion
to relatively large volume fractions of oil
(i.e., 25-40%), and work for extended periods of

TABLE I

Properties of Dynamically Formed Silica Membranes On
0.2 um Membrane Acroflux Capsules (1000 cm$_2$ area)

Capsule	Trial	Membrane Formation Conditions Pressure (atm)	Crossflow Rate (ℓpm)	Hydraulic Permeability, L_p (cm/min-atm)	Intrinsic Rejection of 10^{-3}M Na$_2$SO$_4$
10	1	0.5	2.5	0.40	27
10	2	0.67	2.5	0.34	28
10	3	1.0	2.5	0.20	33
4	4	2.3	2.5	0.17	-
11	5	0.67	3.25	0.29	27
11	6	0.67	3.75	0.23	28
11	7	0.67	4.5	0.37	21
11	8	0.67	5.5	0.34	21

TABLE II

Ultrafiltration Trials of Various Silica Dynamic Membranes
with Pazomus BB Oil Emulsion

Membrane Formation Trial Number*	TOC Feed Concentration (ppm)	TOC Average (ppm)	Concentration of Permeate Species Containing CH$_2$Functionality (ppm)	% Rejection Conductivity
1	20,000	220 ± 10	99	59 ± 2
2	20,000	180 ± 10	95 ± 5	59 ± 2
3	17,000	225 ± 10	96	51
4	12,500	170 ± 30	48	-
5	23,000	250 ± 10	137	50
6	22,000	280 ± 30	108	46
7	22,000	235 ± 5	46	51
8	19,000	230	36	42

*   cf Table I for conditions of membrane formation.

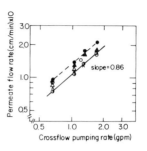

*Figure 10.   Dependence of the permea-
tion rate on the crossflow pumping rate
in the UF of a 3% oil emulsion by a dynamically formed SiO₂ membrane in a
pleated crossflow module:* ◑, *Trial 2;* ✕,
Trial 3; ▲, *Trial 4;* ●, *Trial 6;* ○, *Trial
7;* △, *Trial 8.*

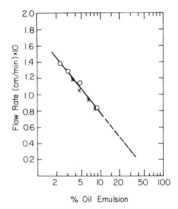

*Figure 11.   Permeate flow rate vs. batch
oil emulsion concentration*

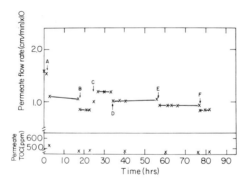

*Figure 12.   Long-term UF performance of a dynamically formed SiO₂ membrane
in a pleated crossflow module:* P_{ar} = 1.5 atm; 1.67-gpm crossflow initial feed concentration = 3.6%; T = 32°C.

time, these aspects were also examined. In Figure 11, the results of two batch concentration trials are shown, in which the flow rate has been plotted vs. log C_B, the oil emulsion concentration. As observed earlier in our study of UF membranes[3], a straight line relation is obtained. For the clean "Paz" emulsion, fluxes of 0.02 cm/min (approximately 7 gfd) can still be anticipated for emulsions containing 40-50% oil.

A test of over 80 hrs. operation on a single dynamically formed layer was also undertaken to examine the continuous operation behaviour. During this time, the membrane was subjected to several shut-downs and restarts, as well as a concentration cycle. As may be seen from Figure 12, the membrane showed almost no change either in flux or rejection after an initial drop in flux which occurred after the first three hours of operation. However, in addition, the membrane appears to have taken the shut-down and restart operation with no ill effects. It should be pointed out that this was not always the case. The Acroflux module used in this trial was tightly packed and showed no visible movement of the pleats when pressurized, whereas earlier units sometimes showed such effects. Movement of the pleats upon re-pressurization cracked the dynamic layer in earlier trials and caused an oil leak into the product compartment. In such cases, a new dynamic membrane had to be formed, and feed introduced without allowing system shut-down.

Nomenclature

Symbols	Q	=	Volumetric Flow Rate
	P	=	Pressure
	C	=	Concentration
Subscripts	c	=	Flow Channel
	m	=	Membrane
	P	=	Permeate Stream
	F	=	Feed Stream
	R	=	Retentate Stream
Terms	Q_R	=	Volumetric flow rate of the retentate stream (gal or liters per min.)
	Q_P	=	Volumetric flow rate of the permeate stream (gal or liters per min.)
	ΔP_c	=	Pressure drop across flow channel (psi or kg/cm^2)
	$\overline{\Delta P_m}$	=	Average pressure drop across membrane (psi or kg/cm^2)

ΔP_F = Pressure drop across membrane at inlet (psi or kg/cm^2)

P_F = Pressure of the feed stream (psig or kg/cm^{2}g)

P_P = Pressure of the permeate stream (psig or kg/cm^{2}g)

P_R = Pressure of the retentate stream (psig or kg/cm^{2}g)

ΔP_c = $P_F - P_R$ = Pressure drop across channel

ΔP_F = $P_F - P_P$ = Pressure drop across membrane at inlet

$\quad = \dfrac{2\overline{\Delta P}_m + \Delta P_c}{2}$

ΔP_R = $P_R - P_P$ = Pressure drop across membrane at outlet

$\overline{\Delta P}_m = \dfrac{\Delta P_F + \Delta P_R}{2} = \dfrac{P_F + P_R}{2} - P_P = $ Avg. pressure drop across membrane.

$\dfrac{\overline{\Delta P}_m}{Q_P}$ = Resistance of membrane to flow of liquid

$X \quad = \dfrac{Q_R}{Q_P} \qquad = $ Cross-flow ratio

$RR \quad = \dfrac{Q_R}{Q_F} \qquad = $ Recovery Ratio

$R \quad = 1 - \dfrac{C_P}{C_F} = $ Rejection

$R_m \quad = $ Membrane Resistance

Appendix 1

Performing the integration of Eq. 4 yields:

$$\frac{1}{n+1}\left(Q_F^{n+1} - Q_R^{n+1}\right) = \frac{1}{aR_m}\left(\frac{P_F^2}{2} - P_F P_P - \frac{P_R^2}{2} + P_R P_P\right) \quad (1)$$

Inserting into the right-hand side of the equation

$$\frac{P_F P_P}{2} - \frac{P_F P_R}{2}$$

enables us to rearrange and restate this right side

$$= \frac{1}{aR_m} \left[P_F \left(\frac{P_F}{2} + \frac{P_R}{2} - P_P \right) - P_R \left(\frac{P_R}{2} + \frac{P_F}{2} - P_P \right) \right] \qquad (2)$$

$$= \frac{1}{aR_m} \left[(P_F - P_R) \left(\frac{P_F + P_R}{2} - P_P \right) \right]$$

Where from the identities in equation 2, and assuming n above is 2, we obtain

$$\frac{1}{3} \left(Q_F^3 - Q_R^3 \right) = \frac{1}{aR_m} (\Delta P_c) (\overline{\Delta P_m}) \qquad (3)$$

Equation #3 can be written as follows:

$$Q_P^3 Z = K_1 \overline{\Delta P_m} \Delta P_c \qquad (4)$$

where

$$Z = \frac{1}{3} \left((1+X)^3 - X^3 \right) \quad \text{and} \quad X = \frac{Q_r}{Q_p}$$

$$K_1 = 1/aR_m$$

Rearrangement of equation 4 can be done using the following substitution:

$$\Delta P_c = 2 \Delta P_m \left(1 - \frac{\Delta P_r}{\overline{\Delta P_m}} \right)$$

This equation can be written as follows:

$$\Delta P_m = \Delta P_c / 2 \left(1 - \frac{\Delta P_r}{\overline{\Delta P_m}} \right) \qquad (5)$$

Substitution of the above in equation #4 will obtain:

$$Z Q_P^3 = \frac{K}{2} \Delta P_c^2 \left(\frac{1}{1 - \Delta P_R / \overline{\Delta P_m}} \right)$$

Rearrangement will obtain

$$\Delta P_c = \left(\frac{2Z}{K} \right)^{1/2} Q_P^{3/2} \left(1 - \Delta P_r / \overline{\Delta P_m} \right)^{1/2} \quad (6)$$

Knowing that

$$\left(1 - \frac{\Delta P_r}{\Delta P_m} \right)^{1/2} = 1 - \frac{\Delta P_r}{2 \Delta P_m} + \frac{\Delta P_r^2}{8 \Delta P_m} \cdots$$

and assuming that only the first two terms of the series can be used

when $\Delta P_r \approx \Delta P_m$ then $\gamma = 1 - \dfrac{\Delta P_r}{2 \Delta P_m} \approx \dfrac{1}{2}$

when $\Delta P_r \ll \Delta P_m$ then $\gamma = 1 - \dfrac{\Delta P_r}{2 \Delta P_m} \approx 1$

Therefore equation 6 can be written as follows:

$$P_c = \left(\frac{2Z}{K} \right)^{1/2} Q_P^{3/2} (\gamma) \quad \text{where} \quad \frac{1}{2} < \gamma < 1 \quad (7)$$

In the case of laminar flow through the channel, the value of n will be 1 and then

$$dp = a_L Q$$

where a_L is a friction coefficient respective to laminar flow at the channel. In this case equation 3 will have the following form:

$$\beta Q_P^2 = K_L \Delta P_c \Delta \overline{P}_m \quad (8)$$

where $\beta = \left((1+X)^2 - X^2 \right) 1/2$ $X = \dfrac{Q_r}{Q_p}$

and $K_L = 1/(a_L R_m)$

substitution of eq. 5 into eq. 8 results in

$$\beta \; Q^2 = K_L \, \Delta \, P_c^2 / 2 \; \left(1 - \frac{\Delta \, P_r}{\Delta \, P_m} \right)$$

or

$$\Delta \, P_c = \left(\frac{2\beta}{K_L} \right) Q_p \left(1 - \frac{\Delta \, P_r}{\Delta \, P_m} \right)^{1/2}$$

thus, when the square root term is developed into a series, then

$$\Delta \, P_c = \left(\frac{2\beta}{K_L} \right)^{1/2} Q_P \left(1 - \frac{\Delta \, P_r}{2 \Delta \, P_m} \right)$$

and therefore,

$$\Delta \, P_c = \frac{2\beta}{K_L} Q_p \gamma \qquad \text{where} \quad 1/2 < \gamma < 1 \qquad (9)$$

One can <u>assume</u> that in a case of laminar flow through a short channel $\overline{\Delta \, P_m} \sim \Delta \, P_r$ and thus $\beta \sim 1/2$ and

$$\Delta \, P_c = Q_p \left(\frac{\beta}{2K_L} \right)^{1/2}$$

REFERENCES

1. Brandon, C.H., 5th. Seminar on Memb. Sep. Tech., Clemson University, S.C., May 12, 13, 14, 1980.

2. Friberg, S. <u>Chem. Tech.</u>, 1976, p. 124.

3. Tanny, G. B.; Heisler, M. A.C.S. Symp. Ultra Filtration Membr., Washington, D.C., 1979.

4. Tanny, G.B.; Hauk, D. <u>Separation Sci. and Tech.</u>, 1980, <u>15</u>, 317.

5. Perry, R.H.; Chilton, C.H. <u>Chem. Eng. Handbook</u> (5th. Edition), McGraw Hill.

6. Tanny, G.B.; Perry, R.H. <u>Separation & Pur. Methods</u>, 1978, <u>7</u>(2), 183-220.

7. Belfort, G.; Reed, R.H. 5th. Seminar on Memb. Sep. Tech.,
    Clemson University S.C., May 12, 13, 14, 1980.

8. "Standard Methods for the Examination of Water and Waste-
    water"; Am. Pub. Health Assoc., Inc., NY 1979.

9. Frelich, D.; PhD Thesis, Feinberg Graduate School, Weizmann
    Institute, Rehovot, Israel.

10. Shor, A.J.; Kraus, K.H.; Johnson, J.S.; Smith, W.T. Ind.
    Eng. Chem. Fund., 1968, 7, 44.

11. Chilton, T.H.; Colburn, A. Ind. Eng. Chem., 1934, 26, 1183.

RECEIVED December 18, 1980.

Engineering Aspects of the Continuous Membrane Column

JOHN M. THORMAN[1] and SUN–TAK HWANG

Chemical and Materials Engineering, The University of Iowa, Iowa City, IA 52242

The partial enrichment of gas mixtures via membranes has long been recognized as a novel separation technique. Prior to 1950 only a limited amount of research had been conducted in this field. Early applications were unique and included hydrogen purification through silver-palladium alloys, helium recovery through silica glass, and uranium isotope separation. However, in recent years there has been an explosion of activity directed toward the imminent and widespread commercialization of gas permeation technology. Gas permeation separations are becoming less novel and more practical.

In particular, substantial progress has been made during the past decade. Plug-flow separation models of capillary permeators have been confirmed experimentally by several investigators (1,2, 3,4). Specific studies of capillary membranes and permeators have also been made concerning axial pressure loss (2,5,6,7), capillary deformation (4,5,8), process variables and broken fibers (7), flow patterns and purge streams (9), the pressure dependency of permeability coefficients (10,11,12,13), and two-membrance permeators (15,16). Work with axisymmetric membranes has been initiated (17). Cascade separations have been advanced by other researchers (18,19,20,21,22). Commerical units, such as the Du Pont Permasep (23) and Monsanto Prism Separator (24), have been developed for enriching hydrogen, carbon monoxide, ammonia, and other industrial gases. Extensive reviews of these and other recent advances in the area of gas permeation can be found in books by Hwang and Kammermeyer (25) and Meares (26).

In addition to the above contributions another idea, referred to as "the continuous membrane column," was developed in the late 1970's (27,28,29). In essence this concept states that the gas permeation cell, traditionally regarded as a single-stage separation unit, is actually a self-contained continuous cascade. The

---

[1] Current address: Monsanto Chemical Intermediates Company, Texas City, TX 77590.

more permeable gas is stripped from the high-pressure stream along the membrane; however, when the cell is operated in the countercurrent, plug-flow mode, and the amount of permeation is maximized relative to product stream flow rates, a strong internal reflux action is created. In principle, the components of a binary mixture can be enriched indefinitely, provided that the membrane employed exhibits some finite selectivity.

Although the separation mechanisms for membrane and equilibrium processes differ, operation of a membrance column is analogous to that of packed distillation and extraction columns. As shown in Figure 1, a feed stream is centrally introduced, and product streams are withdrawn from the ends of the column. The column can be divided into stripping and enriching sections. Note that gas on the low-pressure side of the membrane is recycled to the high-pressure side via a compressor. In this manner the more permeable gas is continually carried toward and collected near the compressor, while the less permeable gas is steadily transferred toward and concentrated at the opposite end of the column. The absence of backmixing is very important, since any axial mixing will tend to equalize compositions. The degree of separation achieved depends on product flow rates, membrane selectivity, amount of local permeation, and column length.

Earlier papers on the continuous membrane column (28,29) have discussed the separation of CO_2-N_2, CO_2-O_2 and O_2-N_2 (air) mixtures in stripper, enricher and total column units composed of 35 silicone rubber capillaries. A characterization of the membrane column using a membrane unit concept (analogous to transfer unit concept — HTU, NTU) has also been presented. The purpose of this paper is to present some new data and discussions on the extended study of continuous membrane column. Specifically, the topics of multicomponent separations, inherent simulation difficulties, composition minima in the enriching section, variation of experimental parameters, and local HMU variation along the column will be covered.

Multicomponents Systems

Thus far, only binary mixtures have been separated in the total membrane column. Results of this work have been discussed elsewhere (28,29). A sample shell-side composition profile from a total column experiment with a CO_2-O_2 mixture is shown in Figure 2. Table I summarizes the total column data obtained to date.

One of the next steps in developing the continuous membrane column will be to obtain extensive data on multicomponent systems. Some preliminary experiments with a $CO_2-CH_4-N_2$ mixture using a stripper have already been conducted. The results of two such experiments are presented in Figures 3 and 4. The agreement between experiment and model is excellent.

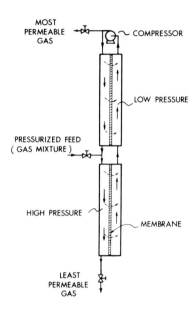

Figure 1. Schematic of the total column

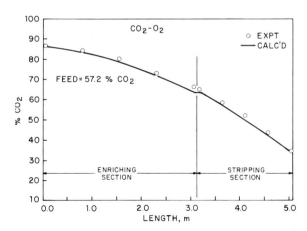

Figure 2. Shell-side composition profile of the total membrane column for the CO_2–O_2 mixture

TABLE I. PERFORMANCE OF THE CONTINUOUS MEMBRANE COLUMN

Gas System	CO_2–N_2	CO_2–N_2	CO_2–O_2	CO_2–O_2	O_2–N_2	O_2–N_2
Feed Composition (% 1st Gas)	54.8	52.6	57.2	57.0	21.0	20.9
Top Product Composition (% 1st Gas)	94.5 (94.4)	94.6 (95.2)	87.3 (86.3)	88.3 (88.7)	36.8 (36.8)	41.7 (41.7)
Bottom Product Composition (% 1st Gas)	17.8	8.2	20.5	22.6	15.1	19.6
Top Product Flow Rate (μmol/s)	4.83	2.37	7.90	7.46	1.79	0.993
Bottom Product Flow Rate (μmol/s)	5.77	2.59	6.74	7.10	4.34	12.92
Feed Flow Rate (μmol/s)	10.60	4.96	14.64	14.56	6.13	13.853
Compressor Load (μmol/s)	(87.7)	(91.7)	(84.0)	(88.69)	(12.66)	(13.13)
Total Column Length (m)	5.12	5.12	5.12	5.12	4.24	4.24

TABLE I. (cont'd.)

Enriching Section Length (m)	3.11	3.11	3.11	3.11	2.13	2.13
Stripping Section Length (m)	2.01	2.01	2.01	2.01	2.11	2.11
Pressure at Compressor (kPa)	226.62 (224.89)	223.86 (222.73)	224.85 (223.31)	223.89 (222.56)	230.14 (230.28)	227.34 (227.11)
Enriching Section Pressure Loss (kPa)	7.62 (5.98)	8.06 (6.92)	7.35 (6.03)	7.81 (6.82)	0.83 (0.88)	1.03 (1.03)
Stripping Section Pressure Loss (kPa)	1.24 (1.16)	0.80 (0.80)	2.04 (1.80)	2.28 (1.96)	0.71 (0.80)	2.04 (1.80)
Shell-Side Pressure (kPa)	99.27	98.78	99.07	99.27	101.22	98.59
Enriching Section Temperature (K)	298.3	298.5	297.8	302.7	296.3	297.1
Stripping Section Temperature (K)	298.7	299.4	299.5	302.7	296.3	297.1

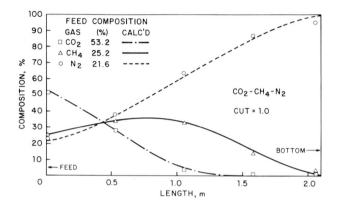

Figure 3.   Shell-side composition profiles for the CO_2–CH_4–N_2 mixture in a stripper at total reflux

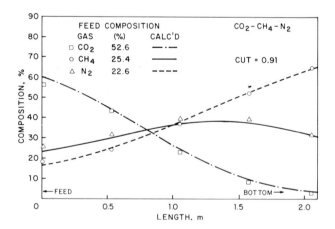

Figure 4.   Shell-side composition profiles for the CO_2–CH_4–N_2 mixture in a stripper with bottom product

In modeling multicomponent systems it is necessary to modify the axial pressure loss, gas permeation and concentration gradients previously described (28). The governing equations, required to execute the numerical simulation over infinitesimal segments along the membrane column as shown in Figure 5 are:

$$\frac{dP}{dz} = \frac{K_1 \bar{\mu} q RT}{\pi N(r_i)^4 P} \left(\frac{1}{K_2} - \frac{4 Re_w z}{Re_z r_i} \right) - \frac{4/r_i}{Re_z/(3P) - \pi N(r_i)^3 P/(2\bar{\mu} q RT)} - \frac{8\bar{\mu} q RT}{\pi N(r_i)^4 P}$$

(1)

$$\frac{dq}{dz} = \frac{2\pi N}{\ln(r_o/r_i)} \sum_j [Q_j(x_j P - y_j P_o)]$$

(2)

and

$$\frac{dx_j}{dz} = \left[\frac{2\pi N Q_j (x_j P - y_j P_o)}{\ln(r_o/r_i)} - x_j \frac{dq}{dz} \right] / q$$

(3)

for $j = 1, 2, \ldots, n-1$

where

$$K_1 = 8 \left(1 + 0.75 Re_w - 0.0407 Re_w^2 + 0.0125 Re_w^3 \cdots \right)$$

(4)

$$K_2 = -1 + 0.056 Re_w - 0.0153 Re_w^2 \cdots$$

(5)

The following overall and component balances are also required:

$$q - q_B = G - G_B$$

(6)

$$x_j q - x_{B_j} q_B = y_j G - y_{B_j} G_B \quad \text{for} \quad j = 1, 2, \cdots, n-1$$

(7)

Of course,

$$\sum_j x_j = 1$$

(8)

All procedures for executing the numerical simulation of a multicomponent separation are similar to those described for a binary system, except for evaluating the initial permeate composition at the residue end of the stripper. Again, the initial permeate composition will be that of the mixture which permeates through the endmost increment of the membrane. The appropriate relations are:

$$y_{B_j} \frac{dq}{dz} = \frac{2\pi N}{\ln(r_o/r_i)} \; Q_j \left(x_{B_j} P - y_{B_j} P_o \right) \tag{9}$$

$$\text{for} \quad j = 1, 2, \cdots, n$$

and

$$\sum_j y_{B_j} = 1 \tag{10}$$

A trial-and-error solution is necessary. By estimating the value of dq/dz each of the component equations (9) and (10) can be solved for y_{B_j}. If $y_{B_j} > 1$, $y_{B_j} < 0$ or $\sum_j y_{B_j} \neq 1$, then dq/dz must be revised. Determination of dq/dz can be facilitated by employing an iterative numerical technique, such as interval halving or the secant method (30).

The multicomponent data obtained from operating a stripper at total reflux and with bottom product are particularly interesting. The feed mixtures were comparable in each case, roughly 53% CO_2-25% CH_4-22% N_2, as were feed pressure (225 kPa), ambient pressure (99 kPa) and temperature (300 K). The pure-gas permeabilities of carbon dioxide and methane are approximately 12 and 3.3 times greater than that of nitrogen, respectively. Figures 3 and 4 show that at steady-state the composition of the most permeable gas, carbon dioxide, steadily decreases, while that of the least permeable gas, nitrogen, increases along the column. The composition of methane, with an intermediate permeability, passes through a maximum.

The curves shown in Figures 3 and 4 are simulated composition profiles based on experimental data. The calculated trends fit the experimental compositions quite well, and in each case the experimental methane peak is well described. This demonstrates that the basic model for the membrane column can be applied to multicomponent systems as well as to binary mixtures.

The existence of a methane peak is not considered a phenomenon that will always occur with intermediately permeable gases in multicomponent mixtures. Rather, the peak is thought to be the result of a combination of factors. These factors include composition of the feed mixture, pure-gas permeabilities, and the internal reflux ratio. For instance, Figure 3 indicates that the intermediate-gas composition profile will steadily decrease in a stripper 1.0 m long, but otherwise identical to the column used in this study, fed with a 63.6% N_2 - 32.3% CH_4 - 4.1% CO_2 mixture under similar total reflux conditions. The presence of an intermediate peak, however, is reminiscent of multicomponent distillation profiles and raises the possibility of withdrawing a side stream enriched with an intermediate gas.

Local HMU Variation

   The performance of the continuous membrane column was characterized earlier (28) in a manner analogous to the transfer unit
concept for packed columns. The expressions developed for NMU
(difficulty of separation) and HMU (efficiency) were

$$ NMU \equiv \int_B^T \frac{dx}{x - yP_r - x\{(1 - Q_r)(x - yP_r) + Q_r(1 - P_r)\}} \qquad (11) $$

and

$$ HMU \equiv \frac{Z}{\int_B^T \frac{2\pi NQ_1 P}{q \ln(r_o/r_i)} \, dz} \qquad (12) $$

Figure 6 illustrates the change in HMU and NMU over 100 mm sections along the column. The curves are for the CO_2-O_2 system,
but qualitatively represent both the enriching and stripping
sections for all of the CO_2-N_2, CO_2-O_2 and O_2-N_2 systems investigated.
   The HMU trend shows that efficiency goes up (HMU goes down)
significantly as the axial flow rate decreases within the column.
In some instances, local HMU values change almost an order of
magnitude. Since HMU and NMU vary inversely over a given interval, the number of membrane units achieved in each section increases dramatically with decreasing flow rates. Note that it is
the modification of column operating variables contained in the
HMU expression that ultimately determine the value HMU when the
column length is fixed.

Composition Minima

   Usually in an enricher or the enriching section of the membrane column, the more permeable component is steadily concentrated from the feed inlet to the compressor. However, some of
the results show that the shell-side and even the tube-side composition profiles can pass through a minimum. Note the experimental data in Figures 7 and 8. In these cases the feed flow is
relatively slow and reflux action, rather than bulk flow, is predominant. Figure 8 illustrates that a composition minimum can
also occur during operation of the total column when the residue
flow rate from the enriching section is too slow.
   Figures 7 and 8 incorporate calculated tube- and shell-side
concentration profiles for the unique CO_2-N_2 and O_2-N_2 (air) data,
and also illustrate local permeate composition variation. Each
figure shows that the concentration of more permeable gas steadily
decreases in the direction of flow along the high-pressure (tube)

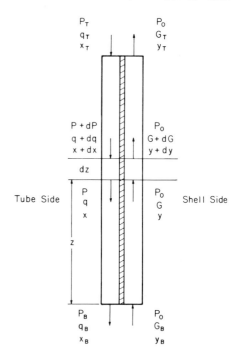

*Figure 5. Modeling of the membrane
column*

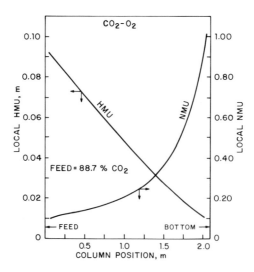

*Figure 6. Local variation of NMU and HMU within a section of the membrane
column*

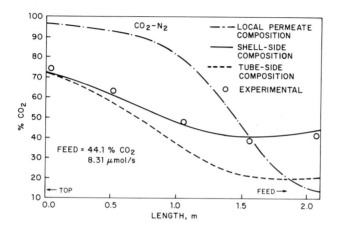

Figure 7. Composition minima for the CO_2–N_2 system in an enricher with top product

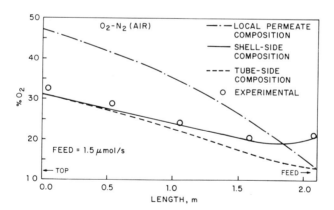

Figure 8. Composition minimum for the O_2–N_2 (air) system in an enricher with top product

side of the enricher. This results in a lower percentage of more permeable gas passing through the membrane. Eventually, because of strong reflux action, the local permeate composition matches the shell-side (low-pressure side) composition. At that point enrichment ceases. Continuing toward the bottom of the enricher, the shell-side concentration of more permeable gas declines until the relative amount of permeate is insufficient to further lower the concentration of the incoming low-pressure stream. The profile then increases toward the feed inlet. Hence a shell-side concentration minimum is formed.

Figure 7 shows that a concentration minimum can also occur on the high-pressure side proceeding again toward the bottom of the enricher, the concentration of more permeable gas passing through the membrane gradually becomes less than that on the tube (high pressure) side. Thus, the concentration of the more permeable gas increases toward the bottom product outlet. There is no tube-side composition minimum in Figure 8, since the local permeate composition does not fall below the tube-side composition profile.

It should be pointed out that operation of an enricher and total column (Figure 9) is less efficient when a concentration minimum occurs. In other words, the same enrichment can be accomplished with a shorter column. This condition can be easily remedied by increasing the flow rate on the high-pressure side of the membrane.

Simulation Difficulties

The numerical simulation of the total membrane column works well, but does contain some inherent problems. These problems relate to restrictions in the direction that integrations are executed, and to the influence of propagated errors in the final results.

All calculations, except those involving a total reflux stripper, should be initiated at the bottom of a column section for two reasons. First, numerical instability is observed in a stripping section with a bottom product when integration is directed from the feed point toward the bottom outlet. Integration is stable, however, from the bottom outlet to the feed point, except in some instances of wide-open flow. Secondly, at the top of the column it is difficult to accurately measure flow rates of streams entering and exiting the enriching section near the compressor. Were values of these flow rates provided, along with gas composition and pressure at the compressor, integration could be executed from the top of the enriching section to the feed point.

The propagation of measurement and calculation errors can also be a problem. In general, experimental errors in boundary conditions at the bottom of the column and calculation errors in the model are propagated along the stripping section, introduced

to and further compounded in the material balance around the feed
point, and amplified again in the enriching section. If at any
step in the simulation the absolute values of composition or flow
rates become comparable with their respective errors, there is a
strong likelihood that the ensuing calculated profiles will
deviate significantly from the experimental profiles. The most
susceptible quantities in the simulation are the boundary conditions at the residue outlets of the stripping and enriching sections.

The effect of perturbing a boundary condition at the bottom of a stripping section is illustrated in Figure 10. The
experimental composition of the bottom product for the CO_2-N_2
system is only 1.7% CO_2. The simulated shell-side composition
profile based on this value follows the experimental trend, but
is consistently higher. After slightly altering the bottom composition to 1.3% CO_2, the calculated profile and conditions at
the opposite end of the stripper agree closely with the experimental data. In this example only one initial condition was
varied. It should be remembered that both the composition and
flow rate of the bottom product may contain measurement errors
comparable to their absolute values. In such cases it is recommended that measurements be taken carefully and that initial conditions in the simulation be perturbed within the range of experimental error in order to appreciate the possible range of calculated results.

The inherent simulation difficulty accompanying a low
residue flow rate from the enriching section of a total column is
shown in Figure 11. Referring to Figure 1, the material balance
around the feed point involves an external feed and the residue
stream from the enriching section, which combine to form an internal feed to the stripping section. In the column simulation the
composition and flow rate of the residue stream are determined
using experimental values for the external feed, and calculated
values for the internal feed to the stripping section. In some
cases the calculated and experimental errors may negate one
another. However, when the *actual* residue flow rate is small
relative to the external feed, it is more likely that errors in
the calculated flow rate and composition of internal feed to the
stripping section will be amplified in determining the *calculated*
values of the residue stream from the enriching section. Depending on how sensitive the enriching section simulation is to propagated errors in the boundary conditions, the calculated profiles
for the enriching section can differ markedly from experimental
profiles.

Should the calculated profiles in the enriching section be
erroneous due to uncertainties in the boundary conditions the correct profiles can be found by employing a shooting technique. The
input data for the simulation are again based on measurements subject to experimental error. By perturbing one or more values
within the bounds of experimental error, the enriching section

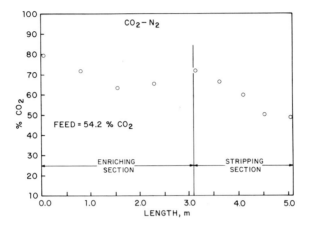

Figure 9.   Shell-side composition profile minimum for the CO_2–N_2 mixture in the total membrane column

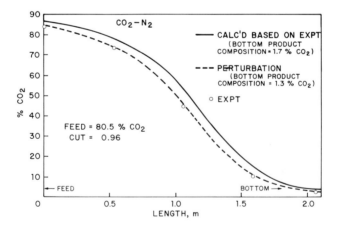

Figure 10.   Sensitivity of the stripper shell-side composition profile to the bottom product composition

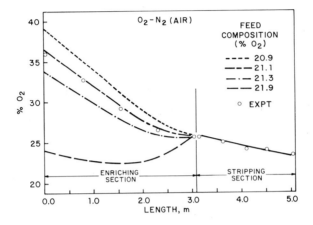

Figure 11.   Sensitivity of the shell-side composition profile to the feed composition in the total column simulation

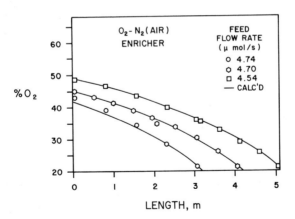

Figure 12.   Effect of column length on enrichment in a total reflux enricher

boundary conditions can be recalculated. This procedure is one
of trial-and-error and can be exercised when an experimental profile, such as the shell-side composition is available for fitting.
Figure 11 illustrates the application of this shooting technique
by perturbing only the external feed composition.

Parameter Variation

The effect of column length on the degree of enrichment in a
total reflux enricher is shown in Figure 12. Feed flow rates were
practically the same to total reflux enrichers 3, 4 or 5m in
length. The output pressure of the compressor was comparable in
each instance, ranging from 229-231 kPa. The data indicate that
extra membrane surface area results in a further accumulation of the
more permeable gas in the enricher. The amount of permeation becomes greater relative to the feed flow rate; hence greater enrichment of mixture occurs along the column. For this specific
case, an O_2-N_2 (air) mixture, the level of oxygen at the compressor increased approximately 4% with each additional meter of tube
bundle.
Figure 13 shows that essentially identical profiles are
obtained when strippers of 3, 4 and 5m are operated at the same
"cut" (ratio of permeate to feed). However, unlike the experimental work leading to Figure 12, feed flow rates were varied with
column length in order to maintain the value of "cut" constant.
Once again, the experimental and calculated composition profiles
are in excellent agreement.
The effect of feed flow rate on the performance of a total
reflux enricher of fixed length was discussed in an earlier paper
(29). In general, the degree of enrichment increased as the
amount of permeation became greater relative to the feed flow
rate.

Conclusions

1. According to membrane unit analysis, the efficiency of a
    permeation cell increases significantly as axial flow rate
    decreases.

2. A composition minimum can occur in an enricher or in the
    enriching section of a total column on the low- and high-
    pressure sides of the membrane. Such operation is ineffi-
    cient, and can be remedied by increasing the axial flow rate
    on the high-pressure side of the column.

3. The separation model, which was previously applied only to
    binary systems, has been successfully extended to describe
    the separation of a multicomponent gas mixture.

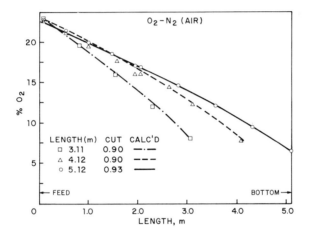

Figure 13. Shell-side composition profile variation with a comparable cut and a variable column length

4. Inherent difficulties accompany some simulations of the
    continuous membrane column. Perturbation of boundary con-
    ditions within the range of experimental error may be
    necessary in certain instances to achieve a proper fit of
    experimental data.

5. Increasing the amount of permeation relative to the feed
    flow rate in a total reflux enricher enhances the degree
    of enrichment of the more permeable gas.

Acknowledgment

This material is based upon work supported by the National
Science Foundation under Grant No. ENG78-10850.

Nomenclature

G $=$ shell-side flow rate, μmole/s

HMU $=$ height of a membrane unit as defined by Equation (12), n

K_1 $=$ function of Re_w as defined by Equation (4)

K_2 $=$ function of Re_w as defined by Equation (5)

n $=$ total number of components in mixture

N $=$ number of capillaries

NMU $=$ number of membrane units as defined by Equation (11)

P $=$ absolute local tube-side pressure, kPa

P_o $=$ atmospheric pressure, kPa

P_r $=$ P_o/P

q $=$ tube-side flow rate, μmol/s

Q $=$ permeability coefficient mol-m/s-m^2-Pa

Q_r $=$ Q_2/Q_1

r $=$ capillary radius, n

R $=$ gas constant

Re_w $=$ Reynolds number at wall defined as $r_k v_{rw} \rho/\bar{\mu}$

Re_z $=$ axial Reynolds number

T   =   absolute temperature, K

v_{rw} =   radial velocity at wall, m/s

x   =   mole fraction of more permeable component on tube side

y   =   mole fraction of more permeable component on shell side

z   =   axial coordinate measured from bottom of column, m

Z   =   total column height, m

Greek Letter

$\bar{\mu}$ =   viscosity of gas mixture, Pa-s

π =   3.14159 $\cdots$

ρ =   gas density, kg/m^3

Subscripts

1   =   more-permeable component

2   =   less-permeable component

B   =   at bottom of column

i   =   inside

o   =   outside

r   =   ratio

T   =   at top of column

w   =   at capillary wall

z   =   axial direction

Abstract

    Engineering aspects of "the continuous membrane column," an innovation in membrane separation technology are discussed. The gaseous permeation cell is no longer regarded as a single stage, but rather as a continuous cascade. The membrane column exploits the countercurrent plug-flow operation of modern gas permeators. By maximizing the amount of permeation relative to product stream flow rates, a strong internal reflux action is created. Thus, a binary feed mixture can be introduced to the membrane column, and nearly complete separation can be achieved on a continuous basis.

Experiments were conducted with a permeator composed of 35 silicone rubber capillaries (pressurized internally). Results are presented for the binary systems O_2-N_2 (air), CO_2-N_2, CO_2-O_2, and the multicomponent system CO_2-CH_4-N_2. Particular attention is given to separation of the CO_2-CH_4-N_2 mixture in a stripper, conditions for observing composition minima in the enriching section, inherent simulation difficulties in modeling the membrane column, variation of experimental parameters, and local HMU variation along the column.

Literature Cited

1. Blaisdell, C.T.; Kammermeyer, K. Chem. Eng. Sci., 1973, 28, 1249.

2. Thorman, J.M.; Rhim, H.; Hwang, S.T. Chem. Eng. Sci., 1975, 30, 751.

3. Ohno, M.; Morisue, T.; Ozaki, O.; Heki, H.; Miyauchi, T. Radiochem. Radioanal. Lett., 1976, 27, 299.

4. Stern, S.A.; Onorato, F.J.; Libove, C. AIChE J., 1977, 23, 567.

5. Thorman, J.M.; Hwang, S.T. Chem. Eng. Sci., 1978, 33, 15.

6. Pan, C.-Y.; Habgood, H.W. Can. J. Chem. Eng., 1978b, 56, 210.

7. Antonson, C.R.; Gardner, R.J.; King, C.F.; Ko, D.Y. Ind. Eng. Chem. Process Des. Develop, 1977, 16, 463.

8. Blaidell, C.T.; Kammermeyer, K. AIChE J., 1972, 18, 1015.

9. Pan, C.-Y.; Habgood, H.W. Ind. Eng. Chem. Fundam., 1974, 13 323.

10. Stern, S.A.; Mullhaupt, J.T.; Gareis, P.J. AIChE J., 1969, 15, 64.

11. Stern, S.A.; Fang, S.-M.; Jobbins, R.M. J. Macromol. Sci.-Phys., 1971, B5(1), 41.

12. Stern, S.A.; Fang, S.-M.; Frisch, H.L.; J. Polymer. Sci., 1972, Part A-2, 201.

13. Fang, S.-M.; Stern, S.A.; Frisch, H.L: Chem. Eng. Sci., 1975, 30, 77.

14. Ohno, M.; Morisue, T.; Ozaki, O.; Miyauchi, T. J. Nucl. Sci. Technol., 1978a, 15, 411.

15. Ohno, M.; Morisue, T.; Ozaki, O.; Miyauchi, T. J. Nucl. Sci. Technol., 1978b, 15, 376.

16. Ohno, M.; Ozaki, O.; Saito, H.; Kimura, S.; Miyauchi, T. J. Nucl. Sci. Technol., 1977, 14, 589.

17. Sourirajan, S.; Agrawal, J.P. "Reverse Osmosis in Synthetic Membranes," S. Sourirajan (Ed.), Natl. Res. Council Can., 1977, Chapter 26.

18. Higashi, K.; Doi, H.; Saito, T.; Energ. Nucl., 1970, 17, 98.

19. Rainey, R.H.; Carter, W.L.; Blumkin, S. Report ORNL-4522, Oak Ridge National Laboratory, Oak Ridge, Tenn., April 1971.

20. Yamamoto, I.; Kanagawa, A.; J. Nucl. Sci. Technol., 1975, 12, 120.

21. Higashi, K.; Miyamoto, Y. J. Nucl. Sci. Technol., 1976, 13, 30.

22. Pan. C.-Y.; Habgood, H.W. Can. J. Chem. Eng., 1978a, 56, 197.

23. Gardner, R.J.; Crane, R.A.; Hannan, J.F. Chem. Eng. Prog., 1977, 73(10), 76.

24. Knieriem, M. Jr. Hydrocarbon Processing, 1980, 59(7), 65.

25. Hwang, S.-T.; Kammermeyer, K. "Membranes in Separations," Wiley-Interscience, New York, 1975.

26. Meares, P. (Ed.) "Membrane Separation Processes," Elsevier, New York, 1976.

27. Thorman, J.M. "Engineering Aspects of Capillary Gas Permeators and the Continuous Membrane Column," Ph.D. Thesis, University of Iowa, Iowa City, Iowa, 1979.

28. Hwang, S.-T.; Thorman, J.M.; AIChE J., 1980, 26, 558.

29. Hwang, S.-T.; Thorman, J.M.; Yuen, K.M. Sep. Sci. Technology, 1980, 15(4), 1069.

30. Beckett, R.; Hurt, J. "Numerical Calculations and Algorithms," McGraw-Hill, New York, 1967.

RECEIVED December 4, 1980.

Chemically Resistant Asymmetric Membranes Made from PVA for the Separation of Organic Solvents and Phenols from Aqueous Solutions

S. PETER and R. STEFAN

Lehrstuhl für Technische Chemie, Universität Erlangen–Nürnberg,
Egerlandstrasse 3, D-8520 Erlangen, West Germany

The increasing quantities of industrial wastes requiring treatment are becoming an important problem. Relatively high demands on the quality must be fulfilled, if the water has to be discharged or recycled. The effluents requiring purification frequently contain a wide variety of compounds with differing properties. Generally the concentrations of these organic and inorganic pollutants may range between 0,5 and 5% by weight, often making an expensive treatment of industrial wastes necessary. Reverse osmosis could possibly become an attractive alternative to the classical separation processes such as distillation, extraction, evaporation etc., which are currently in use. Reverse osmosis may be used to increase the concentration of the compounds present in the wastes so that their reextraction with the aid of classical separation methods becomes economical. Also it can be used as a step in the treatment of wastes before drain off.

The differing properties of the compounds present in industrial effluents require membranes that are stable against the solvents in question. Futhermore, the membranes have to be sufficiently permeable. Thermal stability and durability over a wide pH range (1-14) are also required as well as a sufficiently high selectivity with regard to the compounds to be separated. The demand of general stability against solvents is met by cross-linked membranes.

Material used

For the investigations reported here polyvinyl alcohol (PVA) and its derivatives such as polyvinyl acetate, polyvinyl ether etc. were used as the basic polymeric materials. These compounds can easily be converted into polymeric analogues [1]. It was shown in an earlier work [2] that PVA-membranes with an asymmetrical structure can be obtained by phase-inverted precipitation similar to the method of Loeb and Sourirajan [3]. These membranes can also be rendered insoluble in water by

0097–6156/81/0154–0281$05.00/0

cross-linking [4]. The following substances were mainly used:
PVA with a hydrolysis grade of 98% and a molecular weight of
90 000, Polyvinylacetate with a molecular weight of 110 000,
polyvinylbutyrate with a molecular of 7000 and 12-16% of free
OH-groups.

Method of producing the membranes

Films were cast from the polymer solution and after that
immersed in a precipitation bath. The asymmetric membranes
obtained are soluble in water and have to be made insoluble
by cross-linking. During the cross-linking reactions the
asymmetric structure produced by the phase-inverted precipitation must remain unchanged. This can be performed by treating
the asymmetric membrane in a fixing bath of an acidic salt
solution. After this treatment, cross-linking is possible by
organic   and   inorganic reagents without reduction of the
asymmetry.

Cross-linking renders the membranes insoluble in water;
additionally, the retention of the organic compounds is improved.
The best results were obtained for the cross-linking either by
using both organic and inorganic reagents together in one step
or by applying them one after another. Cross-linking by means
of metal salts can equally well precede or follow the treatment with an organic reagent.

Properties of the membranes

The influence of different cross-linking reagents on the
properties of the membranes was investigated by reverse osmosis
experiments. A procedure for preparing the membranes was
devised that yielded membranes of medium retention of phenol
against an aqueous phenol solution of 2 g/litre at pH 13.
The membranes were always prepared in exactly the same way.
Thus the influence of the different cross-linking agents could
be compared better than under optimum conditions of preparation.
After cross-linking by means of organic compounds, some of the
membranes were additionally treated with a solution containing
Cr(III)-salts [5].

The osmotic properties of the membranes were tested at
room temperature and a pressure difference of 50 bar. Phenol
retention and product flux were measured.

The stability of the membranes obtained against various
solvents was investigated by immersing the membranes in the
solvent concerned at 40°C for about three weeks. After that
their mechanical and osmotic properties were tested again and
compared with their properties before the treatment. The results
of the experiments are shown in table I. The stability of the
membranes subjected to cross-linking by an organic reagent is
very satisfactory. Additional treatment with Cr(III) solutions

Table I: Chemical stability of PVA-membranes in organic and inorganic solutions at 40°C

solvent mixtures		Membrane type I	Membrane type II	reactant	Composition+ weight%	Membrane type I	Membrane type II
$CH_3OH-C_2H_5OH-H_2O$	25:25:50	1	1				
$DMSO- C_2H_5OH-H_2O$	60:30:10	1	1				
$DMSO- C_2H_5OH$	50:50	1	1	HCOOH	98-100	3	2
$DMSO- DMF$	75:25	1	1	CH_3COOH	100	2	1
$DMSO-C_2H_5OH-FA$	60:30:10	1	1				
$DMSO-CH_3OH-FA$	60:30:10	1	1	NaOH	20	2	2
$C_2H_5OH-H_2O$	50:50	1	1	H_2SO_4	50	3	2
	25:75	1	1	NH_4OH	25	1	1
	75:25	1	1				
	100:1	1	1	HNO_3	12	2	2
isopropyl alcohol-H_2O	50:50	1	1	benzene	100	2	2
	25:75	1	1				
	75:25	1	1	toluene	100	3	1
	100:1	2	2	xylene	100	2	2
dioxane- H_2O	50:50	1	1	phenole	3,5	1	1
	25:75	1	1				
	75:25	1	1	cresol (o,m,p)	7	1	1
	100:1	2	2	pyridine	6	2	2
DMSO - H_2O	50:50	1	1	formaldehyde	35	3	2
	25:75	1	1	isobuty-			
	75:25	1	1				
	100:1	3	2	-methyl-ketone	100	2	2
DMF - H_2O	50:50	1	1				
	25:75	1	1				
	75:25	1	1				
	100:1	1	1				
cyclohecanone - H_2O	50:50	2	1				
	25:75	2	1				
	75:25	2	1				
	100:1	3	2				
formamide - H_2O	50:50	1	1				
	25:75	1	1				
	75:25	1	1				
	100:1	1	1				
CH_3OH-H_2O	50:50	1	1				
	25:75	1	1				
	75:25	1	1				
	100:1	1	1				

1 = stable, no change in membrane properties

2 = not stable

3 = destruction of membrane

Type of membrane I = PVA, cross-linked by organic compounds

Type of membrane II = PVA, cross-linked by organic compounds and treated with Cr(III)

+ Concentrations refer to aqueous solutions.

increases the stability as well as the phenol retention as is
shown later.

In Fig. 1 the phenol retention of membranes cross-linked
in saturated solutions of dicarboxylic acids is represented
as a function of the number of carbon atoms of the dicarboxylic
acid. The solubility of the dicarboxylic acids in water
is also represented. As can be seen, the alternating behavior
of homologous series with the number of carbon atoms is
reflected in the phenol retention of the cross-linked membranes.
The results of the investigation are specified in table II.
Besides the retention of phenol, the retention of Na_2S was,
similarly measured. The tabulated values are mean values for
the membranes obtained from about 3 separate trials. The
reproducibility of the measurements amounts to about 2% for the
retention and 0.003 $m^3/(m^2d)$ for the product flux. The additional
treatment of the membranes in Cr(III) salt solutions caused a
notable improvement in phenol retention while the flux remained
practically unaltered.

The behavior of membranes cross-linked by various ketones
was investigated in the same way. These membranes possess
exceptionally good mechanical properties. Moderate values for
flux and phenol retention were found (see table III). Since
the object only was to compare different cross-linking reagents,
no further attempt was made to improve the flux and the retention.

Table IV gives the retention and product flux for membranes
cross-linked by dicarbonyl compounds in presence of various
aqueous solutions of phenol, sodium sulfide, pyridine and
ammonia. The strong concentration dependence of the retention
in the presence of phenol and the dependence of the flux on the
solute is interesting. Membranes with 95% retention for phenol
at fluxes of about 0.100 $m^3/(m^2d)$ can be easily obtained.

In biotechnology, the products concerned are removed from
aqueous solution by extraction with methylacetate, butylacetate,
isobutyl methyl ketone etc. The remaining aqueous substrate is
saturated with the extraction solvents. Sometimes this causes
problems with regard to environmental regulations. Table V
shows that the solvents can be removed almost entirely by
reverse osmosis. The concentrate consists of two phases,
namely, the solvent saturated with water and the water
saturated with solvent. These can be separated by means of a
settler. The water phase is recirculated to the reverse osmosis.
The saturated solubility in Water at room temperature is
19 000 mg/litre for isobutyl methyl ketone, 3300 mg/litre for
butyl acetate and 9 500 mg/litre for methyl acetate. As the
results in table V show, the retention   for isobutyl-methyl
ketone increases with increasing concentration. This result is
remarkable, as generally a decrease in retention is observed
with increasing concentration.

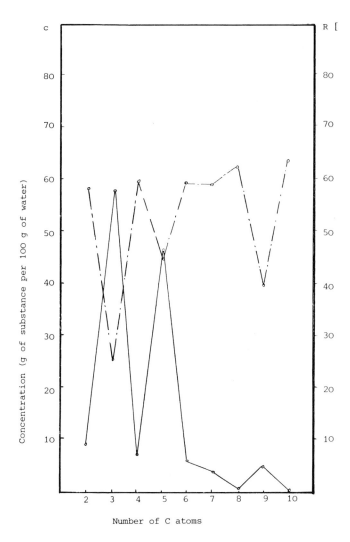

*Figure 1.   Concentration of carboxylic acid and retention of the PVA membrane:
(———) concentration of acid in the cross-linking solution; (— — —) retention on 0.2
wt %, phenol, pH = 13.*

Table II: PVA-Membranes Cross-linked by Dicarboxylic Acids and Cr(III) solution

Number of C-atoms in molecule	Acid	MW	Cr(III)	Retention [%] phenole 2000 [mg]	Retention [%] ammonia 2400 [mg]	Product Flux $\left[\frac{m^3}{m^2 d}\right]$ phenole 2000 [mg]	Product Flux $\left[\frac{m^3}{m^2 d}\right]$ ammonia 2400 [mg]
2	Oxalic Acid	90.04	–	58		0.070	
			+	65		0.066	
3	Malonic Acid	104.06	–	25		0.120	
			+	38		0.250	
4	Succinic Acid	118,00	–	66		0.078	
			+	74		0.060	
5	Glutaric Acid	132,11	–	45		0.105	
			+	69		0.075	
6	Adipic Acid	146,14	–	58	10	0.090	0.119
			+	65		0.080	
7	Pimelic Acid	160,17	–	58		0.105	
			+	66		0.080	
8	Suberic Acid	174,19	–	63		0.100	
			+	69	20	0.075	0.200
9	Azelaic Acid	188,22	–	40		0.130	
			+	46	25	0.105	0.220
10	Sebacic Acid	207,25	–	64		0.080	
			+	70	10	0.075	0.300

$\Delta p = 50$ bar $T = 25^{\circ}C$

Table III: PVA membranes cross-linked by ketones

K E T O N E	C-atoms in molecule	MW	mole fraction of ketone in the cross-linking solution	phenole content of feed	
				2000 $[\frac{mg}{l}]$ R [%]	pH 13 PR $[\frac{1}{m^2 d}]$
acetophenone	8	120.14	0.138	59	100
propiophenone	9	134.17	0.124	69	185
benzylmethylketone	9	134.17	0.124	46	100
butyrophenone	10	148.20	0.112	73	100
acetone	3	58.08	0.286	60	26
ethylmethylketone	4	72.10	0.230	68	80
iso-butylmethylketone	6	100.16	0.166	63	96
cyclohexanone	6	98.14	0.169	59	420
dimethylcyclohexanone	8	126.20	0.132	66	74
diacetyl	4	86.09	0.193	69	32
benzil	14	210.22	0.079	63	62
acetylacetone	5	100.11	0.166	61	268
benzoylacetone	10	162.18	0.102	56	167

Δp = 50 bar   T = 25°C

Table IV: membranes cross-linked by dicarbonyl compounds

Dicarbonyl compound in the cross-linking solution	polymer	solvent for polymer	RETENTION [%]						PRODUCT FLUX $[\frac{1}{m^2 d}]$					
			phenole a pH 13			Na_2S	Pyri-dine	NH_3	phenole at pH 13			Na_2S	Pyri-dine	NH_3
			485	2000	30000	400	13000	2400	485	2000	30000	400	13000	2400
glyoxal	PVA	H_2O		66			26	17		70			85	40
		$DMSO, H_2O$		70		96	30	8		60		90	120	140
		CH_3OH, H_2O		62		78	24	14		80		95	100	90
glutar-dialdehyde	PVA	H_2O	97	95	66	96	53	28	70	150	75	80	70	80
		$DMSO, H_2O$	99	97	57	93	56	30	85	90	82	82	65	90
		CH_3OH, H_2O	99	99		81	50	30	60	70		97	90	110
	PVB	C_2H_5OH, DMF		55						140				
	PVAC	CH_3OH, CH_3COCH_3		33						300				
adipic-aldehyde	PVA	H_2O		63		38	36	10		55		80	100	320
		$DMSO, H_2O$		65		50	32			80		70	140	
		CH_3OH, H_2O		80		63	35			60		65	125	

$\Delta p = 50$ bar $T = 25°C$ conc. $[\frac{mg}{1}]$

Table V   Separating performance of PVA   cross-linked membranes
for certain solvents

ISOBUTYL METHYL KETONE		N-BUTYL-ACETATE	METHYLACETATE		DMSO
$19\ 000\ \frac{mg}{l}$	$9\ 000\ \frac{mg}{l}$	$3\ 300\ \frac{mg}{l}$	$9\ 500\ \frac{mg}{l}$	$6\ 400\ \frac{mg}{l}$	$40\ 000\ \frac{mg}{l}$
R PR	R PR	R PR	R PR	R PR	R PR
70 90	35 120	75 80	35 100	45 105	60 200

$$\Delta p = 50\ bar \qquad t = 25^{\circ}C \qquad R\ [\%] \qquad PR\ [\frac{1}{m^2 d}]$$

Table VI gives the retention and product flux of a PVA cross-
linked membrane for the organic and inorganic compounds in
effluent from a coking plant.

Several membranes with good values for the retention of
organic and inorganic compounds were investigated by reverse
osmosis experiments with the effluents from the manufacture
of organic intermediate products. The composition of the
effluents were complex with analysis as follows:

Type B	pH = 9	TOC	14 000	[mg/l]
		COR	40 800	"
		BOD_5	1 900	"
ion concentration			51 000	"
Type C	pH = 8	TOC	14 600	"
		COR	40 400	"
		BOD_5	6 000	"
ion concentration			67 725	"

The tests were carried out under the following conditions:
a) at room temperature and 50 bar and 85 bar respectively
b) at 42°C and 50 bar.
Each test lasted a week. In all cases no change in the retention
or flux was observed during the experiment. The following
retention values were obtained at a product flux of about
20 litre/(m^{2}d) and were found to be independent of the pH
value of waste:

phenolic compounds	60-90%
TOC	60-70%
SO_4^{2-}	76-82%

Table VI: Retention and product flux with regard to organic and inorganic compounds of cross-linked PVA-membranes in waste water from a coke plant

Type of membrane	Feed cokery waste water						
	RETENTION [%]				PRODUCT FLUX $[\frac{m^3}{m^2 d}]$	R [%] phenolic OH-groups 4500 $[\frac{mg}{l}]$	PR $[\frac{m^3}{m^2 d}]$+ phenolic OH-groups
	phenolic OH-groups+ 15000 $[\frac{mg}{l}]$	sulphide 12000 $[\frac{mg}{l}]$	ammonia free 5000 $[\frac{mg}{l}]$	ammonia in ammonia salts 65000 $[\frac{mg}{l}]$			
I	67	14	54	24	0.048	77	0.292
II	58	14	62	21	0.043	72	0.415
III	66	17	56	26	0.450	69	0.860
IV	57	10	62	15	0.080	59	0.432
V	18				0.961	35	6.262

+ phenolic OH-groups in phenol equivalents

$\Delta p = 50$ bar   T = 25°C

After the investigation into the handling and the action of the most important reagents has been completed, further research can be done to improve those methods that are most promising. Initial trials have resulted in membranes giving a flux of 1 $m^3/(m^2d)$ and a phenol retention of 70% for a phenol concentration of 2 g/litre at pH = 13. Membranes cross-linked by dicarbonyl compounds have been found to possess high thermal stability; retention and product flux remained unaltered after one week of testing in an phenol solution of 2 g/litre at 50°C. It is worth remarking with regard to the treatment of effluents discharged at high temperature, that the thermal stability of these membranes makes heat recycling by means of reverse osmosis a possibility.

This work was supported by the Ministerium fuer Forschung und Technologie (BMFT) of the German Federal Government.

Abstract:

Asymmetrical membranes were initially produced from polyvinylalcohols of suitable molecular weight using phase-inverted precipitation. They were then treated with acid solutions of sodium formate and sodium acetate. The asymmetrical structure was stabilised as a result of the slight cross-linking of the polymers produced. A cross-linked membrane so prepared can then be made insoluble in water and permanent in the presence of solvents by further cross-linking. This was effected by treatment with various compounds containing one or two aldehyde groups or with one or more carboxyl groups (saturated and unsaturated dicarboxylic and tricarboxylic acids); in this way is was possible to maintain the primary asymmetry completely. The chemical activity, chain length and chain structure of the individual compounds used resulted in different degrees of cross-linking of the polyvinyl alcohols in the membran. The cross-linked membranes produced have good chemical, mechanical and thermal durability in an pH – range of 1-14. The membranes have been tested in reverse-osmosis experiments in aqueons solutions of phenols, methyl isobutyl ketone, acetic acid esters etc. The retention and permabilily properties in the presence of the above-mentioned solvents are reported.

Literature Cited

1) F. Kainer, Polyvinylalkohole, Ferdinand Enke Verlag Stuttgart (1949)
2) S.Peter, N. Hese, R. Stefan, Desalination, 19 (1976) 161-167; S. Peter, R. Stefan, Proc. 6 th Int. Symp. Fresh Water from the Sea, Vol. 3 (1978) 239-246;
3) S. Loeb, S. Sourirajan, Advanced Chem. Series 38 (1962) 117.
4) DOS 2441 311 (1974); DOS 27 30 528 (1977)
5) N. Hese, Thesis (1976) Erlangen

RECEIVED December 4, 1980.

Solute Preferential Sorption in Reverse Osmosis

J. M. DICKSON[1] and DOUGLAS R. LLOYD[1]

Department of Chemical Engineering, Virginia Polytechnic Institute and
State University, Blacksburg, VA 24061

Since the early days of research in reverse osmosis (RO), it
has been recognized that, in comparison to the separation of salt
solutions, certain solutes exhibit anomalous performance behavior.
A typical example is the negative separation observed for aqueous
phenol solutions when using cellulose acetate membranes; i.e., the
permeate stream is more concentrated in phenol than is the feed
stream. This anomalous behavior can be accounted for by postulating
that solutes such as phenol are preferentially attracted to or
preferentially sorbed by the cellulose acetate membrane material.
It is to this topic of solute preferential sorption in reverse
osmosis that this paper is dedicated. Specifically, this discussion
will involve a description of solute preferential sorption, an
overview of the literature in the area, and finally a presentation
of some recent work on the removal of aromatic hydrocarbons from
water. The significance of this work is at least two-fold. From
a practical point of view the classes of solutes which demonstrate
preferential attraction to the membrane material tend to be organic
compounds and the removal and recovery of these solutes from water
is environmentally and economically important. From a theoretical
point of view an understanding of the phenomena involved is
essential to the achievement of a fundamental description of the
RO process. Although this paper deals solely with aqueous
solutions and cellulose acetate membranes, it is important to
recognize that the concepts discussed can be extended to include
other membrane materials and non-aqueous systems.

Solute Preferential Sorption

At this point, it is important to describe exactly what is
meant by solute preferential sorption and the consequences that
result from this situation. Consider first the classical case of
the separation of aqueous NaCl solutions by cellulose acetate
membranes. In this instance the membrane material has a stronger
affinity for the solvent than it has for the solute. The result

[1] Current address: Department of Chemical Engineering, University of Texas, Austin,
TX 78712.

0097–6156/81/0154–0293$05.50/0

is the existence of essentially pure water on the surface of and
within the membrane. This water is subsequently transported
through the membrane in the RO process. While this description
holds true for a number of solutes (in particular ionized solutes),
there are certain solutes which exhibit anomalous behavior. In
such cases the membrane material has a stronger affinity for the
solute than for the solvent. The result may be pictured as the
establishment of a sorbed layer of solute which may subsequently
be transported through the membrane. The consequence of the
solute being preferentially sorbed is that the observed performance
behavior is different than in the case of water preferential
sorption. The main differences in performance can be summarized
as follows:

For the case of water preferential sorption –

i) increasing the operating pressure usually increases
separation

ii) the decrease in permeate flux with increasing concentration
is due to the osmotic pressure of the solution

iii) separation is always positive

iv) separation increases with decreasing pore size on the
membrane surface.

However, for the case of solute preferential sorption –

i) increasing the operating pressure usually decreases
separation

ii) the permeate flux is less than the pure water flux, even
when the osmotic pressure effects are negligible

iii) separation may be positive, zero, or negative depending
on the solute and the specific operating conditions

iv) separation may exhibit a maximum, a minimum, or both with
decreasing pore size on the membrane surface.

The list of solutes that are known to be preferentially sorbed
by cellulose acetate membranes includes many alcohols, phenols,
un-ionized carboxylic acids and hydrocarbons (1). Although solute
preferential sorption is a common occurrence with a number of
important aqueous organic systems little experimental or
quantitative work has appeared in the literature. The purpose
of the current work is to rectify this situation.

Literature Review

A number of models have been developed over the years to
describe reverse osmosis. These models include the solution-
diffusion model, the finely porous model, and the preferential
sorption - capillary flow model. In each case, the model was
originally developed based on the separation of aqueous salt
solutions. The application of each of these models to systems
which exhibit anomalous behavior will be discussed in this section.

Solution-Diffusion Model (2). In this model, the solute and
solvent are transported through the membrane by first dissolving

in the homogeneous skin layer and then diffusing through it. Thus, permeability is the product of the solubility and the diffusivity of the compound in the membrane material. The original attempts to apply this model to the phenol-water system were made by Lonsdale et al. (3). Phenol was found to be readily soluble in the cellulose acetate membrane and the diffusivity of phenol in cellulose acetate was approximately the same as that of water. The result was negative separation in RO application. The solution-diffusion model in its existing form proved to be insufficient to quantitatively describe the negative separation. Therefore, the authors suggested the development of a coupled flow model (i.e. the solute flux is coupled to the water flux). Subsequent attempts to develop such a model met with only moderate success (4). Anderson et al. (5) conducted studies that paralleled the work of Lonsdale. The emphasis was placed on separately measuring equilibrium sorption and diffusion coefficients for the solute in the membrane material. They attributed the negative separation to the strong interaction between the phenol and the cellulose acetate membrane material. Pusch et al. (6) also studied the separation of phenol and water. Dialysis and sorption experiments were performed, and the results were consistent with the negative separation observed in RO. The decrease in water flux in the presence of phenol was attributed to the decrease in membrane water content under these conditions.

   Finely Porous Model. In this model, solute and solvent permeate the membrane via pores which connect the high pressure and low pressure faces of the membrane. The finely porous model, which combines a viscous flow model and a friction model (7,8), has been developed in detail and applied to RO data by Jonsson (9-12). The most recent work of Jonsson (12) treated several organic solutes including phenol and octanol, both of which exhibit solute preferential sorption. In his paper, Jonsson compared several models including that developed by Spiegler and Kedem (13) (which is essentially an irreversible thermodynamics treatment), the finely porous model, the solution-diffusion imperfection model (14), and a model developed by Pusch (15). Jonsson illustrated that the finely porous model is similar in form to the Spiegler-Kedem relationship. Both models fit the data equally well, although not with total accuracy. The Pusch model has a similar form and proves to be less accurate, while the solution-diffusion imperfection model is even less accurate. In all models, the largest discrepancy between the predicted performance and the experimental data occurred when negative separation was observed. Jonsson concluded that the finely porous model is preferred over the alternatives, although the Pusch relationship is easier to use and yields reasonable results in most cases.

   Preferential Sorption-Capillary Flow Model. An alternative approach to those mentioned above has been presented by

Sourirajan (16) and is illustrated schematically in Figure 1.   In
this approach the cellulose acetate membranes are considered to be
porous.   Separation is jointly governed by the preferential
sorption of one of the constituents of the solution at the
membrane-solution interface, and the number, size, and size
distribution of the pores on the membrane surface.   In the case
of salt solutions, water is preferentially sorbed.   This means
that a sharp concentration gradient exists in the vicinity of the
membrane material, leading to a layer of almost pure water on the
surface of the membrane.   Applying pressure allows this pure water
to be continuously withdrawn through the membrane pores. Smaller
pore size leads to higher separation.   This situation of water
preferential sorption is applicable to most salt solutions and
many organic solutes.   The transport of these solutions is
quantitatively described by the Kimura-Sourirajan analysis (16,17).
With this model, it is possible to predict solute separation and
flux for many systems which exhibit water preferential sorption
(17,18).
     However, some solutes exhibit a strong attraction to the
membrane material and are therefore preferentially sorbed compared
to the solvent water.   This can lead to positive, zero, or negative
separation depending on both the magnitude of the attractive
forces and the mobility of the solute at the solution-membrane
interface (relative to the mobility of water in this region). Both
the polar and nonpolar character of the solute may be important
in the separation process.   Consider the case of a polar solute.
Since the cellulose acetate membrane material has a net proton
acceptor nature (1), any polar compound is attracted to the
membrane surface.   The more polar the compound the stronger the
attraction.   When the solute is more polar than the solvent, as is
the case in phenol-water systems, the solute is preferentially
sorbed by the membrane. [Note: the polar nature of a compound can
be conveniently and quantitatively expressed by the Taft number
(1,19).]   Since the solute and the solvent are both polar, a
strong interaction exists between the two solution components.
This interaction allows the solute to be relatively mobile in the
vicinity of the pore, and thus it can be carried through the pore
with the water, resulting in negative separation.
     On the other hand, for a hydrocarbon solute such as benzene,
the nonpolar forces predominate.   The cellulose acetate membrane
material has a nonpolar character due to its carbon backbone.
This nonpolar character results in the attraction of nonpolar
solutes.   Since the solute has little polar character, it is more
strongly immobilized on the membrane surface than is water.   Thus,
the solvent passes through the membrane relatively fast and
positive separation is observed.   The strength of this nonpolar
attraction, quantitatively represented by the modified Small's
number (1,20), will, in part, determine the extent of separation.
     The presence of preferentially sorbed solute on the membrane
surface will block or impede the flow of the solvent water.   This

pore blocking effect results in the permeate flux for feed
solutions, even dilute solutions of negligible osmotic pressure,
being less than the flux observed for a pure water feed under
similar operating conditions; i.e., permeate flux (PF) is less
than pure water flux (PWF).

The advantage of the preferential sorption-capillary flow
approach to reverse osmosis lies in its emphasis on the mechanism
of separation at a molecular level. This knowledge is useful when
it becomes necessary to predict membrane performance for unknown
systems. Also, the approach is not restricted to the so-called
"perfect", defect-free membranes, but encompasses the whole range
of membrane pore size. Until recently, the application of a
quantitative model to the case of solute preferential sorption
has been missing. Attempts to change this situation have been
made by Matsuura and Sourirajan (21) by using a modified finely
porous model. In addition to the usual features of this model
(9-12), a Lennard-Jones type of potential function is incorporated
to describe the membrane-solute interaction. This model is
discussed elsewhere in this book.

Separation of Aromatic Hydrocarbons

In this paper, the removal of two aromatic hydrocarbons,
benzene and toluene, from water is investigated. Toluene can be
shown to be more nonpolar than benzene by comparing the modified
Small's numbers (1), which are 549 and 425 (cal cm^3)$^{\frac{1}{2}}$/mol
for toluene and benzene, respectively. The greater nonpolar
character of toluene (indicated by the larger modified Small's
number) suggests that, in comparison to benzene, toluene will be
more strongly attracted to the membrane, and therefore will exhibit
lower mobility. The result is that under identical operating
conditions the separation of toluene from water should be greater
than the separation of benzene from water. The validity of this
assumption is checked in the present study. In a previous study
of these solutes, data was reported for a single feed concentration
(22). The effect of feed concentration on membrane performance
is examined in this work.

The quantitative treatment of the data generated in the present
study will initially be based on a set of equations recently
reported (23). These equations, which have proven to be adequate
for dilute p-chlorophenol-water systems, are as follows:

$$1 - \frac{PF}{PWF} = K_1 \; X_{A2}{}^{n_1} \qquad\qquad (1)$$

$$N_A = K_2 \; X_{A2}{}^{n_1} \; P^{n_2} \qquad\qquad (2)$$

$$X_{A2} = X_{A3} + (X_{A1} - X_{A3}) \exp (PF/k\rho) \qquad\qquad (3)$$

$$k = k_{ref}(D_{AB}/D_{AB,ref})^{2/3} \qquad (4)$$

The nomenclature is defined in the Legend of Symbols section at the conclusion of this paper and is illustrated in Figure 1. Equation 1 is an empirical relation which describes the extent of pore blocking, expressed by the pore blocking factor 1-(PF/PWF). In the case of the RO separation of a dilute solute-containing feed stream in which there is no pore blocking by the solute, the flux of the permeating stream is equal to the flux obtained for a similar experiment in which the feed stream is pure water (i.e., permeate flux (PF) equals pure water flux (PWF)). In this case, the flux ratio PF/PWF is unity and the pore blocking factor 1-(PF/PWF) is zero. Conversely, when the pores are completely blocked PF is zero, and thus, the pore blocking factor is unity. Equation 1 indicates that the pore blocking factor is proportional to the concentration of the boundary layer (X_{A2}) raised to a power of n_1 This relationship will be discussed below. Equation 2 is an empirical relation which relates solute flux (N_A) to both X_{A2} (again raised to a power of n_1) and the operating pressure (raised to a power of n_2). The exponents n_1 and n_2, as well as the proportionality factors K_1 and K_2, are functions of pore size and the nature of the solute. Equation 3, which allows the calculation of X_{A2} from experimental data, is based on a simple "film" theory for mass transfer and is derived elsewhere (17,23). Equation 4 allows the mass transfer coefficient on the feed side, k, to be calculated for any solute based on the value obtained for a reference solute (usually sodium chloride) in the same test cell. The possibility of using equations of this form for aromatic hydrocarbon solutions will be examined in this paper.

Experimental

The cellulose acetate membranes used were batch 316(0/25) – type membranes (24) made by the general Loeb-Sourirajan technique (25). The six flat cast membranes were shrunk at different temperatures (from 68 to 85°C) prior to loading the membranes into the reverse osmosis test cells. This treatment adjusts the average surface pore size of each membrane so that a range of porosities could be studied. A prepressurization at a pressure of 11 720 kPa for 2 hours was used to stabilize the membranes for subsequent use at pressures of 6900 kPa or lower. (All pressures listed are gauge pressure.)

The general experimental procedure was similar to that reported in the literature (25). The six flow type reverse osmosis cells were connected in series and were constructed in a design similar to that reported by Sourirajan (25). The cells were placed in a constant temperature box and the system was controlled to 25 ± 1°C. The feed flow rate was maintained constant at 400

ml/min. For each experiment, the pure water flux (PWF) and the
permeate flux (PF) were measured. In addition, the solute
concentration was determined in the feed and permeate solutions and
the separation, f, was calculated as

$$f = \frac{m_1 - m_3}{m_1} \qquad\qquad (5)$$

where m_1 and m_3 are the feed and permeate molalities respectively.
For dilute solutions this can be approximated as

$$f = \frac{ppm1 - ppm3}{ppm1} \qquad\qquad (6)$$

where ppm1 and ppm3 are the feed and permeate concentrations
expressed in parts per million. The solute concentrations for
benzene and toluene samples were analyzed using an Oceanography
International Corporation Total Carbon Analyzer. The sodium
chloride solutions were analyzed with either a Laboratory Data
Control Differential Refractometer or a YSI Model 31 Conductivity
Meter. The water used was deionized and distilled and all other
chemicals were analytical reagent grade.

Results and Discussions

   Membrane Characterization. The six cellulose acetate membranes
were characterized according to the sodium chloride performance
data. These data are presented in Table I. Actual experiments
were repeated at regular intervals in order to monitor the membrane
change, and the illustrated data represent the average of nine
tests. Since the solute transport parameter $D_{AM}/K\delta$ for sodium
chloride, and hence ln C^*_{NaCl}, remained essentially constant over
the experimental time period it can be assumed that the membrane
pore size remained constant. The quantity ln C^*_{NaCl} is representative
of the average pore size on the membrane surface and is independent
of the solute under consideration (26). Briefly, a decrease in
the value of ln C^*_{NaCl} indicates a decrease in the average pore
size. The values of ln C^*_{NaCl} for the membranes tested cover a
wide range of surface pore size, thereby maximizing experimental
design. The pure water permeability constant A tended to decrease
over the period of several experiments; this decrease was attributed
to membrane compaction. This change in A varied from a 10%
decrease for the membranes of largest pore size to a 5% decrease
for the membranes of smallest pore size. The rate of compaction
for these hydrocarbon studies was slightly higher than would
normally be observed for salt solution experiments. This
accelerated decrease in A may be the result of the detrimental
effect that high interfacial concentration of organics have on the
cellulose acetate. The average separation and the permeate flux
for aqueous NaCl solutions measured under the indicated conditions
are also listed in Table I.

TABLE I

Characterization and Performance of the Cellulose Acetate Membranes[a]

	Film Number					
	1	2	3	4	5	6
Pure water permeability constant, A, (mol H_2O)/(m^2 s kPa), $\times 10^4$	0.7051	0.8547	1.268	1.868	2.331	2.487
Solute transport parameter, $(D_{AM}/K\delta)_{NaCl}$, m/s, $\times 10^7$	0.6914	1.342	2.846	8.653	29.69	66.15
ln C^*_{NaCl}	-13.25	-12.59	-11.84	-10.73	-9.49	-8.69
Mass transfer coefficient, k, m/s, $\times 10^6$	28.3	38.2	38.5	44.0	47.0	29.3
Solute Separation, %	98.8	98.1	97.0	93.5	82.8	61.7
Permeate flux, $\dfrac{kg}{m^2\ s}$, $\times 10^3$	7.43	9.05	13.27	19.38	24.41	25.80

a) Film area, 1.443 $\times 10^{-3} m^2$; operating pressure 6900 kPa; feed concentration 10 000 ppm NaCl; temperature 25°C; feed flow rate 400 ml/min.

Benzene – Water Reverse Osmosis Data. The experimentally determined performance for the separation of benzene and water at four different pressures is illustrated in Figures 2 through 5. The separation and pore blocking factor observed for several different feed concentrations are plotted as a function of the membrane pore size, $\ln C^*_{NaCl}$. Although there is scatter in the data, it is possible to observe trends that apply consistently in Figures 2 through 5. As the pore size decreases the separation increases. As the feed concentration increases, the separation increases. The extent of this concentration effect is small for the membranes of large pore size, and increases with decreasing pore size until the greatest influence is observed for the membrane of smallest pore size. In all cases, the extent of pore blocking increases linearly with decreasing pore size. In addition, increasing the feed concentration increases the extent of pore blocking.

The effect of solute concentration on separation is illustrated by extracting the data for any given membrane from the curves in Figures 2 through 5, and replotting the data in the form of separation as a function of solute concentration in the feed stream. Typical results are shown in Figure 6. This relationship clearly illustrates that separation increases with increasing concentration, eventually leveling off at a constant value. This plot also allows the comparison of separation at different pressures. For the range of pressures 690 to 3450 kPa, the separation increases with decreasing pressure, which is consistent with the general behavior of preferentially sorbed solute systems as discussed above and with the data previously obtained (1). However, the data for 6900 kPa does not follow this trend and indicates that separation passes through a minimum with increasing pressure. This behavior will be investigated in more detail in the future.

The trends in Figures 2 to 6 are consistent with the qualitative features of solute preferential sorption discussed earlier in this paper. The permeate flux is lower than the pure water flux due to pore blocking. This effect is enhanced by either decreasing the pore size or increasing the feed concentration. Both of these factors lead to a relative increase in the solute content of the pore and thus, to restricted water transport through the pore. Since the solute is relatively immobile at the membrane surface, positive separation is observed. Both increasing the feed concentration and decreasing the pore size lead to higher separation. The additional solute retained on the high pressure side must also be relatively immobile. It is hypothesized that benzene can be sorbed in multiple layers which are bound to the membrane. The layers in the immediate vicinity of the membrane material/pore wall are strongly bound to the membrane. The strength of the attraction force decreases as the distance between each subsequent layer and the membrane surface increases.

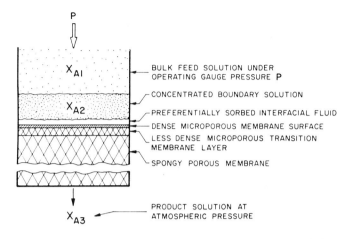

NRCC Publications

Figure 1.   Schematic of RO transport under steady-state conditions (16)

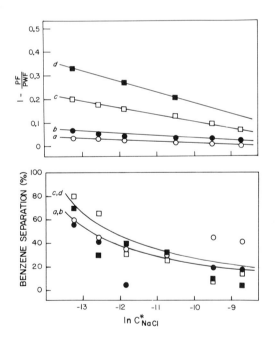

Figure 2.   Effect of feed concentration on the RO performance for the benzene–water system. Operating conditions: membrane material = CA; membrane area = 1.443 × 10⁻³ m²; ln C*$_{NaCl}$ obtained at 6900 kPa; feed flow rate = 400 mL/min; T = 25°C; operating pressure = 690 kPa. Curve a (○) 20.6 ppm; Curve b (●) 31.7 ppm; Curve c (□) 54.0 ppm; Curve d (■) 96.0 ppm.

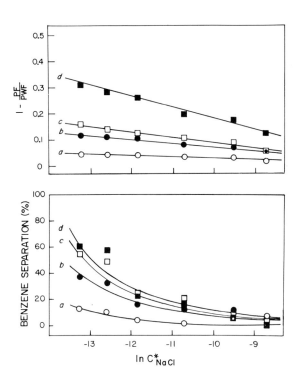

Figure 3.   Effect of feed concentration on the RO performance for the benzene–water system. The operating conditions are identical to those of Figure 2 except that the operating pressure = 1725 kPa. Curve a (○) 18.0 ppm; Curve b (●) 29.8 ppm; Curve c (□) 49.0 ppm; Curve d (■) 98.8 ppm.

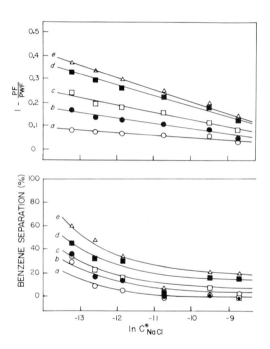

Figure 4.   Effect of feed concentration on the RO performance for the benzene–water system. The operating conditions are identical to those of Figure 2 except that the operating pressure = 3450 kPa. Curve a (○) 20.9 ppm; Curve b (●) 31.0 ppm; Curve c (□) 44.8 ppm; Curve d (■) 54.5 ppm; Curve e (△) 92.6 ppm.

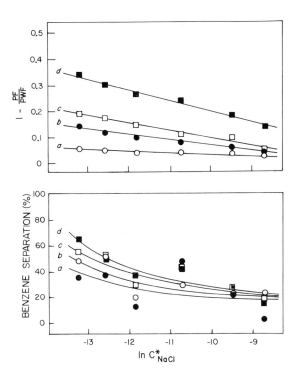

Figure 5. Effect of feed concentration on the RO performance for the benzene–water system. The operating conditions are identical to those of Figure 2 except that the operating pressure = 6900 kPa. Curve a (○) 13.5 ppm; Curve b (●) 23.2 ppm; Curve c (□) 46.1 ppm; Curve d (■) 84.6 ppm.

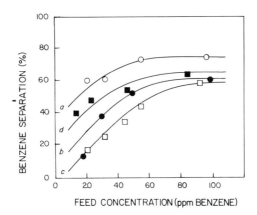

Figure 6. Effect of feed concentration and operating pressure on separation for the benzene–water system. Data illustrated for the CA membrane with ln C^*_{NaCl} = −13.25. Curve a (○) 690 kPa; Curve b (●) 1725 kPa; Curve c (□) 3450 kPa; Curve d (■) 6900 kPa.

The results observed for the benzene-water system can be compared to those observed for the p-chlorophenol-water system. In the latter case, higher feed concentrations and smaller pore size lead to lower separation (23). As discussed earlier in this report, this difference in behavior is consistent with the differences in mobility of the two solutes. With both benzene and p-chlorophenol, increasing the concentration increases the amount of solute bound to the membrane pore wall. Since the p-chlorophenol is more highly hydrated it can move through the pore with the water, which decreases the separation. For benzene, the solute is relatively immobilized, and with increasing concentration more and more of the pore is occupied with immobilized solute. The result is higher separation. Thus, it appears that the separation and pore blocking factor are both controlled by the relative amount of immobilized solute in the pore. This relative quantity of solute can be increased by increasing the feed concentration at a fixed pore size or by decreasing the pore size at a fixed feed concentration. As concentration is increased, the additional solute assumes a position in sorbed layers which are increasingly far from the membrane surface. Thus, the attraction forces exerted by the membrane material on the solute are progressively less, and the additional solute is not so tightly bound. The result is the permeation of a portion of the concentrated boundary layer. Therefore, there is a leveling off in separation with increasing concentration.

Correlation of X_{A2} with Pore Blocking for Benzene-Water Data. The blocking of the pores on the membrane surface by the preferentially sorbed solute, which was discussed qualitatively in the preceding section, is now treated more quantitatively. Equation 4 was used to estimate the appropriate k value for each cell. The diffusivity of the solute in water was estimated by the method of Wilke and Chang (27), and the diffusivity of sodium chloride in water used was 1.60×10^{-5} cm^2/s (26). Then X_{A2} was calculated for each run from Equation 3. Figure 7 illustrates the relationship between $1 - (PF/PWF)$ and X_{A2}. Within the scatter of this data, it is reasonable to use a straight line through the origin for all six membranes. This data corresponds to an n_1 value of 1.0 in Equation 1. The K_1 values, obtained by least squares analysis of the data in Figure 7, are plotted in Figure 8 as a function of ln $C*_{NaCl}$. This relationship can be described by the equation

$$K_1 = -2189 \ln C*_{NaCl} - 12840 \qquad (7)$$

For the membranes used in this study, K_1 varied from 6×10^3 to 16×10^3. It should be noted that Figures 7 and 8 included data from all pressures tested and therefore Equation 7 will predict K_1 for all pressures and concentrations within the range studied. The inverse dependence of K_1 on ln $C*_{NaCl}$ reflects the increased

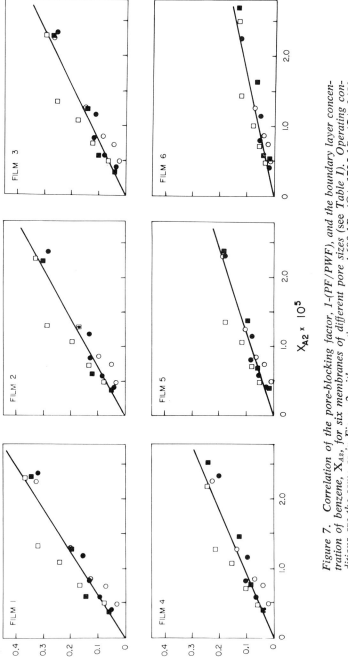

Figure 7. Correlation of the pore-blocking factor, 1-(PF/PWF), and the boundary layer concentration of benzene, X_{A2}, for six membranes of different pore sizes (see Table I). Operating conditions are the same as in Figure 2 with operating pressures of 690 kPa (○), 1725 kPa (●), 3450 kPa (□), 6900 kPa (■).

importance of solute pore blocking for the membranes of smaller pore size. Equation 7, therefore, can be used to estimate the extent of pore blocking that will be caused by preferentially sorbed benzene. This estimation can be performed by simply conducting experiments with NaCl-water systems to determine the ln $C*_{NaCl}$ value for the membrane in use. The application of Equation 7 to aqueous systems containing benzene plus a solute such as NaCl will be explored in future studies.

Toluene-Water Reverse Osmosis Data. Data for the reverse osmosis separation of aqueous toluene solutions at 3450 kPa and three different concentrations, using the same six membranes as above, are illustrated in Figure 9. These results are qualitatively similar to those for the benzene studies. That is, separation and extent of pore blocking increase with both increasing concentration and decreasing pore size. Further studies to investigate the effects of pressure are currently underway.

Correlation of X_{A2} with Pore Blocking for Toluene-Water Data. An analysis similar to that used for the benzene data was applied to the toluene data to investigate pore blocking as a function of concentration. Figure 10 illustrates this relationship for all six membranes. The data for membranes 5 and 6 can be approximated by a straight line; therefore, n_1 was set to 1.0 in Equation 1. For the other films, a least squares parameter estimation was applied and the n_1 and K_1 values generated. The results are illustrated in Figure 11, where K_1 (plotted as ln K_1 for convenience) and n_1 are shown as functions of ln $C*_{NaCl}$. For the region of ln $C*_{NaCl}$ less than -10.5 both n_1 and K_1 increase with ln $C*_{NaCl}$. Above this value n_1 and K_1 level off at 1.0 and 40 x 10^3 (i.e., ln K_1 = 10.6), respectively. This result is similar to that obtained previously in p-chlorophenol studies (23), where n_1 was found to level off at ln $C*_{NaCl}$ values greater than -12.0.

In general, the separation and pore blocking data for the toluene-water system are consistent with those obtained for the benzene-water system. Positive separation occurs, and the general trends of increasing separation and pore blocking with increasing concentration and decreasing pore size are observed. This is not surprising since toluene and benzene are similar in structure. However, based on the modified Small's number for these solutes, as discussed earlier in this paper, it would be expected that toluene would be more strongly sorbed by the membrane than is the benzene. If this is true, then at otherwise identical conditions toluene should demonstrate greater pore blocking and higher separation than benzene. Curve c in Figure 9 for toluene and curve a in Figure 4 for benzene are at the same pressure and approximately the same molar concentration. In all cases, the expected result is found. For example, for membrane 2, the separations are 41% and 9% and the pore blocking factors are 0.30 and 0.08 for toluene and benzene, respectively. Thus, the modified Small's

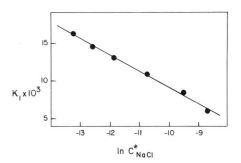

Figure 8. Correlation of K_1 of Equation 1 with membrane pore size (ln C^*_{NaCl}) for separation of the benzene–water system

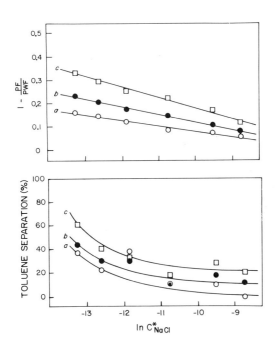

Figure 9. Effect of feed concentration on the RO performance for the toluene–water system. The operating conditions are identical to those of Figure 2 except that the operating pressure = 3450 kPa. Curve a (○) 8.7 ppm; Curve b (●) 12.4 ppm; Curve c (□) 20.8 ppm.

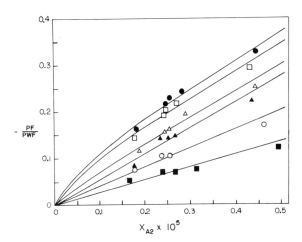

Figure 10.   Correlation of the pore-blocking factor, 1-(PF/PWF), and the boundary layer concentration of toluene, X_{A2}. The operating conditions are the same as in Figure 9 with Membranes 1 (●), 2 (□), 3 (△), 4 (▲), 5 (○), and 6 (■) as designated in Table I.

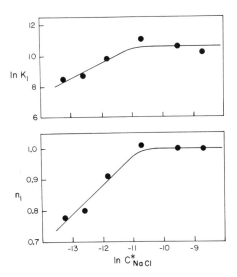

Figure 11.   Correlation of ln K_1 and n_1 of Equation 1 with membrane pore size (ln C^*_{NaCl}) for separation of the toluene–water system

number is a useful tool for qualitatively predicting differences in the reverse osmosis performance for toluene–water and benzene–water systems.

Conclusions

In conclusion, several important points of this work should be reiterated. An understanding and quantitative description of solute preferential sorption is imperative to the advancement of a fundamental knowledge of the separation mechanism and to the application of reverse osmosis. For the systems studied, increasing the feed concentration was found to increase separation and decrease permeate flux. This behavior can be contrasted to the case of water preferential sorption where both separation and permeate flux would remain constant for these dilute concentrations. The results for the benzene studies and the toluene studies were similar in that separation increased and flux decreased with increasing feed concentration or decreasing pore size. The benzene studies showed a minimum in separation with increasing pressure. At similar experimental conditions the toluene system showed higher separation and lower flux than the benzene system. This observation is consistent with the difference in the nonpolar character of the solutes as expressed by the Small's number. Further work is needed in order to improve the quantitative understanding of systems which exhibit solute preferential sorption.

Legend of Symbols

A	= pure water permeability constant, mol $H_2O/$ $(m^2$ s kPa)
D_{AB}	= diffusivity of A in B, m^2/s
$D_{AM}/K\delta$	= solute transport parameter, m/s
f	= separation
k	= mass transfer coefficient, m/s
K_1,K_2	= proportionality factors defined in Equations 1 and 2, respectively
ln C^*_{NaCl}	= relative measure of the membrane pore size
m_i	= concentration, molality
n_1,n_2	= exponents defined in Equations 1 and 2, respectively
N_A	= solute flux, mol/$(m^2$ s)
P	= operating pressure, kPa gauge
PF	= permeate flux, kg/$(m^2$ s)

ppm   = concentration, parts per million

PWF   = pure water flux, $kg/(m^2 s)$

X   = concentration, mole fraction

ρ = solution density, kg/m^3

Subscripts

1   = feed solution

2   = boundary layer solution

3   = permeate solution

M   = membrane phase

A   = solute

B   = solvent

ref   = reference solute

Acknowledgements

The authors wish to thank The Engineering Foundation for their support of this research and the Natural Sciences and Engineering Research Council of Canada for the scholarship support of one of the authors (JMD).

Literature Cited

1.   Sourirajan, S.; Matsuura, T. in "Reverse Osmosis and Synthetic Membranes"; Sourirajan, S., Ed.; National Research Council of Canada: Ottawa, 1977; Chapter 2.

2.   Lonsdale, H.K.; Merten, U.; Riley, R.L. J. Appl. Polymer Sci. 1965, 9, 1341-1362.

3.   Lonsdale, H.K.; Merten, U.; Tagami, M. J. Appl. Polymer Sci. 1967, 11, 1807-1820.

4.   Merten, U.; Lonsdale, H.K.; Riley, R.L.; Tagami, M. presented at NATO Advanced Study Institute on Synthetic Polymer Membranes, Ravello, Sept. 1966.

5.   Anderson, J.E.; Hoffman, S.J.; Peters, C.R. J. Phys. Chem. 1972, 76, 4006-4011.

6.   Pusch, W.; Burghoff, H.G.; Staude, E. 5th Intern. Symp. on Fresh Water from the Sea 1976, 4, 143-156.

7.   Merten, U., Ed. "Desalination by Reverse Osmosis"; M.I.T. Press: Cambridge, Mass., 1966; p. 15-54.

8.   Spiegler, K.S. Trans. Faraday Soc. 1958, 54, 1408-1428.

9.   Jonsson, G.; Boesen, C.E. Desalination 1975, 17, 145-165.

10. Boesen, C.E.; Jonsson, G. 5th Intern. Symp. on Fresh Water from the Sea 1976, 4, 259-266.

11. Boesen, C.E.; Jonsson, G. 6th Intern. Symp. on Fresh Water from the Sea 1978, 3, 157-164.

12. Jonsson, G. Desalination 1978, 24, 19-37.

13. Spiegler, K.S.; Kedem, O. Desalination 1966, 1, 311-326.

14. Sherwood, T.K.; Brian, P.L.T.; Fisher, R.E. Ind. Eng. Chem. Fundamentals 1967, 6(1), 2-12.

15. Pusch, W. Ber. Bunsenges. Physik. Chem. 1977, 81, 269-276.

16. Sourirajan, S.; Matsuura, T. in "Reverse Osmosis and Synthetic Membranes"; Sourirajan, S., Ed.; National Research Council of Canada: Ottawa, 1977; Chapter 3.

17. Sourirajan, S. "Reverse Osmosis"; Academic Press: New York, 1970; Chapter 3.

18. Matsuura, T.; Dickson, J.M.; Sourirajan, S. Ind. Eng. Chem. Process Des. Dev. 1976, 15(1), 149-161.

19. Taft, R.W., Jr. in "Steric Effects in Organic Chemistry" Newman, M.S., Ed.; Wiley: New York, 1956; p. 556-675.

20. Small, P.A. J. Appl. Chem. 1953, 3, 71-80.

21. Matsuura, T.; Sourirajan, S. Ind. Eng. Chem. Process Des. Dev. in press.

22. Matsuura, T.; Sourirajan, S. J. Appl. Polymer Sci. 1973, 17, 3683-3708.

23. Dickson, J.M.; Matsuura, T.; Sourirajan, S. Ind. Eng. Chem. Process Des. Dev. 1979, 18(4), 641-647.

24. Pageau, L.; Sourirajan, S. J. Appl. Polymer Sci. 1972, 16, 3185-3206.

25. Sourirajan, S. "Reverse Osmosis"; Academic Press: New York, 1970; Chapter 2.

26. Matsuura, T.; Pageau, L.; Sourirajan, S. J. Appl. Polymer Sci. 1975, 19, 179-198.

27. Wilke, C.R.; Chang, P. AIChE J. 1955, 1, 264-270.

RECEIVED December 4, 1980.

Estimation of Interfacial Forces Governing the Reverse-Osmosis System: Nonionized Polar Organic Solute–Water–Cellulose Acetate Membrane

TAKESHI MATSUURA, YUTAKA TAKETANI, and S. SOURIRAJAN

Division of Chemistry, National Research Council of Canada,
Ottawa, Ontario K1A 0R9 Canada

This extends the previous work (1) in which the Lennard-Jones type surface potential function and the frictional function representing the interfacial forces working on the solute molecule from the membrane pore wall were combined with solute and solvent transport through a pore to calculate data on membrane performance such as those on solute separation and the ratio of product rate to pure water permeation rate in reverse osmosis. In the previous work (1) parameters involved in the Lennard-Jones type and frictional functions were determined by a trial and error method so that the solutions in terms of solute separation and (product rate/pure water permeation rate) ratio fit the experimental data. In this paper the potential function is generated by using the experimental high performance liquid chromatography (HPLC) data in which the retention time represents the adsorption and desorption equilibrium of the solute at the solvent-polymer interface.

The frictional force is expressed by a function of the ratio of a distance associated with steric repulsion at the interface, to the pore radius. The frictional function increases steeply with increase in the latter ratio. The method of calculating reverse osmosis separation data by using the surface potential function and the frictional function so generated, in conjunction with the transport equation is illustrated by examples involving cellulose acetate membranes of different porosities and 40 nonionized organic solutes in single solute aqueous solution systems.

Experimental

HPLC Experiments. The liquid chromatograph model ALC 202 of Waters Associates fitted with a differential refractometer was used in this work. The method of column preparation and the general experimental technique used were the same as those reported earlier (2). All experiments were carried out at the laboratory temperature (23-25°C). The solvent (water) flow rate

through the column was fixed at 0.27 cm^3/min. The pressure drop
through the column was 1034kPa(=150psi)/ft. Forty solutes
including alcohols, polyalcohols, phenols, ketones, ethers,
aldehydes, esters, amines, amides, nitriles and nitrocompounds
were injected into the column which was made from cellulose
acetate Eastman E-398 polymer. 10μL of sample solution (solute
concentration in the range 1~10%) was injected into the column,
and the retention time for each solute was determined. Raffinose
whose retention time was the least, was used as the unretained
component to establish the position of solvent front. The
retention time measurements were duplicated and the average
values obtained were used for computations; in most cases, the
results of duplicated measurements were identical. It was
already established (2) that changes in column length, particle
size, packing density of column material, solvent velocity
through the column, operating pressure and sample size did not
affect the retention time ratio for different solutes under
otherwise identical experimental conditions.

Reverse Osmosis Experiments. This work makes further use of
reverse osmosis data already reported with respect to membranes
made from cellulose acetate Eastman E-398 polymers (3,4,5,6).
Data on amides, nitriles and nitrocompounds were newly added in
this work. The experimental details are briefly as follows.
Each membrane was subjected to an initial pure water pressure of
2068kPa gauge(=300psig) for about 2h prior to subsequent use in
reverse osmosis experiments all of which were carried out at
1724kPa gauge(=250psig) and at laboratory temperature (23-25°C).
For purposes of membrane specifications in terms of pure water
permeability constant A (in kg-mol of H$_2$O/m^2·s·kPa) and solute
transport parameter (D$_{AM}$/Kδ)(treated as a single quantity, m/s),
aqueous feed solutions containing 3500 ppm of NaCl were used (7).
Data on A and (D$_{AM}$/Kδ) thus obtained are listed in Table I with
respect to all membranes used in this work together with
experimental reverse osmosis data of sodium chloride solute. In
all other experiments, the solute concentrations in the aqueous
feed solutions were so low (0.001 to 0.006 molal) that the
osmotic pressures involved were negligible compared to the
operating pressure. In each experiment, the fraction solute
separation defined as:

$$f = \frac{\text{solute concentration in feed-solute concentration in product}}{\text{solute concentration in feed}}$$

membrane permeated product rate (PR) and pure water permeation
rate (PWP) in g/h for the effective area of membrane surface used
(=13.2 cm^2 in this work) were determined at the specified
operating conditions. All reverse osmosis experiments were for
single solute systems. The concentrations of sodium chloride
were determined using a conductivity bridge; the concentrations
of organic solutes were determined by a Beckman total carbon

analyzer Model 915A. Data on specifications and performances of all films used in this work are given in Table I.

Theoretical

In the earlier work (1) transport equations were developed on the basis of surface force-pore flow model in which a surface potential function and a frictional function are incorporated. The results can be briefly summarized as follows:
Defining the following dimensionless quantities,

$$\rho = r/R \tag{1}$$
$$C_A(\rho) = c_{A3}(\rho)/c_{A2} \tag{2}$$
$$\alpha(\rho) = u_B(r)\delta\chi_{AB}/\tilde{R}T \tag{3}$$
$$\beta_1 = \eta/\chi_{AB}R^2 c_{A2} \tag{4}$$
$$\beta_2 = (P_i - P_o)/\tilde{R}T c_{A2} \tag{5}$$
$$\Phi(\rho) = \phi(r)/\tilde{R}T \tag{6}$$

the solute separation, f', on the basis of the boundary concentration, c_{A2}, can be calculated by

$$f' = 1 - \frac{\int_0^1 \left[\exp(\alpha(\rho))\bigg/1 + \frac{b(\rho)}{e^{-\Phi(\rho)}}\left\{\exp(\alpha(\rho)-1)\right\}\right]\alpha(\rho)\rho d\rho}{\int_0^1 \alpha(\rho)\rho d\rho} \tag{7}$$

The dimensionless radial velocity profile, expressed by $\alpha(\rho)$ is obtained by solving the differential equation

$$\frac{d^2\alpha(\rho)}{d\rho^2} + \frac{1}{\rho}\frac{d\alpha(\rho)}{d\rho} + \frac{\beta_2}{\beta_1} + \frac{1}{\beta_1}\left(1-e^{-\Phi(\rho)}\right)\left(C_A(\rho)-1\right)$$

$$-(b(\rho)-1)\alpha(\rho)C_A(\rho)/\beta_1 = 0 \tag{8}$$

where

$$C_A(\rho) = \exp(\alpha(\rho))\bigg/1 + \frac{b(\rho)}{e^{-\Phi(\rho)}}\left\{\exp(\alpha(\rho))-1\right\} \tag{9}$$

with boundary conditions:

$$\frac{d\alpha(\rho)}{d\rho} = 0 \qquad \text{when } \rho = 0 \tag{10}$$

and

$$\alpha(\rho) = 0 \qquad \text{when } \rho = 1 \tag{11}$$

Table I. Experimental Reverse Osmosis Data[a] for the System NaCl-H$_2$O and Glycerol-H$_2$O Using Porous Cellulose Acetate Membranes and Parameters Characterizing Membranes

Film No.	1	2	3	4	5	6	7	8	9	10	11	12	13	14
$A \times 10^7$, kg-mol/m^2·s·kPa	1.726	1.544	2.955	3.485	2.044	2.513	1.622	3.559	3.430	2.810	1.728	1.535	3.438	5.189
$(D_{AM}/k\delta)_{NaCl} \times 10^7$, m/s	2.515	2.772	10.15	25.75	3.302	6.759	2.230	18.36	25.13	9.833	2.195	2.877	26.81	62.81
$k_{NaCl} \times 10^6$, m/s	22.6	21.1	35.0	40.0	26.0	30.6	22.0	40.6	39.5	33.5	23.0	21.1	39.5	45.0
(PWP), g/h	25.45	22.77	43.57	51.38	30.14	37.06	23.91	52.47	50.57	41.43	25.48	22.64	50.70	76.51
NaCl experimental data	b	b	b	b						b	b	b	b	b
(PR), g/h	20.40	18.90	34.40	42.20	28.18	34.34	22.23	49.09	46.67	36.00	21.53	20.49	43.84	66.64
Solute separation, %	93.5	92.2	85.8	74.0	93.4	89.4	94.4	81.3	75.5	85.6	94.3	91.9	73.0	62.0
Glycerol experimental data[c] Solute separation, %	82.9	82.8	75.0	60.2	82.5	79.2	83.2	66.2	60.6	75.6	83.3	82.7	59.5	40.0
Pore radius, Å	7.36	7.48	8.61	9.39	7.62	8.24	7.20	9.14	9.37	8.57	7.20	7.54	9.42	10.09
Solutes studied	Alcohols				Ketones, Esters, Ethers					Amides, Nitriles, Nitro-compounds				

a. Operating pressure, 1724 kPa gauge (=250 psig)
   Flow rate, 400 cm^3/min
   Effective membrane area, 13.2 cm^2.
   Sodium chloride concentration in feed, 0.026 molal unless otherwise stated.

b. Sodium chloride concentration in feed, 0.06 molal.

c. Glycerol feed concentration in feed, 0.002 molal, (PR) ≈ (PWP).

Table I Continued

Film No.	15	16	17	18	19	20	21	22	23	24
$A \times 10^7$, kg-mol/m²·s·kPa	4.263	1.564	2.291	3.198	3.917	2.593	4.338	1.546	2.271	3.219
$(D_{AM}/k\delta)_{NaCl} \times 10^7$, m/s	58.64	2.319	7.610	13.09	29.63	17.50	61.43	2.371	7.199	13.06
$k_{NaCl} \times 10^6$, m/s	45.00	21.4	28.5	37.1	44.1	31.4	45.0	21.0	28.2	37.3
(PWP), g/h	62.86	23.05	33.78	47.16	57.78	38.24	63.96	22.80	33.48	47.46
NaCl experimental data (PR), g/h	60.36	21.63	31.64	44.65	54.51	36.15	60.53	21.58	31.69	44.92
Solute separation, %	61.8	94.0	87.3	84.6	74.8	77.2	61.0	93.8	87.8	84.7
Glycerol experimental data[c] Solute separation, %	43.3	82.9	78.3	74.3	58.0	63.9	41.8	83.1	78.6	71.3
Pore radius, Å	9.98	7.36	8.35	8.66	9.47	9.24	10.04	7.30	8.31	8.86
Solutes studied	Polyalcohols, Carbohydrates						Phenols, Anilines			

All symbols used are defined at the end of the paper. The ratio of product rate to pure water permeation rate, (PR)/(PWP), is obtained from the relation.

$$(PR)/(PWP) = 2 \int_{0}^{1} \alpha(\rho)\rho d\rho / (\beta_2/8\beta_1) \tag{12}$$

In the above equations the dimensionless potential function expressing the solute-pore wall surface interaction can be written as

$$\Phi(\rho) = \begin{cases} 10 & \text{when } 1-\rho \leqq \dfrac{D}{R} \\[2ex] \dfrac{-B/R^3}{(1-\rho)^3} & \text{when } 1-\rho > \dfrac{D}{R} \end{cases} \tag{13}$$

in a non-dimensional form, particularly for the organic solutes for which Lennard-Jones type interfacial potential function is applicable. Further, $b(\rho)$ was written in the previous work (1) using a non-dimensional frictional function in the form

$$b(\rho) = \begin{cases} e^{10} & \text{when } 1-\rho \leqq \dfrac{D}{R} \\[2ex] \exp \dfrac{E/R}{1-\rho} & \text{when } 1-\rho > \dfrac{D}{R} \end{cases} \tag{14}$$

In eq 13 and 14, D is the distance between the polymer surface and the solute molecule at which $\Phi(\rho)$ becomes very large, and E is the frictional force constant for the transport of solute through the pore. As it is clear from eq 14 the frictional force is a function of D. Therefore, b and D are directly related. Further, since the distance D is associated with steric repulsion at the interface, and since the latter directly parallels the effective size of the solute molecule concerned, it is reasonable to consider that D is a function of the effective size of the solute molecule. Therefore, both D and b can be related to the effective size of the solute molecule. For the purpose of mathematical analysis, the location of a molecule inside a pore may be considered as the location of the center of the molecule, assuming spherical shape for the molecule. Therefore, the lowest limiting distance D at which surface repulsion for the molecule is the highest is actually the radius of the molecule itself, since it cannot be any closer to the membrane surface. Further, for nonionic solutes which are subject to short range hydrogen bonding and/or dispersion forces of attraction and repulsion, the actual distance D cannot be too far different from the radius of the molecule. Therefore, as a matter of practical approximation the distance D is considered identical to an effective radius of the molecule for purposes of analysis in this work.

It has to be noted that for the solution of eq 7 and 8 together with boundary conditions given by eq 10 and 11, only pore radius, R, and parameters B, D and E are necessary. The other quantities involved in the above equations are all available in terms of the experimental conditions used. In other words, the solute separation, f', which is defined on the basis of the boundary concentration c_{A2} is strictly a function of variables R, B, D and E under a given set of operating conditions.

In eq 7, solute separation was defined on the basis of boundary concentration c_{A2} as,

$$f' = \frac{c_{A2} - c_{A3}}{c_{A2}} \tag{15}$$

In order to relate the above solute separation to that on the basis of feed concentration c_{A1},

$$f = \frac{c_{A1} - c_{A3}}{c_{A1}} \tag{16}$$

the following equation based on the basic transport equation established earlier ($\underline{7}$)

$$c_{A2} = c_{A3} + (c_{A1} - c_{A3}) \exp\left(\frac{v_s}{k}\right) \tag{17}$$

can be employed using the fact that the molar density remains essentially constant for the present system. In eq 17, v_s is the linear velocity of the permeate solution through the membrane, which is essentially the same as $v_w^* = A(P_i - P_o)/c$ for dilute solutions. Furthermore, from previous work the mass transfer coefficient k can be represented as a function of pure water permeability constant, A, as shown in Figure 1 ($\underline{8}$). Combining eq 15, 16 and 17 we obtain

$$f = \frac{f'}{f' + \left\{(1-f')\exp\left(\frac{v_s}{k}\right)\right\}} \tag{18}$$

which equation relates f' defined by eq 15 to f defined by eq 16.

Analysis of High Performance Liquid Chromatography (HPLC) Data

On the basis of analysis of retention time data obtained from liquid chromatography experiments reported earlier ($\underline{9}$) the existence of interfacial water is assumed at the solution polymer interface and the equilibrium concentration of solute between stationary- and mobile-phases is regarded as that between

interfacial- and bulk-water phases. This model is schematically
described in Figure 2. Expressing average concentration of
solute in the interfacial region as $\overline{c}_{Ai}$ and the concentration of
solute in the bulk solution phase c_{Ab}, the equilibrium constant
K' can be written as

$$K' = \frac{\overline{c}_{Ai}}{c_{Ab}} \tag{19}$$

It is further assumed that the equilibrium constant for D_2O is
the same as that of ordinary water and is unity. Then, K' for
other solutes can be calculated from the relation (9)

$$K' = \frac{[v_R'] - [v_R']_{min}}{[v_R']_{water} - [v_R']_{min}} \tag{20}$$

where $[v_R']$ is the experimental retention volume, $[v_R']_{water}$ is
$[v_R']$ of D_2O and $[v_R']_{min}$ is $[v_R']$ of a reference solute, raffinose
in this particular system, which exhibits the lowest retention
volume among solutes injected (9). From eq 20, values of K' for
water and reference solute are one and zero, respectively. Using
the equilibrium constant defined by eq 20, retention volume $[v_R']$
for any solute can be given by

$$[v_R'] = [v_R']_{min} + K' v_s \tag{21}$$

where V_s represents the volume of stationary phase water and is
equal to the volume of the interfacial water in this case. In
eq 20, the value of K' may be equal to, greater than or less
than unity depending on details of concentration gradient in the
interfacial region. Further, the interfacial water layer thickness, t_i in Figure 2, evaluated in the previous work (9) to be
9.5Å for cellulose acetate E-398 polymer material, is used in
this work.
     Since membrane pore surface and the chromatography packing
surface are both made out of the same polymer material, identical
interfacial forces have to govern both membrane transport and
chromatography equilibrium. The only difference between the two
systems is that in the latter case, there is no effect of solute
movement (kinetic effect) on the retention volume data, and
therefore the interfacial force governing the chromatography
equilibrium may be represented only by surface potential working
on the solute, which may be expressed by a Lennard-Jones type
equation.
     The equilibrium constant, K', can be related to the Lennard-
Jones type potential function as follows. The concentration
profile of the solute at polymer-solution interface may be
described schematically as shown in Figure 3a and 3b.

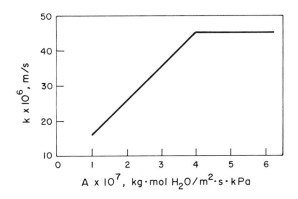

Figure 1.   Effect of the PWP constant on the mass-transfer coefficient for sodium chloride

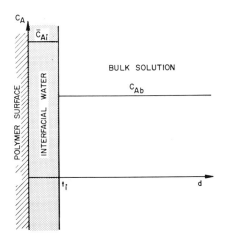

Figure 2.   Equilibrium of solute between interfacial water and bulk solution

Using the potential function, ϕ, as a function of the distance from the polymer surface,

$$\phi(d) = \begin{cases} 10RT & \text{when } d \leq \underset{\sim}{D} \\[3ex] -\dfrac{\underset{\sim}{B}}{d^3} RT & \text{when } d > \underset{\sim}{D} \end{cases} \qquad (22)$$

(dimensionless potential function eq 13 was derived from eq 22), and Boltzmann's law, solute concentration in the range $0 \leq d \leq \underset{\sim}{D}$ is effectively equal to zero (because the location of solute molecule is assumed to be its geometric center) and increases discontinuously to $c_{Ab}e^{\underset{\sim}{B}/D^3}$ at $d = \underset{\sim}{D}$ and then gradually diminishes according to the functional form

$$c_{Ai} = c_{Ab} \exp(\underset{\sim}{B}/D^3) \qquad (23)$$

until it finally reaches the bulk concentration, c_{Ab}.

According to definition, surface excess, Γ, can be calculated by

$$\Gamma = \int_{\underset{\sim}{D}_{water}}^{\underset{\sim}{D}} (0 - c_{Ab}) d(d) + \int_{\underset{\sim}{D}}^{\infty} \left\{ c_{Ab} \exp(\underset{\sim}{B}/d^3) - c_{Ab} \right\} d(d) \qquad (24)$$

where $\underset{\sim}{D}_{water}$ denotes the effective radius of a single water molecule ($= 0.87\text{Å}$ (10)). Since there exists effectively no water, and therefore no solution, between $d = 0$ and $d = \underset{\sim}{D}_{water}$ integration starts from $\underset{\sim}{D}_{water}$ in eq 24, where the concentration in excess of the bulk concentration is integrated from $d = \underset{\sim}{D}_{water}$ to $d = \infty$. Supposing this excessive amount of solute is compressed in the region of interfacial water, whose thickness is t_i (see Figure 3) and averaged out, the result becomes,

$$\bar{c}_{Ai} = \frac{\Gamma}{t_i} + c_{Ab}$$

$$= \frac{\displaystyle\int_{\underset{\sim}{D}_{water}}^{\underset{\sim}{D}} (-c_{Ab}) d(d) + \int_{\underset{\sim}{D}}^{\infty} \left\{ c_{Ab} \exp(B/d^3) - c_{Ab} \right\} d(d)}{t_i} + c_{Ab} \qquad (25)$$

Using eq 19

$$K' = \cfrac{\displaystyle\int_{\underset{\sim}{D}water}^{\underset{\sim}{D}} (-1)d(d) + \int_{\underset{\sim}{D}}^{\infty} (\exp(\underset{\sim}{B}/d^3)-1)d(d)}{t_i} + 1$$

$$= \cfrac{-(\underset{\sim}{D}-\underset{\sim}{D}water) + \displaystyle\int_{\underset{\sim}{D}}^{\infty} (\exp(\underset{\sim}{B}/d^3)-1)d(d)}{t_i} + 1 \tag{26}$$

Eq 26 indicates that the equilibrium constant K' is uniquely related to parameters $\underset{\sim}{B}$ and $\underset{\sim}{D}$ which characterize the Lennard–Jones type potential function.

Frictional Function

It is a well accepted concept that the movement of the molecule is restricted in the pore of diameters which are comparable to those of solute molecules. Many groups have attempted so far to describe the restricted molecular motion in small pores quantitatively. Even though the degree of restriction depends on the distance of the solute molecule from the pore wall (11), it has been common in the literature to express the frictional force as a function of the ratio of the molecular radius to the pore radius, designated as λ.

In this work, λ is defined as

$$\lambda = \frac{\underset{\sim}{D}}{R} \tag{27}$$

considering $\underset{\sim}{D}$ equal to the effective molecular radius for practical purpose. According to eq 27, λ and hence b are both independent of the position of the solute molecule in the pore.

Faxen suggested that the reduced diffusivity in fine pores (D_m) resulting from an increased frictional drag on the solute which is in the proximity of solid walls can be expressed by (12)

$$\frac{D_m}{D_{AB}} = 1 - 2.104\lambda + 2.09\lambda^3 - 0.95\lambda^5 \tag{28}$$

Since the frictional function b can be written as

$$b = 1/(D_m/D_{AB}) \tag{29}$$

b is related to the quantity λ by

$$\frac{1}{b} = 1 - 2.104\lambda + 2.09\lambda^3 - 0.95\lambda^5 \tag{30}$$

When combined with a solute repulsion factor $(1-\lambda)^2$ eq 30 was found valid in the range of λ below 0.2 using membranes whose pore sizes ranged from 45 to 300Å (13). Satterfield, Colton and Pitcher on the other hand studied restricted diffusion in heterogeneous solid almina bead catalysts which possessed a pore radius of 16Å, by unsteady diffusion and observed a more severe restriction of the solute diffusion in the pore (14).

When there is no interaction between solute and the pore wall, effective diffusivity in the pore could be expressed by

$$\log_{10}(D_{eff}/D_{AB}) = -0.37 - 2.0\lambda \tag{31}$$

or

$$D_{eff}/D_{AB} = 0.427 \times 10^{-2.0\lambda}$$

When there is strong interaction between solute and the pore wall and the former is strongly adsorbed to the latter, the ratio, D_{eff}/D_{AB}, is even less than the quantity obtained by eq 31.

Though their D_{eff} includes the effect of tortuosity and does not denote the diffusivity in the pore in a strict sense of the definition, the frictional function can be written, in analogy to eq 29, as

$$\frac{1}{b} = \left(\frac{D_{eff}}{D_{AB}}\right) = 0.427 \times 10^{-2.0\lambda} \tag{32}$$

Eq 32 implies that the frictional function includes also the effect of tortuosity.

In Figure 4, 1/b described by eq 30 and 32 are both illustrated with an experimental correlation of Satterfield et al., when there is a strong interaction between solute and the pore wall, in the form of the correlation shown by Lane and Riggle (15). Obviously Satterfield's correlation lies far below that of Faxen. While Faxen's equation can well demonstrate the frictional drag in the range of $\lambda \leq 0.2$ (13) it is obviously underestimating the reduction in pore diffusivity in the range of higher λ values, particularly when there is a solute-pore wall interaction. Satterfield's correction seems to be better representing the relationship between 1/b and λ. In an attempt to make the best use of both correlations, a new function was generated, in which both Faxen's and Satterfield's correlations were combined. The new function thus synthesized is also illustrated in Figure 4. It has to be noted that the value 1/b

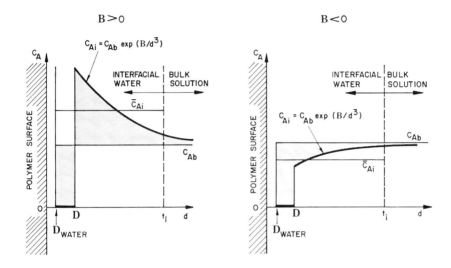

Figure 3. Solute concentration profile at the polymer–solution interface

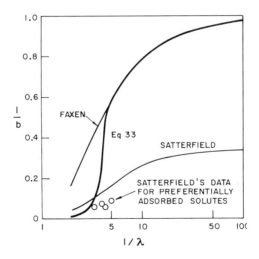

Figure 4. Correlation of $1/\lambda$ vs. $1/b$

in the higher range of λ resembles more Satterfield's experimental data on solutes under interaction force from the pore wall. The new function can be expressed as

$$\frac{1}{b} = \begin{cases} 1 - 2.104\lambda + 2.09\lambda^3 - 0.95\lambda^5 & \text{when } \lambda \leq 0.22 \\ 1/(44.57 - 416.2\lambda + 934.9\lambda^2 + 302.4\lambda^3) & \text{when } \lambda > 0.22 \end{cases} \tag{33}$$

Eq 33 was used throughout this work in order to represent the effect of λ on b.

Effect of Size of Water Molecule on Solvent Transport through Pore

When the size of the pore is comparable to the molecular size, the effect of solvent water on membrane transport cannot be ignored. In a pore there is an area into which the center of water molecule cannot enter due to its collision onto the pore wall. This area is illustrated in Figure 5 as the area surrounded by coaxial circles of radii R_1 and R_2. The quantity R_2-R_1 corresponds to the molecular radius of water ($D_{water} = 0.87$Å in this work). The pore radius used in the Poiseuille equation should be, therefore, the smaller radius designated by R_1. On the other hand, the interaction force expressed by a potential function such as eq 13 or the frictional function such as eq 39 are exerted throughout the larger pore radius R_2. These two radii have to be strictly distinguished. Following the previous work, the pore radius used in the Poiseuille equation, i.e. R_1, is defined as the pore radius and this definition is used throughout this work.

Results and Discussion

Calculation of Pore Radius of Membrane. By choosing an appropriate reference solute the pore radius of the membrane can be calculated in the following way:
Step 1. Using the diffusivity of the reference solute at infinite dilution and the Stokes equation

$$D_{AB} = \frac{kT}{6\pi\eta r_A} \tag{34}$$

where k, T, μ and r_A are the Boltzmann gas constant, absolute temperature, solution viscosity (viscosity of pure water in this case) and the solute radius, respectively, calculate r_A. Solute radius, r_A, thus obtained is considered equal to D of the reference solute for purposes of analysis.
Step 2. Using eq 26 and data on K' from liquid chromatography experiment determine B. Use $t_i = 9.5$Å and $D_{water} = 0.87$Å in eq. 26.

Step 3. Assume R_1 as pore radius, defined by Figure 5, and calculate λ by eq 27 where $\underset{\sim}{D}$ is set equal to $R_2 = R_1 + D_{\underset{\sim}{water}}$. Then calculate b by eq 33. This b is used as a constant throughout the entire range of ρ in eq 7-9.

Step 4. Assume c_{A3} and calculate c_{A2} by eq 17. The value of k found in Figure 1 as a function of A listed in Table I is used in this calculation.

Step 5. Calculate dimensionless parameters β_1 and β_2 from eq 4 and 5 using data on operating pressure and c_{A2} obtained above. The viscosity data of pure water can be used for η. χ_{AB} is calculated from the relation

$$\chi_{AB} = \frac{\underset{\sim}{RT}}{D_{AB}} \tag{35}$$

where D_{AB} is the diffusivity of solute at infinite dilution. Note that R in eq 4 corresponds to R_1 (Figure 5).

Step 6. Combine eq 8, 9 and 13 and solve the differential eq 8 with boundary conditions eq 10 and 11 using $\underset{\sim}{D}$, $\underset{\sim}{B}$, b, β_1 and β_2 obtained in steps 1, 2, 3 and 5. R in eq 13 must be $R_1 + D_{\underset{\sim}{water}}$.

Step 7. Since $\alpha(\rho)$, as function of ρ, is now known, f' can be calculated from eq 7.

Step 8. Use f' calculated above in eq 15 and calculate c_{A3} using the value of c_{A2} obtained in step 4. When c_{A3} agrees with the value assumed in step 4, f' is regarded as valid, in which case go to the next step. Otherwise go back to step 4 and repeat.

Step 9. Using f' obtained above calculate f from eq 18. If it agrees with the experimental separation data, R_1 assumed in step 3 is regarded as the final solution and the pore radius is thus determined. Otherwise go back to step 3 and repeat the entire procedure.

Glycerol was chosen as the reference solute and the pore radius R_1 was determined for all the membranes used in this study. The experimental results on glycerol separation and the pore radius, R_1, so calculated are both listed in Table I.

The quantities $\ln R_1$ and $\ln(PWP)$ were then subjected to least squares analysis. As a result, it was found that

$$\ln(PWP) = -3.12 + 3.2 \ln R_1$$
$$\text{or } (PWP) = 0.04 \, R_1^{3.2} \tag{36}$$

Assuming the number of pores is equal for all membranes involved in this work, eq 36 indicates that the pore flow is very much like Poiseuille flow as assumed in the entire scheme of this calculation.

Calculation of Molecular Radius of Solutes. The membranes of smallest pore sizes (films 1, 7, 11, 16 and 22) were then chosen and the characteristic constants $\underset{\sim}{D}$ and $\underset{\sim}{B}$, describing the interfacial attractive potential function, were determined for each solute involved in this work from experimental results of reverse osmosis and liquid chromatography. The method used was as follows:

Step 10. Assume solute radius $\underset{\sim}{D}$.

Step 11. Same as step 2 before, calculate $\underset{\sim}{B}$.

Step 12. R_1 is now known for the membrane under consideration; calculate b.

Step 13. Same as step 4 before, assume c_{A3} and calculate c_{A2}.

Step 14. Same as step 5 before, calculate β_1 and β_2.

Step 15. Same as step 6 before, calculate $\alpha(\rho)$ as a function of ρ.

Step 16. Same as step 7 before, obtain f'.

Step 17. Same as step 8 before, obtain c_{A3}. If it agrees with the value assumed in step 13, go to the next step. Otherwise, go to step 13.

Step 18. Calculate f from f'. If it agrees with experimental f, $\underset{\sim}{D}$ assumed in step 10 is regarded as the final solution. Otherwise, go back to step 10.

By the method described above $\underset{\sim}{D}$ and $\underset{\sim}{B}$ were calculated for all solutes involved except the reference solute glycerol. In Table II, $\underset{\sim}{D}$ and $\underset{\sim}{B}$ are listed together with equilibrium constant obtained by liquid chromatography data. For comparison molecular radius, r_A, calculated from eq 34 is also listed using experimental D_{AB} data available in the literature. The agreement between $\underset{\sim}{D}$ and r_A is surprisingly good for most of the solutes except ethyl acetate, phenol and resorcinol for which $\underset{\sim}{D}$ values calculated by combination of reverse osmosis and liquid chromatography data were significantly smaller than r_A. It must be noted that $\underset{\sim}{D}$ was evaluated without any reference to r_A. Therefore, this agreement testifies the validity of surface force-pore flow model for reverse osmosis transport, and also the form of the potential function and particularly that of the frictional function b. Figure 6 and 7 illustrate the potential functions for two special cases where the solute is strongly rejected from the membrane pore (solute=glucose) and the solute is strongly adsorbed onto the membrane pore wall (solute=t-butyl i-propyl ether).

Reverse Osmosis Separation of Various Organic Solutes Using Membranes of Different Porosities. Since R_1 for all membranes, $\underset{\sim}{B}$ and $\underset{\sim}{D}$ for all solutes involved in this work are now available (Table I and II), it is possible to calculate the solute separation, f, for all membranes other than those used for the determination of $\underset{\sim}{B}$ and $\underset{\sim}{D}$ and for all solutes other than the reference solute.

The calculation is straight from step 3 to step 9 described

Table II. Diffusivities of Solutes, Equilibrium Constants Calculated from HPLC Data and Characteristic Constants Defining Interfacial Forces for the System Cellulose Acetate (Eastman E-398) - Water

Solute	$D_{AB} \times 10^9$, m²/s at 25°C [c]	K'	D, Å	r_A, Å [b]	B, Å³
Methanol	1.69	1.077	1.85	1.45	8.31
Ethanol	1.19	1.474	2.03	2.05	21.54
1-Propanol	1.15	2.385	2.15	2.12	37.77
2-Propanol	1.08	1.564	2.45	2.26	38.40
1-Butanol	1.05[a]	4.705	2.10		47.27
2-Butanol	1.05[a]	3.154	2.45		62.15
2-Methyl-1-propanol	0.80	4.205	2.75	3.05	95.57
2-Methyl-2-propanol	0.73	1.897	3.67	3.35	134.3
1-Hexanol	1.24	23.03	1.97	1.97	56.76
Acetone	1.28	2.308	1.91	1.91	26.90
Methyl ethyl ketone	1.08[a]	4.307	1.92	1.92[d]	35.87
Methyl isopropyl ketone	0.943[a]	7.923	2.45		83.67
Methyl isobutyl ketone	0.853[a]	15.69	2.45		97.88
Cyclohexanone	0.883[a]	10.59	2.72		120.8
Diisopropyl ketone	0.786[a]	28.46	2.62		131.7
Methyl acetate	1.19[a]	4.821	1.73		27.88
Ethyl acetate	1.02	7.308	1.83	2.39	36.41
Ethyl propionate	0.91[a]	14.33	1.88		45.63
Ethyl butyl ether	0.834[a]	6.333	2.53		86.45
Ethyl t-butyl ether	0.834[a]	20.44	5.30		901.2
Isopropyl t-butyl ether	0.767[a]	11.72	5.60		918.2
Propionamide	1.09	1.410	1.98	2.24	19.13
Acetonitrile	1.66	4.128	1.78	1.47	28.49
Propionitrile	1.32[a]	7.436	1.78		34.20
Nitromethane	1.48[a]	8.077	1.80		36.00
1-Nitropropane	1.22[a]	28.15	2.05		65.76
Phenol	1.16	75.21	1.71	2.10	45.39
Resorcinol	0.89	55.87	1.73	2.74	45.16
Aniline	1.01[a]	46.46	1.80		48.98
Dimethyl aniline	0.816[a]	47.97	2.50		125.8
1,2-Ethanediol	1.16	0.692	2.20	2.11	-16.82
Glycerol	1.06	0.513	2.30	2.30	-52.30
2,3-Butanediol	0.994[a]	0.846	2.75		-11.97
Xylitol	0.815[a]	0.308	3.30		-135.0
1,2,6-Hexanetriol	0.796[a]	0.667	2.82		-16.95
D-Sorbitol	0.739[a]	0.205	4.64		-180.2
D-Glucose	0.67	0.180	3.36	3.66	-203.1
D-Fructose	0.758[a]	0.205	4.51		-181.8
Sucrose	0.52	~0	5.11	4.67	-343.2
Maltose	0.49	~0	4.98	4.98	-346.0

a. From Wilke-Chang equation (16).

b. Molecular radius was calculated by eq 34 only when measured diffusivity data were available in the literature.

c. From literature (17,18). Diffusion coefficients were converted to values at 25°C by eq 34.

d. Data obtained from diffusion in benzene.

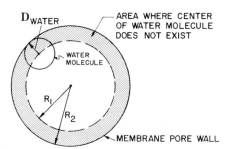

Figure 5. Position of water molecule in the membrane pore

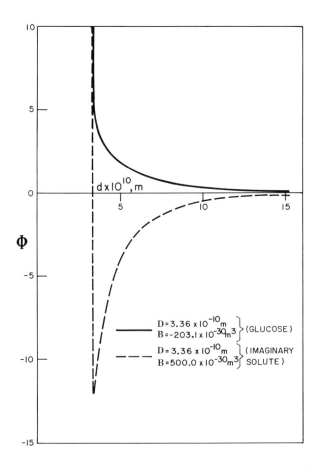

Figure 6. Potential curve of interfacial force for the system CA (E-398) material–water–glucose and an imaginary solute

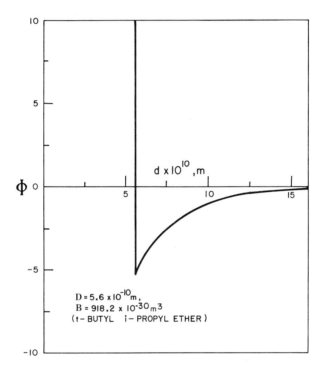

Figure 7.   Potential curve of interfacial force for the system CA (E-398) material–water–t-butyl-iso-propyl ether

above without any assumption in values of R_1, B, and D. The
calculated separation data so obtained versus experimental values
are plotted in Figure 8. A total of 140 data points obtained are
crowded along the diagonal line, indicating the good agreement
between calculated and experimental values. This result again
testifies the validity of the surface force-pore flow model, and
also the form of the potential function of the interfacial force
working on the solute and the frictional function affecting
diffusion in membrane pores.

Effect of Potential Function on Solute Separation. As shown
in Figures 6 and 7, glucose is strongly repelled from the membrane
pore wall as the result of the positive potential working in the
entire range of the distance of solute from the pore wall, while
t-butyl i-propyl ether is strongly adsorbed onto the pore wall as
the result of the deep negative value of the potential in the
vicinity of the interface. Assume that there is a solute which
has the same molecular radius as glucose and yet very strongly
adsorbed onto the pore wall; then what kind of solute separation
will take place as the reverse osmosis performance data with a
particular membrane porosity? In order to answer this question
the effect of operating pressure on f and (PR)/(PWP) for glucose
solute and for an imaginary solute, whose D and B are each equal
to 3.36Å and 500Å^3, as indicated by the dotted line in Figure 6,
was calculated and the result is illustrated in Figure 9 for the
membrane whose pore size, R_1, is 7.36Å.
     The result obtained clearly shows the effect of the
potential function on the reverse osmosis experimental data. The
following three conclusions can be reached immediately from
Figure 9.
1. The imaginary solute with a high adsorption capacity to the
membrane pore wall shows significantly less separations than
glucose.
2. Data on (PR)/(PWP) for the imaginary solute is also significantly less than unity while that for glucose is essentially
unity indicating considerable pore blocking in the former system.
3. As pressure increases the separation of the imaginary solute
tends to decrease while that of glucose tends to increase. All
the above results are entirely consistent with experimental
results discussed in the previous work (1).

Conclusion

     In this work HPLC experimental data were combined with
surface force-pore flow model to determine the parameters
involved in the surface potential function and the frictional
function which represent the surface force working on the solute
molecule at the polymer-solution interface in the membrane pore.
     The use of the potential and frictional functions so
obtained enables one to calculate the solute separation for each
solute studied under a given operating condition. The good

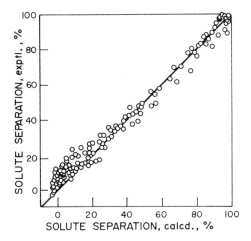

Figure 8. Comparison of calculated and experimental solute separation for various undissociated polar organic solutes. Membrane material, CA (E-398); operating pressure = 1724 kPa·gauge (250 psig); feed flow rate = 400 cm³/min; dilute solution systems.

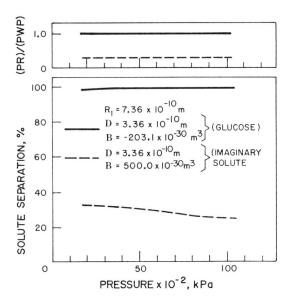

Figure 9. Effect of pressure on the (PR)/(PWP) ratio and solute separation of glucose and an imaginary solute. Membrane material, CA (E-398); membrane pore radius = 7.36 Å; feed flow rate = 400 cm³/min; feed concentration = 1 mol/m³.

agreement between the calculated and experimental values testifies the validity of the model used and the forms of potential as well as frictional functions.

It was also shown that the change of reverse osmosis performance data of a particular solute with the change in pore size of the membrane and the experimental operating condition such as operating pressure depends significantly on the relative magnitude of the distance associated with the steric repulsion at the interface and the quantity representing the affinity of the solute molecule to the polymer surface.

The frictional function which was described as a function of the ratio of the distance associated with the steric repulsion at the interface to the pore radius, however, is still an approximation at most, though it is convenient to use, due to its simplified form. A more appropriate functional form including both steric repulsion and interfacial affinity effects on the restricted motion of the solute molecule in the membrane pore is yet to be developed. A further research effort in this direction is called for.

Nomenclature

A	= pure water permeability constant, kg-mol H_2O/m^2s kPa
B	= constant characterizing potential function, m^3
b	= frictional function defined by eq 33
C_A	= dimensionless solute concentration defined by eq 2
c	= molar concentration of solution, mol/m^3
c_A	= molar concentration of solute, mol/m^3
c_{AB}	= molar concentration of solute in the bulk solution, mol/m^3
c_{Ai}	= molar concentration of solute in the interfacial solution, mol/m^3
D	= distance associated with steric repulsion at the interface, m
D_{water}	= molecular radius of water, m
D_{AB}	= diffusivity of solute in water, m^2/s
D_{eff}	= effective diffusivity of solute in the pore including totuosity factor, m^2/s
D_m	= effective diffusivity of solute in the pore, m^2/s
$(D_{AM}/K\delta)$	= solute transport parameter (treated as a single quantity), m/s
d	= distance between pore wall and the center of solute molecule, m
E	= constant characterizing frictional function, m
f	= fraction solute separation based on the feed concentration
f'	= fraction solute separation based on the solute concentration in the boundary phase
K'	= equilibrium constant between concentrations of interfacial solution - and bulk solution phase

k   = mass transfer coefficient for solute on high pressure side of membrane, m/s
$\underset{\sim}{k}$ = Boltzmann constant
P_i = operating pressure, Pa when used in eq 5, kPa when used with A
P_o = atmospheric pressure, Pa when used in eq 5, kPa when used with A
(PR)   = membrane permeated product rate for given area of membrane surface, g/h
(PWP)   = pure water permeation rate for given area of membrane surface, g/h
R   = pore radius, m
R_1, R_2 = pore radii defined in Figure 5, m or Å when used in eq 36
$\underset{\sim}{R}$ = gas constant
r   = radial distance in cylindrical coordinate, m
r_A = molecular radius of solute, m
T   = absolute temperature, K
t_i = thickness of interfacial water layer, m
u_B = velocity of solvent in the pore, m/s
$[V_R']$ = chromatography retention volume, m^3
V_s = volume of stationary phase water, m^3
v_s = permeation velocity of product solution, m/s
v_w^* = pure water permeation velocity, m/s

Greek Letters

α = dimensionless quantity defined by eq 3
β_1 = dimensionless quantity defined by eq 4
β_2 = dimensionless quantity defined by eq 5
Γ = surface excess, mol/m^2
δ = length of cylindrical pore, m
η = solution viscosity, Pa·s
λ = quantity defined by eq 27
ρ = dimensionless quantity defined by eq 1
Φ = dimensionless quantity defined by eq 6
ϕ = potential function of force exerted on solute molecule by pore wall, J/mol
χ_{AB} = quantity defined by eq 35

Subscripts

1   = bulk feed solution
2   = concentrated boundary solution on the high pressure side of membrane
3   = membrane permeated product solution on the low pressure side of membrane

Acknowledgments

The authors are grateful to A.G. Baxter for his valuable assistance in the progress of these investigations. One of the authors (Y.T.) thanks the National Research Council of Canada for the award of a postdoctoral research associateship.

Literature Cited

1. Matsuura, T.; Sourirajan, S. Ind. Eng. Chem., Process Des. Dev., (in press).
2. Matsuura, T.; Blais, P.; Sourirajan, S. J. Appl. Polym. Sci., 1976, 20, 1515.
3. Matsuura, T.; Sourirajan, S. J. Appl. Polym. Sci., 1971, 15, 2905.
4. Matsuura, T.; Sourirajan, S. J. Appl. Polym. Sci., 1972, 16, 1663.
5. Matsuura, T.; Sourirajan, S. J. Appl. Polym. Sci., 1973, 17, 1043.
6. Matsuura, T.; Baxter, A.G.; Sourirajan, S. Ind. Eng. Chem., Process Des. Dev., 1977, 16, 82.
7. Sourirajan, S., "Reverse Osmosis"; Academic: New York, 1970; Chap. 3.
8. Rangarajan, R.; Matsuura, T.; Goodhue, E.C.; Sourirajan, S. Ind. Eng. Chem., Process Des. Dev., 1976, 15, 529.
9. Matsuura, T.; Sourirajan, S. J. Coll. Int. Sci., 1978, 66, 589.
10. Robinson, R.A.; Stokes, R.H., "Electrolyte Solutions", 2nd ed.; Butterworths: London, 1959; p. 13.
11. Anderson, J.L.; Quinn, J.A. Biophys. J., 1974, 14, 130.
12. Faxen, H. Kolloid Z., 1959, 167, 146.
13. Beck, R.E.; Schultz, J.S. Biochim. Biophys. Acta, 1972, 255, 253.
14. Satterfield, C.N.; Colton, C.K.; Pitcher, W.H., Jr. A.I.Ch.E.J., 1973, 19, 628.
15. Lane, J.A.; Riggle, J.W. Chem. Eng. Progr. Symposium Ser., 1959, 55 (24) 127.
16. Wilke, C.R.; Chang, P. A.I.Ch.E.J., 1955, 1, 264.
17. National Research Council of the United States of America, "International Critical Tables of Numerical Data", Vol. V, First ed.; McGraw-Hill: New York, 1929.
18. Landolt-Boernstein, "Zahlenwerte und Funktionen aus Physik-Chemie-Astronomie Geophysik und Technik", 6th ed., Vol. 2, No. 5; Springer: Berlin, 1969.

Issued as NRC No. 18590

RECEIVED December 4, 1980.

Reverse-Osmosis Separations of Alkali Metal Halides in Methanol Solutions Using Cellulose Acetate Membranes

BRIAN A. FARNAND and F. D. F. TALBOT

Department of Chemical Engineering, University of Ottawa, Ottawa

TAKESHI MATSUURA and S. SOURIRAJAN

Division of Chemistry, National Research Council of Canada, Ottawa

Virtually all reverse osmosis separations have been made with water as the major component, and the general case of aqueous salt solutions has been well documented in the literature (1, 2). While separations in nonaqueous solution systems have been investigated (3, 4, 5), no organized study of such systems has been made and there are no reports in the literature of using reverse osmosis to separate inorganic salts in nonaqueous solutions. For these reasons, the reverse osmosis separation of alkali metal halides in methanol solutions using porous cellulose acetate membranes has been studied in this work.

Previous work with aqueous solution systems has been successful in treating both completely ionized salts as well as incompletely ionized salts (2, 6). This work incorporates both of these cases in methanol solutions and uses the Kimura-Sourirajan analysis for the treatment of reverse osmosis data (7). The surface excess free energy parameters ($-\Delta\Delta G/RT$) for the ions and ion pairs involved were determined by the methods established earlier (8). The predictability of membrane performance by the use of data on free energy parameters obtained in this work has been tested.

Removal of dissolved inorganic impurities from methanol is of interest from the point of view of utilization of methanol as an alternative to conventional fuels. Reports show that the corrosion rate of metal alloys used for turbines and fuel transportation is greater in methanol than in water in the presence of traces of chlorine and sodium ions (9, 10). Further, ion complexes in trace quantities have been observed in methanol and there is concern that they could alter the reaction kinetics for processes which use methanol as a feedstock or reaction medium (11). Methanol that is used as a feedstock in the production of single cell protein could be sterilized as well as purified of heavy metals by reverse osmosis which can be integrated in the design of these processes.

Table I. Physical Properties of LiCl–Methanol Solutions

mol fraction × 10^3	π [b] kPa	D_{AB} $m^2/s \times 10^{10}$	$\gamma_\pm$ [a] mol fraction basis
0	0	12.07	1.000
1.0	71	7.74	.496
2.0	155	7.65	.384
3.0	235	8.02	.333
4.0	318	8.47	.304
5.0	403	8.93	.285
6.0	495	9.37	.273
7.0	592	9.79	.265
8.0	675	10.20	.259
9.0	755	10.59	.254
10.0	839	10.95	.251
11.0	925	11.29	.250
12.0	993	11.68	.248

[a] from (14)
[b] from (15)

Table I. – Cont'd
         Physical Properties of LiBr–Methanol Solutions

mol fraction × 10^3	π kPa	D_{AB} $m^2/s \times 10^{10}$	$\gamma_\pm$ [a] mol fraction basis
0	0	12.56	1.000
1.0	71	8.05	.496
2.0	155	7.96	.384
3.0	235	8.35	.333
4.0	318	8.81	.304
5.0	403	9.29	.285
6.0	495	9.75	.273
7.0	592	10.19	.265
8.0	675	10.61	.259
9.0	755	11.02	.254
10.0	839	11.39	.251
11.0	925	11.75	.250
12.0	993	12.15	.248

[a] from (16)

Table I. - Cont'd
Physical Properties of NaCl-Methanol Solutions

mol fraction × 10³	π [c,d] kPa	D_{AB} m^2/s × 10¹⁰	$\gamma_\pm$ [a,b] mol fraction basis
0	0	13.17	1.000
1.0	74	7.25	.428
2.0	155	7.17	.332
3.0	241	7.33	.285
4.0	327	7.51	.257
5.0	406	7.68	.239
6.0	488	7.89	.226
7.0	558	8.09	.217
8.0	648	8.29	.210
9.0	725	8.48	.205
10.0	803	8.69	.202

[a] from (17)

[b] from (18)

[c] from (19)

[d] from (15)

Table I. - Cont'd
Physical Properties of NaBr-Methanol Solutions

mol fraction × 10³	π [b] kPa	D_{AB} m^2/s × 10¹⁰	$\gamma_\pm$ [a] mol fraction basis
0	0	13.37	1.000
1.0	86	12.09	.658
2.0	181	11.31	.581
3.0	282	10.98	.536
4.0	385	10.73	.504
5.0	488	10.54	.479
6.0	594	10.39	.459
7.0	690	10.27	.442
8.0	795	10.17	.427
9.0	898	10.09	.414
10.0	1001	–	.403
12.0	1203	–	.382
14.0	1408	–	.365
16.0	1613	–	.350
18.0	1818	–	.337

[a] from (18)
[b] from (19)

Table I. - Cont'd
Physical Properties of KI-Methanol Solutions

mol fraction × 10^3	π [b] kPa	D_{AB} $m^2/s \times 10^{10}$	$\gamma_\pm$ [a] mol fraction basis
0	0	15.20	1.000
1.0	74	13.02	.545
2.0	150	11.95	.472
3.0	230	11.40	.428
4.0	306	11.18	.398
5.0	394	10.87	.374
6.0	466	10.64	.355
7.0	538	10.34	.338
8.0	613	10.14	.324
9.0	696	9.85	.311
10.0	780	9.59	.300

[a] from (14)
[b] from (20)

Table I. - Cont'd
Physical Properties of CsCl-Methanol Solutions

mol fraction × 10^3	π [b] kPa	D_{AB} $m^2/s \times 10^{10}$	$\gamma_\pm$ [a] mol fraction basis
0	0	14.98	1.000
1.0	74	7.89	.428
2.0	155	7.81	.332
3.0	241	7.98	.285
4.0	327	8.18	.257
5.0	406	8.36	.239

[a] from (21)
[b] from (15)

Table I. - Cont'd
          Limiting Diffusion Coefficients of Alkali
              Metal Halides in Methanol

Solute	D_{AB} $m^2/s \times 10^{10}$
LiCl	12.07
LiBr	12.56
NaCl	13.17
NaBr	13.37
NaI	14.03
KF	11.88
KCl	14.24
KBr	14.41
KI	15.20
RbCl	14.33
CsCl	14.98
CsBr	15.16

Table II. Bulk Solution Free Energy of Solvation for
           Alkali Metal and Halide Ions in Methanol
                        Solutions

Ion	Crystallographic radius nm	ΔG_B kJ/mol	
Li^+	6.0	481.9[a]	481.9[b]
Na^+	9.5	385.5	385.5
K^+	13.3	314.3	314.3
Rb^+	14.8	289.1	289.0
Cs^+	16.9	249.3	247.2
F^-	13.6	–	–
Cl^-	18.1	305.9	–
Br^-	19.5	282.8	–
I^-	21.6	253.5	–

[a] from (22)

[b] from (23)

Experimental

   Twelve alkali metal halides were used in single solute
methanol solution systems with cellulose acetate batch 316
(10/30) membranes at pressures of 1725 kPa gauge (250 psig) and
3450 kPa gauge (500 psig) (1). The membranes were heat treated
in water and then solvent exchanged to methanol by immersion in
successively concentrated methanol-water solutions. After a pure
methanol immersion had been completed, the membranes were loaded
into cells and subjected to pressures of 120% of the subsequent
operating pressures for one hour. The apparatus used was the
same as reported earlier with the addition of a temperature
controller to keep the temperature of the feed solution at
25 ± 0.5°C (2). The concentrations of the feed solutions
involved were in the range of 0.005 m to 0.45 m and the operating
pressure was either 1725 kPa gauge (250 psig) or 3450 kPa gauge
(500 psig). All experiments were performed at 25°C with a feed
flow rate of 490 cm³/min. For each experiment, pure solvent
permeation rates (PSP) and product rates (PR) as well as solute
separation (f) defined as:

$$f = \frac{\text{feed molality} - \text{permeate molality}}{\text{feed molality}} \tag{1}$$

were determined. Analysis of the concentration of the various
salts in both the feed and the permeate solutions was by either
electrical conductance or atomic absorption spectroscopy.

Results and Discussion

   Physical Properties. The calculation of osmotic pressure
requires values of the solvent's thermodynamic activity for each
solution. The solute mean activity coefficients, $\gamma_{\pm}$, are
reported in the literature and their transformation to
solvent activities was made by use of the Gibbs-Duhem relation
(12). The diffusion coefficient, D_{AB}, was determined for each
solute by the Nernst-Haskel equation (13). These are presented
in Table I along with osmotic pressures. The free energy of
solvation for the bulk solution (ΔG_B) for each ion considered and
the dissociation constant (K_D) of relevant salts are given in
Tables II and III respectively.

   Basic Transport Equations. The Kimura-Sourirajan analysis
of experimental reverse osmosis data leads to the following basic
transport equations (2, 7, 8):

$$A = \frac{(PSP)}{M_B \cdot S \cdot 3600 \cdot P} \tag{2}$$

$$N_B = A \cdot (P - \pi_2 + \pi_3) \tag{3}$$

$$= \left(\frac{D_{AM}}{K\delta}\right) \cdot \frac{1-X_{A3}}{X_{A3}} \cdot (c_2 X_{A2} - c_3 X_{A3}) \tag{4}$$

$$= k \cdot c_1 \cdot (1-X_{A3}) \cdot \ln\left(\frac{X_{A2} - X_{A3}}{X_{A1} - X_{A3}}\right) \tag{5}$$

All symbols are defined at the end of the paper. In the range of solution concentrations used in this work, the molar density of solution, c, is essentially constant (2.496×10^4 mol/m^3 at 25°C) so that $c_1 = c_2 = c_3 = c$. Equations (4) and (5) then become:

$$N_B = \left(\frac{D_{AM}}{K\delta}\right) \cdot c \cdot \frac{(1-X_{A3})}{X_{A3}} \cdot (X_{A2} - X_{A3}) \tag{6}$$

$$= k \cdot c \cdot (1-X_{A3}) \cdot \ln\left(\frac{X_{A2} - X_{A3}}{X_{A1} - X_{A3}}\right) \tag{7}$$

Using equations 2, 3, 6, and 7, one can calculate the values of A, $D_{AM}/K\delta$, and k for each membrane for each set of experimental (PSP), (PR), and f data corresponding to specified experimental conditions.

For the case of completely dissociated univalent salts in solution the solute transport parameter $(D_{AM}/K\delta)$ has been shown to be (2):

$$\ln\left(\frac{D_{AM}}{K\delta}\right) = \ln C^*_{NaCl} + \sum_i \left(\frac{-\Delta\Delta G}{RT}\right)_i \tag{8}$$

where $\ln C^*_{NaCl}$ represents the porosity of the membrane surface, subscript i represents the ions involved and $\Delta\Delta G$ is the surface excess free energy of solvation defined as:

$$\Delta\Delta G = \Delta G_I - \Delta G_B \tag{9}$$

where ΔG is the free energy of solvation and the subscripts I and B represent the membrane-solution interface and the bulk solution phase respectively.

It is known that in methanol solutions, solutes involving monovalent ions, even in low concentrations, are subject to significant ion pair formation (28a). For solution systems involving both ions and ion pairs, eq. (8) becomes (6):

$$\ln\left(\frac{D_{AM}}{K\delta}\right) = \ln C^*_{NaCl} + \alpha \cdot \left(\sum_i \left(\frac{-\Delta\Delta G}{RT}\right)_i\right) + (1-\alpha) \cdot \left(\frac{-\Delta\Delta G}{RT}\right)_{IP} \quad (10)$$

where the subscript IP represents the ion pair and α represents the degree of dissociation defined as (28b):

$$K_D = \frac{\alpha^2 \cdot \gamma_{\pm}^2 \cdot X_{A2}}{(1-\alpha)} \quad (11)$$

where K_D is the ionic dissociation constant, and $\gamma_{\pm}$ is the mean ionic activity coefficient. Eq. (11) may be solved for α to give:

$$\alpha = \frac{1}{2}\left[-\beta + \sqrt{\beta^2 + 4\beta}\right] \quad (12)$$

where

$$\beta = \left(\frac{K_D}{X_{A2} \cdot \gamma_{\pm}^2}\right) \quad (13)$$

Figure 1 gives the correlation of α with β. It should be noted that for small values of X_{A2}, β is large and approaches unity which corresponds to complete dissociation.

Correlation of k with A. Values of the mass transfer coefficient k were determined by reverse osmosis experiments with NaCl-methanol solutions at 0.15 m using several membranes of different surface porosities. The plot of k versus A in Figure 2 gives a linear correlation which can be expressed by the relation.

$$k = 0.9201 (A \times 10^9 + 12.17) \times 10^{-6} \quad (14)$$

To obtain values of k at other concentrations and also for different solutes, the Schmidt-Sherwood correlation for constant Reynold's number was used (29):

$$k = k_{ref} \cdot \left[\frac{D_{AB}}{(D_{AB})_{ref}}\right]^{2/3} \quad (15)$$

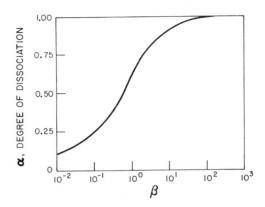

Figure 1.   Degree of dissociation as a function of β for univalent salts

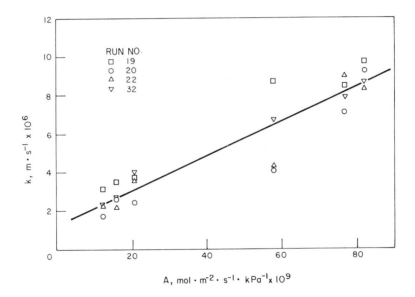

Figure 2.   Mass-transfer coefficient with pure solvent permeability for 0.15m NaCl and 1725 kPa

where D_{AB} is the diffusivity of the solute A in the solvent B and the subscript "ref" refers to the data for NaCl at 0.15 m and 25°C.

$(-\Delta\Delta G/RT)_i$ for Ions. The following relationships have been derived and discussed elsewhere (2):

$$\frac{1}{\Delta G_{B,i}} = \frac{-1}{E_B}r_i - \frac{\Delta_B}{E_B} \tag{16}$$

$$\frac{1}{\Delta G_{I,i}} = \frac{-1}{E_I}r_i - \frac{\Delta_I}{E_I} \tag{17}$$

$$\Delta\Delta G_i = \left(\frac{-E_I}{r_i + \Delta_I}\right) - \left(\frac{-E_B}{r_i + \Delta_B}\right) \tag{18}$$

The quantities E and Δ are constants for each class of ions, and E_B and Δ_B have been determined by a linear plot of $1/\Delta G_B$ with the Pauling ionic radius in Figure 3 which gave E_B and Δ_B values of 656.5 kJ·nm·mol^{-1} and 0.0753 nm respectively for the cations and 492.9 kJ·nm·mol^{-1} and -0.0180 nm respectively for the halide ions. These are compared to those for water in Table IV.
Using eq. (18), eq. (8) may be written as:

$$\ln\left(\frac{D_{AM}}{K\delta}\right)_{M^+X^-} = \ln C^*_{NaCl} + \frac{1}{RT}\left\{\left(\frac{E_I}{r_M + \Delta_I}\right)_{M^+}\right.$$
$$\left. -\left(\frac{E_B}{r_M + \Delta_B}\right)_{M^+}\right\} + \frac{1}{RT}\left\{\left(\frac{E_I}{r_X + \Delta_I}\right)_{X^-}\right.$$
$$\left. -\left(\frac{E_B}{r_X + \Delta_B}\right)_{X^-}\right\} \tag{19}$$

Reverse osmosis experiments were performed with 12 salts and four membranes and the results obtained are given in Table V. These results were used to obtain values for $(D_{AM}/K\delta)_{M^+X^-}$. The unknown quantities $\ln C^*_{NaCl}, (E_I)_{M^+}, (\Delta_I)_{M^+}, (E_I)_{X^-}$, and $(\Delta_I)_{X^-}$ were determined by regression analysis and are given in Table IV. They were used to determine values of $(-\Delta\Delta G/RT)_i$ for different ions which are compared to those for aqueous solutions in Table VI.

$(-\Delta\Delta G/RT)_{IP}$ for Ion Pairs. For the case where ion pairs had a significant effect, eq. (10) was used in place of eq. (19).

Table III. Values of Dissociation Constant,
K_D, for Various Ion Pairs

Ion Pair	K_D mol fraction basis	Ref.
LiCl	.01059	(24)
LiBr	.01058	(24)
NaCl	.004123	(25)
NaBr	.003996	(26)
KI	.004058	(26)
CsCl	.004539	(27)

Table IV. Values of Born Equation Parameters,
Cellulose Acetate (Eastman E-398)

Ion Class	E_B kJ·nm·mol^{-1}	Δ_B nm × 10^2	E_I kJ·nm·mol^{-1}	Δ_I nm × 10^2
Alkali Metal Cation, Methanol	656.5	7.53	665.6	7.81
Halide Anion, Methanol	492.9	-1.80	492.9	-1.80
Alkali Metal Cation, Water[a]	761.5	8.9	824.7	9.76
Halide Anion, Water[a]	504.2	-2.0	477.4	-2.30

[a] from (2)

Table V.   Separations and Permeation Rates for Some Alkali
            Metal Halide Salts

		Membrane							
		1		2		5		6	
Solute	Run Number	(PR)	f	(PR)	f	(PR)	f	(PR)	f
LiCl	39	21.50	.802	5.20	.831	20.05	.806	3.17	.876
LiBr	41	21.78	.782	5.20	.829	20.42	.789	3.11	.888
NaCl	13	21.22	.589	5.32	.729	20.21	.631	3.31	.803
NaCl	27	21.67	.613	5.25	.718	20.12	.622	3.24	.775
NaCl	28	21.66	.612	5.22	.720	20.28	.619	3.24	.783
NaBr	38	21.92	.568	5.25	.661	20.43	.577	3.22	.764
NaI	12	21.39	.543	5.37	.674	20.13	.554	3.24	.759
KF	50	22.01	.603	5.26	.706	20.39	.614	3.23	.774
KCl	42	21.62	.461	5.15	.606	20.11	.470	3.14	.678
KBr	43	21.76	.435	5.15	.577	20.21	.443	3.15	.642
KI	44	21.49	.432	5.05	.563	19.89	.419	3.08	.623
KI	45	21.68	.411	5.14	.560	20.18	.428	3.15	.622
RbCl	15	21.41	.455	5.31	.623	20.09	.464	3.24	.732
CsCl	14	21.59	.437	5.35	.612	20.15	.456	3.27	.670
CsBr	46	21.59	.415	5.06	.566	19.94	.415	3.11	.623

[a]Operating pressure, 1724 kPa gauge; Feed solution, 0.005 m;
Product rates are g/h for 1.32×10^{-3} m^2 membrane surface.

Table VI.   Values of $(-\Delta\Delta G/RT)_i$

Ion	r_i, nm	Methanol $(-\Delta\Delta G/RT)_i$	Water[a] $(-\Delta\Delta G/RT)_i$
Li^+	6.0	−1.36	5.77
Na^+	9.5	−0.427	5.79
K^+	13.3	0.033	5.91
Rb^+	14.8	0.138	5.86
Cs^+	16.9	0.244	5.72
F^-	13.6	−2.34	−4.91
Cl^-	18.1	−1.71	−4.42
Br^-	19.5	−1.58	−4.25
I^-	21.6	−1.41	−3.98

a from (2)

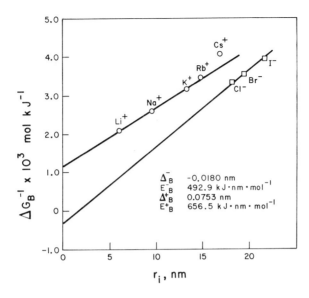

Figure 3. Born Equation for alkali metal and halide ions—bulk-phase free energy of solvation in methanol solutions

Table VII. Values of $\left(\dfrac{-\Delta\Delta G}{RT}\right)_{IP}$

Ion Pair	Average α, for 0.15 m feed, determined at X_{A2}	$\left(\dfrac{-\Delta\Delta G}{RT}\right)_{IP}$
NaCl	0.73	-1.295
NaBr	0.80	-0.343
KI	0.85	5.175
CsCl	0.82	1.706
LiCl[a]	≈ 1.0	-
LiBr[a]	≈ 1.0	-

[a] K_D is so large that α is considered as unity for the concentration ranges used in this work.

Reverse osmosis experiments were performed with the same
membranes that were used previously at concentrations where the
formation of ion pairs was significant. The values of
$(-\Delta\Delta G/RT)_i$ for the unassociated ions that were determined
previously were used in eq. (10) with the values of $\ln(D_{AM}/K\delta)$
for the associated ion experiments to obtain the values of
$(-\Delta\Delta G/RT)_{IP}$ presented in Table VII.

Predictability of Membrane Performance. New membranes were
placed in the cells as before and an experiment was done with a
reference solute (NaCl). With the use of the transport equations
(eq. (2), (3), (6), and (7)) and the correlation of k with A,
eq. (14), $(D_{AM}/K\delta)_{NaCl}$ was determined. The appropriate
$(\Delta\Delta G/RT)_i$'s were used from Table VI to determine C^*_{NaCl} for each
membrane. Calculations of (PR) and f for several salts at
various concentrations and pressures were made and compared to
the experimental results with the new membranes and these are
summarized in Figure 4 and Tables VIII, and IX. The
satisfactory agreement between predicted and experimental
results obtained indicates the practical utility of the
correlations and parameters generated in this work.

Comparison of Water and Methanol Solutions. Comparison of
$(-\Delta\Delta G/RT)_i$ for ions in both water and methanol solutions can be
made by using $(-\Delta\Delta G/RT)_{Na^+}$ and $(-\Delta\Delta G/RT)_{Cl^-}$ as references for
the alkali metal cations and halide anions respectively. These
have been plotted in Figure 5 with the lyotropic numbers for
each ion. Figure 5 shows that with respect to halide ions the
correlation of lyotropic number with $[(-\Delta\Delta G/RT)_i-(-\Delta\Delta G/RT)_{Cl^-}]$
is both linear and identical for both solvents, whereas the
corresponding correlations with respect to alkali metal cations
are different. In particular, with respect to these latter ions,
the change of $[(-\Delta\Delta G/RT)_i-(-\Delta\Delta G/RT)_{Na^+}]$ with lyotropic number is
greater in methanol solutions than in aqueous solutions. This
means that for a given membrane, the variations in solute
separation for alkali metal halide salts with common anions is
much less in aqueous solutions than in methanol solutions, which
is consistent with experimental results. Further, in the case
of methanol solutions, the solute separation increases with
increase in lyotropic number for the alkali metal cation series
and decreases with an increase in lyotropic number for the
halide series.

The lytoropic number for an ion is a fundamental
physicochemical parameter which expresses its relative tendency
for electron transfer (30) which is also the basis for
preferential sorption at interfaces for aqueous solutions
involving polar solutes (31). Since the lyotropic series is
valid in many fields of physical chemistry including solvation,

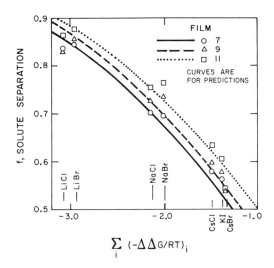

Figure 4. Separation in methanol solutions with surface excess free energy of solvation at 0.005m and 1725 kPa

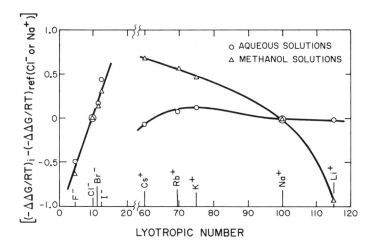

Figure 5. Comparison of the surface excess free energies for alkali metal and halide ions for aqueous and methanol solutions

Table VIII. Experimental and Product Rates,
            (PR), at 0.15 m and 1725 kPa

Membrane	Run	Solute	f Exptl	f Calcd	(PR) Exptl	(PR) Calcd	α
7	32	NaCl	.605	.606	6.32	5.90	.74
	38	CsCl	.351	.361	6.87	6.90	.83
	40	LiCl	.817	.813	5.65	5.52	1.00
	41	LiBr	.780	.792	5.75	5.50	1.00
	42	NaBr	.605	.590	6.04	5.77	.80
	47	KI	.323	.304	5.94	6.89	.87
8	32	NaCl	.658	.636	4.61	4.31	.74
	38	CsCl	.471	.392	4.99	5.03	.83
	40	LiCl	.848	.831	4.08	4.06	1.00
	41	LiBr	.817	.812	4.17	4.05	1.00
	42	NaBr	.639	.619	4.37	4.22	.80
	47	KI	.361	.330	4.39	5.02	.87
9	32	NaCl	.639	.641	3.65	3.41	.74
	38	CsCl	.417	.407	3.94	3.95	.83
	40	LiCl	.836	.835	3.22	3.22	1.00
	41	LiBr	.805	.816	3.30	3.21	1.00
	42	NaBr	.625	.623	3.47	3.33	.80
	47	KI	.349	.335	3.43	3.95	.87
11	32	NaCl	.655	.673	3.60	3.40	.74
	38	CsCl	.431	.434	3.97	3.98	.84
	40	LiCl	.850	.853	3.20	3.24	1.00
	41	LiBr	.822	.835	3.31	3.22	1.00
	42	NaBr	.649	.655	3.47	3.32	.80
	47	KI	.381	.367	3.48	3.95	.87

Table IX. Experimental and Calculated Separation, f, and Product Rate, (PR), at 3450 kPa

Membrane	Run	Solute	Concn m	f Exptl	Calcd	(PR) Exptl	Calcd	α
7	16	LiCl	.4586	.801	.816	9.17	7.61	1.00
	22	LiCl	.4930	.790	.796	8.25	7.34	1.00
	14	LiBr	.4093	.768	.802	9.88	8.49	1.00
	24	LiBr	.2617	.821	.816	11.10	10.20	1.00
	11	NaBr	.3853	.554	.551	11.48	12.12	.73
	26	NaBr	.2686	.583	.552	11.04	10.90	.75
8	16	LiCl	.4586	.835	.852	6.71	5.64	1.00
	22	LiCl	.4930	.828	.838	6.10	5.40	1.00
	14	LiBr	.4093	.814	.841	7.29	6.30	1.00
	24	LiBr	.2617	.856	.853	8.21	7.59	1.00
	11	NaBr	.3853	.616	.615	8.50	8.65	.73
	26	NaBr	.2686	.676	.613	8.15	7.95	.75
9	16	LiCl	.4586	.820	.839	5.38	4.57	1.00
	22	LiCl	.4930	.815	.819	4.86	4.40	1.00
	14	LiBr	.4093	.800	.836	5.79	5.01	1.00
	24	LiBr	.2617	.840	.842	6.53	6.07	1.00
	11	NaBr	.3853	.600	.591	6.73	7.04	.73
	26	NaBr	.2686	.661	.590	6.45	6.17	.75
11	16	LiCl	.4586	.839	.854	5.51	4.73	1.00
	22	LiCl	.4930	.835	.832	5.05	4.49	1.00
	14	LiBr	.4093	.816	.846	5.99	5.24	1.00
	24	LiBr	.2617	.861	.853	6.71	6.27	1.00
	11	NaBr	.3853	.617	.621	6.91	7.18	.73
	26	NaBr	.2686	.684	.619	6.72	6.51	.75
12	16	LiCl	.4586	.748	.792	4.54	3.95	1.00
	22	LiCl	.4930	.737	.766	4.16	3.85	1.00
	14	LiBr	.4093	.729	.887	4.84	3.78	1.00
	24	LiBr	.2617	.771	.790	5.47	5.11	1.00
	11	NaBr	.3853	.515	.517	5.42	6.10	.73
	26	NaBr	.2686	.571	.517	5.34	5.51	.75

sorbability, and surface tension, the correlation of $(-\Delta\Delta G/RT)_i$ with lyotropic number reflects the separation of ions in reverse osmosis.

Conclusions

The physicochemical criteria approach to reverse osmosis separations involving the surface excess free energy of solvation for ionized and nonionized solutes has been demonstrated by this work to include nonaqueous solutions. The parameters and correlations presented in this work permit the prediction of reverse osmosis separations and permeation rates for different alkali metal halides for cellulose acetate (Eastman E-398) membranes of different surface porosities from only a single set of experimental data for a sodium chloride-methanol reference feed solution system.

Abstract

Reverse osmosis separations of 12 alkali metal halides in methanol solutions have been studied using cellulose acetate membranes of different surface porosities. Data for surface excess free energy parameters for the ions and ion pairs involved have been generated for the above membrane material-solution systems. These data offer a means of predicting the performance of cellulose acetate membranes in the reverse osmosis treatment of methanol solutions involving the above ions from only a single set of experimental data.

Nomenclature

A = pure solvent permeability constant (mol solvent)$\cdot$ $m^{-2}\cdot s^{-1}\cdot kPa^{-1}$.

C^*_{NaCl} = constant defined in eq. (8), m/s.

c = molar concentration of solution, mol/m^3.

D_{AB} = diffusivity of solute A in solvent B, m^2/s.

$D_{AM}/K\delta$ = solute transport parameter, treated as a single variable, m/s.

E = constant in modified Born equation, kJ$\cdot$nm$\cdot$mol^{-1}.

f = fraction of solute separation, defined in eq. (1).

ΔG = free energy of solvation, kJ/mol.

$\Delta\Delta G$ = surface excess free energy of solvation, kJ/mol.

K_D = ionic dissociation equilibrium constant based on mol fraction.

k = mass transfer coefficient on the high pressure side of the membrane, m/s.

M_B = molecular weight of solvent B.

N_B = solvent flux through membrane, mol$\cdot$m$^{-2}\cdot s^{-1}$.

P = operating pressure, kPa.

(PR)   = product permeation rate through a given membrane area, g/h.
(PSP)   = pure solvent permeation rate through a given membrane area, g/h.
R   = gas constant, 8.314×10^{-3} $J \cdot K^{-1} \cdot mol^{-1}$.
r_i = Pauling crystallographic radius of ion i, nm.
S   = effective membrane surface area, m^2.
T   = system temperature, K.
X_A = mol fraction of total (dissociated and undissociated) solute A.

Greek Letters

α = degree of ionic dissociation.
β = defined in eq. (13).
$\gamma_{\pm}$ = mean ionic activity coefficient (mol fraction).
Δ = constant in modified Born equation, nm.
π = osmotic pressure of solution, kPa.

Subscripts

1   = bulk solution or feed solution, i.e. X_{A1}.
2   = concentrated boundary solution on the high pressure side of the membrane, i.e. X_{A2}.
3   = membrane permeated solution on the low pressure side of the membrane, i.e. X_{A3}.
A   = pertaining to the solute.
B   = pertaining to the solvent or bulk solution phase.
I   = membrane-solution interface.
i   = ion of type i.
IP   = ion pair.
+, -   = cationic and anionic, respectively.

Acknowledgement

The authors are thankful for the technical assistance of A. Baxter and for the analytical work of V. Clancy, G. Gardner, and H. MacPherson. This work received financial support from the National Science and Engineering Research Council of Canada and from a research contract with the National Research Council of Canada. One of the authors (B.F.) thanks the Province of Ontario for the award of a scholarship.

Literature Cited

1.   Pageau, L.; Sourirajan, S. J. *Appl. Polym. Sci.*, 1972, 16, 3185.
2.   Matsuura, T.; Pageau, L.; Sourirajan, S. J. *Appl. Polym. Sci.*, 1975, 19, 179.

3. Kammermeyer, K.; Haugerbaumer, D. A.I.Ch.E.J., 1955, 1, 215.
4. Sourirajan, S. Nature, 1964, 203, 1348.
5. Nomura, H.; Senō, M.; Takahashi, H.; Yamabe, T. J. Membrane Science, 1979, 5, 189.
6. Rangarajan, R.; Matsuura, T.; Goodhue, E.C.; Sourirajan, S. Ind. Eng. Chem., Process Des. Dev., 1976, 15, 529.
7. Sourirajan, S. "Reverse Osmosis"; Academic Press: New York, 1970; Chap. 3.
8. Matsuura, T.; Blais, P.; Pageau, L.; Sourirajan, S. Ind. Eng. Chem., Process Des. Dev., 1977, 16, 510.
9. Foulkes, F.R. "Literature Survey for the Corrosion and Degradation of Vehicle Components in Methanol"; Ministry of Transport and Communications: Toronto, Ontario, March, 1977.
10. A.P.I. Report No. 4261 "Alcohols: A Technical Assessment of Their Application as Fuels", 1976.
11. Dehn, J.S.; Boyd, J.M.; Slate, J.L.; Leach, H.S. Chem. Eng. Progr., Symp. Ser., 1970, 66, 24.
12. Lewis, G.N.; Randall, M.; Pitzer, K.S.; Brewer, L. "Thermodynamics", 2nd. Ed.; McGraw-Hill: New York, 1961; p. 260.
13. Reid, R.C.; Prausnitz, J.M.; Sherwood, T.K. "Properties of Gases and Liquids", 3rd. Ed.; McGraw-Hill: New York, 1977, p. 591.
14. Shkodin, A.; Shapovalova, L. Ya. Izv. Vyssh. Zaved., Khim Khim Teknol., 1966, 9, 563.
15. Einfeldt, J.; Gerdes, E. Z. Phys. Chem. (Leipzig), 1971, 246, 221.
16. Skabichevskii, P.A. Russ. J. Phys. Chem., 1969, 43, 1432.
17. Vlasov, Y.; Antonov, P. Russ. J. Phys. Chem., 1973, 47, 1278.
18. Izmailov, N.; Ivanova, E. Zhur. Fiz. Khim., 1955, 29, 1422.
19. Ewart, F.K.; Raikes, H.R. J. Chem. Soc., 1906, 1926.
20. Jones, G.; Fernwalt, H. J. Amer. Chem. Soc., 1935, 57, 2041.
21. Minc, S.; Jastrzebska, J. Rocz. Chem., 1968, 42, 719.
22. Izmailov, N. Doklady Akademii Nauk S.S.S.R., 1963, 149, 1364.
23. Allen, C.; Wright, P. J. Chem. Soc. (A), 1967, 892.
24. Skabichevskii, P.A. Russ. J. Phys. Chem., 1975, 49, 181.
25. Evers, C.; Knox, G. J. Amer. Chem. Soc., 1951, 73, 1739.
26. Cussler, E.; Fuoss, R. J. Phys. Chem., 1967, 71, 4459.
27. Kay, R.; Hawes, J. J. Phys. Chem., 1965, 69, 2787.
28. Robinson, R.A.; Stokes, R.H. "Electrolyte Solutions", 2nd. Ed.; Butterworths: London, 1959;
    (a) p. 401;
    (b) p. 396.

29. Matsuura, T.; Sourirajan, S. J. Appl. Polym. Sci., 1973,
     17, 1043.
30. McBain, J.W. "Colloid Science"; Heath Co.: Boston,
     1950; p. 131.
31. Sourirajan, S.; Matsuura, T. "Reverse Osmosis and
     Synthetic Membranes", Sourirajan, S., Ed.; N.R.C.
     Canada: Ottawa, 1977; p. 11.

Issued as NRC No. 18591

RECEIVED December 4, 1980.

Ultrafiltration and Hyperfiltration in the Pulp and Paper Industry for By-Product Recovery and Energy Savings

PER H. CLAUSSEN

Niro Atomizer, Inc., 9165 Rumsey Road, Columbia, MD 21045

The development work with regard to application of DDS-RO(1) membrane filtration systems for treatment of effluents from the pulp and paper industry started in Norway in the beginning of 1972.

Both lab and pilot trials were successful and a Norwegian patent (2) was granted for separation of lignosulfonate from spent sulfite liquor (SSL) by ultrafiltration (UF).

In 1974 a major Norwegian manufacturer of lignin products started regular production of UF-lignosulfonates. The plant has been expanded several times and today the production is some thousand tons per year of product.

A cooperation agreement was made in 1973 between DDS-RO and the Finnish Pulp and Paper Research Institute with the aim to develop products and processes on the basis of membrane filtration of effluents from the pulp and paper industry. The cooperation with Dr. Kaj Forss' section at FPPRI has been very successful. For instance, through an extensive development program UF has been found to be a feasible tool for the preparation of lignin for the Karatex (3) plywood binder. This adhesive, which is made from ultrafiltered spent sulfite liquor (SSL) or kraft black liquor (KBL), can be used for partial replacement of the much more expensive petroleum based phenol-formaldehyde resin in plywood and other wooden boards.

The Swedish Company EKA and DDS-RO have worked together on a 2-year large scale pilot operation in a Swedish kraft mill for color removal from caustic extraction bleach effluent by UF (4).

The results of the program were successful both with regard to color removal efficiency, reliability and membrane lifetime and the first full scale installation will be made this year in Japan.

With the increasing fuel prices, it becomes more and more important to find energy efficient concentration methods for industrial effluents. Hyperfiltration (HF) also called reverse osmosis is in several cases the most favorable method.

Toten Sulphite Mill in Norway realized this in 1976 when a

0097–6156/81/0154–0361$05.00/0
© 1981 American Chemical Society

a demand for additional water removal capacity occurred, and
they installed a HF-system. Over the years substantial fuel
savings have been made.
   So far this paper has been dealing with the past. The table
below shows the situation today with regards to DDS-RO installations in the pulp and paper industry.
   At the end of 1980 about 30,000 ft.^{2} of membrane area of
DDS make will be in operation in this industry.
   By-product capacity will be 15,000-20,000 tons per year of
product solids by UF.
   Water removal capacity is approximately 100,000 gallons per
day.

Main Features of the Systems. The 450 ft.^{2} horizontal mounted
module UF 35-42 and the 300 ft.^{2} vertical module HF 40-28 are
the key components of the described systems, shown in figure 2
and 3.
   Both the UF and the HF systems are multistage continuous
plants according to the concept on figure 4.
   Process control concept is simple but efficient and reliable,
with thermostatic control of supply of steam or cooling water to
the heat exchangers and flow/solids concentration control either
on basis of in-line refractometer at the end of the system or
ratio control between feed and concentrate flow.
   Figure 5 is showing a typical UF-installation in the pulp
and paper industry at Iggesund Kraft Mill in Sweden. Figure 6
is showing the HF-installation at Toten Sulphite mill in Norway.
   Membranes of various polymer materials are used in the UF
systems allowing operating temperatures up to 190°F and pH from
0 to 14, which is favorable when operating on pulping effluents
that either are in the upper or the lower end of the pH-range
and with temperatures close to the limits for the system.
   The systems also allow cleaning with strong alkaline or acid
chemicals, also oxydants as H_2O_2 and $NaOCl$ which in some cases is
necessary to keep the membranes sufficiently clean in the long
run.
   For HF cellulose acetate membranes are used setting limits
for temperature, 85°F, as well as for pH, 2.5 to 8.0. Still with
those limitations it is possible to keep the systems at an accept
ably high performance level for extensive periods of time, when
operating on spent sulphite liquor.
   A proper prefiltration of the liquids is required and is
mainly done in a self-cleaning rotary drum filter with a 25micron
web.

Applications, Experience. Ultrafiltration of SSL. This processing has been going on on a regular commercial basis since 1974
for manufacture of lignosulfonate products with a lignosulfonate
content in the 90%+ range (5). Not only the lignosulfonate
content of the product is of importance, often also the molecular

Yr. Installed	System	Country	Product
1974-1979	UF	Norway	Lignosulfonates
1976	HF	Norway	NH_4-SSL
1978	UF	N.America	Lignosulfonates
1978	HF	Canada	Ca-SSL

Under Construction			
1980	UF	Finland	Kraft liquor
1980	UF	Finland	Lignosulfonates
1980	UF	Japan	Kraft bleach effluent

Larger Pilot Plants			
1978	UF	Sweden	Kraft bleach effluent
1980	HF	Italy	Ca-SSL
1980	HF	Argentina	NSSC waste liquor

Figure 1. DDS–Ro installations in the pulp and paper industry

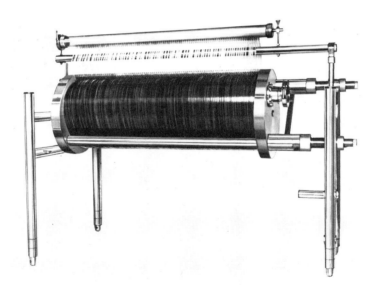

Figure 2. The 450-ft² horizontally mounted UF module UF 35–42

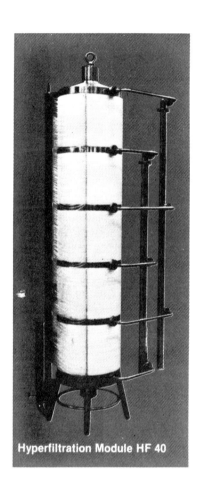

Figure 3.   The 300-ft² vertical HF module HF 40–28

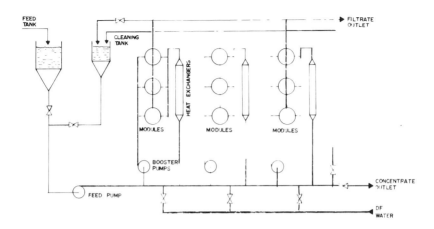

Figure 4. Continuous membrane filtration system

Figure 5. Typical UF installation at Iggesund Kraft Mill in Sweden

weight distribution of the lignosulfonate, Figure 7, is showing
the molecular weight distribution of the lignosulfonate in SSL
and in the two fractions from UF, the concentrate and the filtrate (6). The lignosulfonates from UF are mainly used as
dispersants.

It took a few years before the modules, the membranes, pretreatment and membrane cleaning procedures were sufficiently
developed, but today the UF systems operate as steadily and reliable as other unit operations in this industry.

The process concept is simple and energy efficient, the
pumps are the only moving parts. No chemicals required for the
operation except for minor quantities of harmless cleaning agents.

Membrane cleaning frequency is mainly once every one or two
days.

Lifetime expectancy, based on latest experience is one year
+.

UF is made on both fermented and unfermented SSL. On a
Pekilo-fermented liquor Kaj Forss et al (6) found a 50% higher
production capacity for a UF system of a given size and a given
product composition compared with UF of the unfermented liquor.
The diafiltration water requirement was 55% less for the fermented liquor.

Further details from the above mentioned operations cannot
be disclosed as the involved companies, due to the competitive
situation, prefer to give out as little information as possible.

UF of Kraft Black Liquor. Lignin from kraft black liquor has for
years been used to a limited extent as extender for binders in
various board products.

With the rapidly increasing prices and the outlook of insufficient supplies of PF resin in the future, there is a growing
interest for lignin for such applications.

An extensive development program in Finland, conducted by
Dr. Kaj Forss, has shown that UF is a simple, efficient and inexpensive method for tailoring a lignin product for this purpose.

By selection of the proper membrane and processing parameters, it is possible in a simple way to get a product with the
content of lignin and molecular weight distribution required for
an active binder ingredient which combines chemically with PF
resin for plywood.

So far, a 40% replacement of PF resin has been made without
change in the properties of the plywood.

Successful ultrafiltration/diafiltration has been made on
15% TDS liquor from pulp washers, as well as 30% TDS liquor from
tall oil soap skimming. It appears from Figure 8, that for a
lignin product with a lignin content in the 80-90% range, based
on product solids, the production capacity of a system of a given
size is almost the same in the two cases, but the 30% liquor requires more water to get to the same lignin content.

Figure 6.   HF installation at Toten Sulfite Mill in Norway

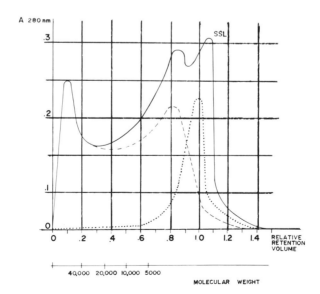

Figure 7.   Molecular-weight distribution of lignin in SSL and UF concentrate and filtrate

368   SYNTHETIC MEMBRANES: HF AND UF USES

The first industrial scale installation will come on stream
towards the end of this year in Finland.

Hyperfiltration-Preconcentration of SSL. Preconcentration of SSL
has been going on since 1976 at Toten Sulphite Mill in Norway and
since 1978 at Reed's Lignosol Plant in Quebec, Canada.
     This method of concentrating weak liquors in combination
with evaporation is becoming more and more attractive with the
rapid increasing fuel prices.
     Figure 9 showing energy requirement for various evaporator
systems compared with hyperfiltration, indicates clearly the advantage of water removal by hyperfiltration.
     Figure 10 is showing the energy savings that can be achieved
by combining HF with an existing evaporator system for SSL at a
given situation.
     By integration of HF, energy input can be reduced by about
50% which should more than pay for the HF installation; and, at
the same time, relieve the steam boiler or make more steam for
other operations available.
     For incremental increases in water removal capacity, HF is,
in most cases, the favorable operation, due to the energy
efficiency and the possibility of adding modules stepwise according to the increasing demand for capacity.
     This fact has been taken advantage of at Toten and Reed.
     Figure 11 is showing some of the essential features from
those two HF plants.
     Both plants are using CA-membranes and despite that pH is
on the lower side of the acceptable pH-range, at Toten occasion-
nally below pH2 on average, membrane lifetime of one year + is
experienced.
     There have been some fouling problems in the systems caused
by pitch-containing small fibers and calcium sulfite. Improved
pretreatment and membrane cleaning procedures are the keys to
the better performance of the systems.
     Power consumption for the systems is in the range 3.5-4.5
Kwh per 1,000 lbs. of water removal.
     Membrane cleaning frequency has been 2-6 times a week for
the two systems.
     Composition of filtrate is not much different from that of
an evaporator condensate.

The Ultrasep Color Removal Process for Caustic Extraction Bleach
Effluent. An extensive large scale pilot plant program was
carried out by the Swedish company, EKA, at Iggesund Kraft Mill
in Sweden, using a four-stage, continuous DDS-RO ultrafiltration
system for this application.
     The system has been in continuous operation for about two
years, separating 10% of the total caustic extraction effluent,
approximately 100 GPM, in two fractions, 4 GPM of concentrate
containing 90% of the color and 96 GPM containing 10% of the
color.

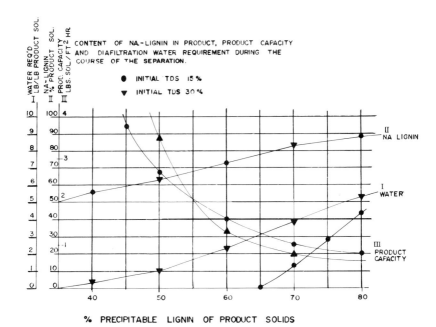

Figure 8.   UF of KBL. Content of NA-lignin in product, product capacity, and diafiltration water requirement during the course of the separation.

Energy-Efficient Concentration by HF (RO)

Common energy requirements for evaporators and HY systems:

System	Btu per 1,000 lbs. of water removal
1 effect with vapor recompression	50,000
6 stage multiple effect evaporator	215,000
5 stage multiple effect evaporator	270,000
4 stage multiple effect evaporator	345,000
3 stage multiple effect evaporator	430,000
Hyperfiltration	15,000

Figure 9.   Energy efficient concentration by HF (RO)

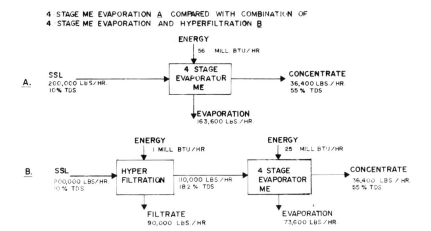

Figure 10. Energy requirement for water removal. Four-stage ME evaporation, A, compared with a combination of the four-stage ME evaporation and HF, B.

Features	Toten	Reed
Installation year	1976	1978
Size sq.ft. membrane area	4215	4817
Configuration	4 stage cont.	4 stage cont.
Product	NH_4-SSL pH 2-2.5	Ca-SSL pH 3-3.5
% TDS feed	6 - 10	10 - 12
% TDS concentrate	12	18
Maximum feed rate GPM	88	132
Max filtration rate GPM	44	44
Avg. filtration rate at		
max. feed	15	13
Nominal power consumption		
approx. Kw.	75	90
Nominal power concumption		
Kwh per 1000 lbs.filtrate	3.4	4.0
No.of membrane replacements	3	1

Figure 11. Features of the HF plants at Totel and Reed as of August 15, 1980

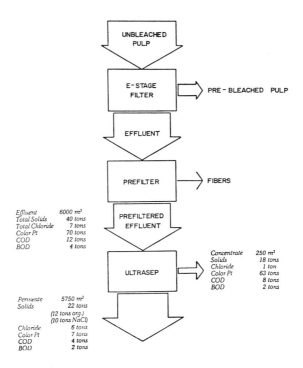

Figure 12.   Ultrasep system for color removal. Materials balance for 600 tons of kraft pulp.

Figure 12 is showing the distribution of other essential substance; for instance, BOD, COD, chloride and TDS in the two fractions.

The operation ran smoothly with few major problems. Membrane cleaning frequency was, on average, once every three weeks.

Different membranes were used; the last set was in continuous operation for more than 8,000 hours without significant change in performance.

This process is found to be competitive to existing color removal processes, both with regard to economy and color removal efficiency.

To which degree it is going to be utilized is depending on what kind of regulations there will be with regard to emmissions from bleach plants. However, the first industrial installation of its kind will be made this year in Japan.

ABSTRACT. Membrane filtration has been in operation for more than five years on a commercial scale in the pulp and paper industry. Continuous, multi-stage plate and frame based systems are being used for purification, and molecular distribution control of lignosulfonate from spent sulfite liquor and preconcentration of weak spent sulfite liquor before evaporation.

Larger scale, long term pilot operations with the similar systems for separation of lignin from kraft black liquor and color removal from bleach plant effluents are going on successfully, advising new and comprehensive applications for membrane filtration process in this industry. The aspect of saving fossile energy is a common feature of most such operations as hyperfiltration is typical low energy concentration method and the lignin products in many cases replace petroleum based chemicals.

Literature Cited

1. DDS Modules, U.S. Patent 3,872,015, GB patent 1,390,671, Italy patent 978,747, Switzerland patent 542,639, New Zealand patent 169,679.
2. L. Janzen, P.H. Claussen, Norway patent 127,545, Swiss patent 560,289, Portugal, France, Brazil, Italy patents.
3. K. Forss, A. Fuhrman, Karatex adhesive, Finland patent 167,647, U.S. patent 4,105,606. Patents GDR, Austria, GB, Hungary, etc.
4. J. Manson, EKA AB Sweden. Proceedings from International Pulp Bleaching Conference in Toronto, June, 1979.
5. P.H. Claussen, Pulp and Paper Canada, March, 1978.
6. K. Forss, R. Kokkonen, H. Sirelius, P.E. Sagfors, Pulp and Paper Canada, December, 1979.

RECEIVED December 17, 1980.

Pressure-Independent Ultrafiltration—Is It Gel Limited or Osmotic Pressure Limited?

DANIEL R. TRETTIN[1] and MAHENDRA R. DOSHI

Environmental Sciences Division, The Institute of Paper Chemistry,
Appleton, WI 54912

Ultrafiltration involves the pressure-activated separation of chemical species which have different permeability through a membrane. Solute retention is achieved on the basis of steric exclusion, that is, a sieving-type of mechanism and solvent passes through by pore flow. As an initially homogeneous solution is pressurized over a selective membrane, solvent permeates through while rejected solute accumulates in the vicinity of the membrane. The net result is a layer of solution adjacent to the membrane surface of substantially greater solute concentration than that of the bulk solution. This phenomenon of concentration polarization always operates to reduce the solvent permeation rate which may become pressure independent in some cases.

In the ultrafiltration of macromolecular solutions, a large number of investigators have observed that as pressure is increased, permeate flux first increases and then remains more or less pressure independent. Blatt, et al. (1970), among others, argued that one of the reasons for the observed pressure independence could be due to the formation of a gel layer on the membrane surface. The permeate rate in this case may be expressed as:

$$|v_w| = \frac{\Delta P - \Delta \pi}{\mu (R_m + R_g)} \qquad (1)$$

where R_m and R_g are the hydraulic resistances of the membrane and gel layer respectively, ΔP and $\Delta \pi$ represent the applied pressure and osmotic back pressure and μ is the permeate viscosity. In the case of pressure independent ultrafiltration of macromolecular solutions, if the applied pressure is much greater than the osmotic pressure difference across the membrane, and since the gel resistance is generally substantially greater than that of a membrane, Eq. (1) can be simplified to:

[1] Current address: Union Camp Corporation, Franklin, VA 23851.

0097–6156/81/0154–0373$09.25/0

$$v_w \simeq \frac{\Delta P}{\mu R_g} , \quad \begin{array}{l} \Delta P >> \Delta\pi \\ R_g >> R_m \end{array}$$

Any increase in pressure after the occurrence of gel formation merely increases gel thickness and hence R_g so that the permeate flux remains essentially independent of pressure.

There could be other possibilities for the observed pressure independence. We know that, in the absence of gel formation, increase in the applied pressure results in the increase in solute concentration at the membrane surface. If osmotic pressure is quite sensitive to the changes in solute concentration, it is possible that an increase in ΔP gives rise to proportional increase in $\Delta\pi$ so that the net driving force, $(\Delta P - \Delta\pi)$ remains virtually constant. From Eq. (1), then, the permeate rate in the absence of gel formation ($R_g = 0$) can be pressure independent due to osmotic pressure limitation. Other phenomena, for example, solute-membrane interactions may give rise to pressure independent permeate rate.

Gel polarized ultrafiltration was recently analyzed for cross flow and unstirred batch cell systems by Trettin and Doshi (1980 a,b). We have shown in these papers that the widely used film theory does not predict the limiting flux accurately. The objective of this paper is to derive an expression for the permeate flux when the pressure independent ultrafiltration of macromolecular solutions is osmotic pressure limited. We will also attempt to distinguish between gel and osmotic pressure limited ultrafiltration of macromolecular solutions.

The effect of osmotic pressure in macromolecular ultrafiltration has not been analyzed in detail although many similarities between this process and reverse osmosis may be drawn. An excellent review of reverse osmosis research has been given by Gill et al. (1971). It is generally found, however, that the simple linear osmotic pressure-concentration relationship used in reverse osmosis studies cannot be applied to ultrafiltration where the concentration dependency of macromolecular solutions is more complex. It is also reasonable to assume that variable viscosity effects may be more pronounced in macromolecular ultrafiltration as opposed to reverse osmosis. Similarly, because of the relatively low diffusivity of macromolecules compared to typical reverse osmosis solutes (by a factor of 100), concentration polarization effects are more severe in ultrafiltration.

An early work considering osmotic pressure in the ultrafiltration of macromolecular solutions was done by Blatt, et al., (1970), who employed a theory which had been developed for cross flow reverse osmosis systems. They essentially suggested that the film theory relationship given by Eq. (2) could be solved simultaneously with Eq. (1) to predict permeate rates, where the

value of k was determined from a Leveque-type solution of the
convective diffusion equation neglecting transverse velocity.

$$|v_w| = k \ln \left[\frac{c_w - c_p}{c_o - c_p} \right] \qquad (2)$$

Presented data were not analyzed in terms of this model, however,
because it was felt that macromolecular solutions generally had
very low osmotic pressures.

Goldsmith (1971) pointed out that developed osmotic pressures for macromolecular solutions were not necessarily negligible.   The ultrafiltration of Carbowax 20M (polyethylene oxide)
and various Dextrans was studied in thin channel and tube flow
as well as stirred batch cell.   Both turbulent and laminar flow
regimes were considered.   Data were analyzed with the use of
Eq. (2) and the phenomenological relationship of Eq. (1) with
R_g = 0.   From Eq. (1) it was possible to calculate an average
value of $\Delta\pi$ where R_m, the membrane resistance, ΔP, and experi-
mental flux $|\bar{v}_w|$ were known.   The average value of c_w could be
extracted from a known osmotic pressure relationship, and an
experimental value of $\bar{k}$ could finally be found from Eq. (2).
Experimental values of $\bar{k}$ were compared to theoretical values to
estimate molecular diffusion coefficient.   The difference between
the experimental and the literature value of the diffusion
coefficient was attributed to the concentration dependency of
viscosity and diffusion coefficient.

Kozinski and Lightfoot (1972) modeled the ultrafiltration of
bovine serum albumin (BSA) through a rotating disk.   Concentration dependent viscosity and diffusivity were assumed, and the
one-dimensional convective diffusion equation, which was coupled
to the appropriate Navier-Stokes equation, was solved numerically.
Osmotic pressure data of Scachard et al. (1944) were used.
Numerical prediction of flux agreed very well with experimental
results for the rotating disk.   Their model was extended to
other flow geometries, such as tubular and thin channel, where
average values of viscosity and diffusivity were used.   The convective diffusion equation in this case was solved through
similarity transformation.   The published data of Blatt, et al.,
(1970) were analyzed in terms of the developed model but agreement was not good.

Mitra and Lundblad (1978) studied the thin channel ultrafiltration of immune serum globulin (ISG) and human serum albumin
(HSA).   Data were interpreted using the film theory relationship
of:

$$|\bar{v}_w| = A \langle u \rangle^B \ln (c_w/c_o) \qquad (3)$$

where multiple regression techniques were employed to solve for
the value of the constants A, B, and c_w. The value of c_w was
assumed to equal the corresponding concentration at which the
developed osmotic pressure approximately equalled the applied
system pressure. Agreement of data with the general model was
not good, the calculated value of A exhibiting a 21% standard
deviation. Large axial pressure drops along the thin channel at
the higher velocities studied may be a partial explanation of
the discrepancy.

Leung and Probstein (1979) studied the ultrafiltration of
macromolecular solutions in steady state, laminar channel flow.
The convective diffusion equation was solved by an integral method. A parabolic concentration profile was assumed. The osmotic
pressure relationship of Vilker (1975) for 0.15M saline BSA solutions at pH 4.5, and a diffusivity relationship obtained by linearly interpolating the diffusion coefficient value between the
gel and dilute solution concentration limits were used. The
determination of this diffusivity relationship has been outlined
in a previous paper [Probstein, et al. (1979)]. The integral
solution was checked in the limiting case of a linear osmotic
pressure-concentration relationship and constant diffusivity with
Brian's (1966) finite difference solution for reverse osmosis
systems. Thin channel ultrafiltration data were acquired by
Leung and Probstein using BSA in 0.10M acetate solution at pH 4.7.

A discrepancy emerges in the use of Vilker's osmotic pressure relationship, however. In an earlier paper, Probstein,
et al., (1979) determined the gelling (solubility limit) concentration of BSA in 0.10M acetate solution (pH 4.7) to be 34 g/100
cc. We have determined the value to be approximately 38.5 g/100
cc [Trettin and Doshi (1980b)]. It is clear from Fig. 5 that
Vilker has determined osmotic pressures for BSA in 0.15M saline
solutions (pH 4.5) up to concentrations of 48 g/100 cc. This
finding suggests the effect of buffer type is substantial in
influencing solute solubility limits and most probably solution
osmotic pressure. Therefore, it is hardly admissible to use
Vilker's saline buffer osmotic pressure data to interpret the thin
channel ultrafiltration data of BSA in acetate buffer without
further confirmation of the effect of buffer type.

The preceding review has shown that although many advances
have been made in the understanding of macromolecular ultrafiltration, some very fundamental questions still remain unanswered.
For instance, the establishment of when an ultrafiltration process
is osmotic pressure limited or gel limited needs to be more clearly defined. In macromolecular ultrafiltration solution osmotic
pressure is often a strong function of moderate-to-high solute
concentration (c_w) due to the increased importance of the second
and third order virial terms in the Flory equation [Brandup and
Immergut (1967), Billmeyer (1971)]. In this event, the ultrafiltration flux may be limited by the osmotic pressure and/or

by the formation of a gel layer depending on the nature of the
solute and operating conditions. The determination of a flux-
limiting cause is the primary concern of this paper.

Theoretical Development

Consider the unstirred batch cell geometry shown in Fig. 1
where the general solute mass balance equation of

$$\frac{\partial c}{\partial t} - |v_w| \frac{\partial c}{\partial y} = D\ \partial^2 c/\partial y^2 \tag{4}$$

applies. It is implicitly assumed in the derivation of Eq. (4)
that the solution density and diffusion coefficient are independent of solute concentration.

The appropriate boundary and initial conditions are:

$$\text{at } y = 0 \quad ; . \quad c = c_w(t) \tag{5}$$

$$-|v_w|\ c_w\ R = D\ \frac{\partial c}{\partial y}\bigg|_{y\,=\,0} \tag{6}$$

$$y \rightarrow \infty,\ c = c_o \text{ for all } t \tag{7}$$

$$t \rightarrow 0\ ,\ c = c_o \text{ for all } y \tag{8}$$

where

$$R = 1 - c_p/c_w$$

The phenomenological equation of permeate velocity is

$$|v_w| = A\Delta P\ (1 - \frac{\Delta\pi}{\Delta P});\ A = \frac{1}{\mu R_m} \tag{9}$$

where

$$\Delta\pi = \pi_w - \pi_p \tag{10}$$

If osmotic pressure is related to solute concentration by a cubic
equation:

$$\pi = b_0 c + b_1 c^2 + b_2 c^3$$

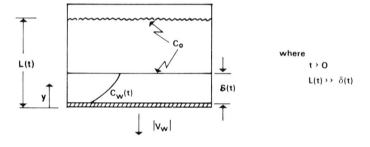

Figure 1.   Batch cell geometry

then

$$\Delta\pi = B \ c_w \ \Delta P \quad \left[1 + \alpha_1 \ c_w + \alpha_2 \ c_w^{\ 2}\right] \tag{11}$$

where

$$B = \frac{Rb_0}{\Delta P} \ , \ \alpha_1 = \frac{b_1 \ (2-R)}{b_0} \text{and } \alpha_2 = \frac{b_2 \ (3-3R+R^2)}{b_0} \tag{12}$$

Our objective is to derive an expression for the permeate velocity when ultrafiltration is osmotic pressure limited. We therefore, introduce equivalent wall concentration, c_{wa}, for which the osmotic pressure is equal to the applied pressure. In the asymptotic case, as $\Delta\pi$ approaches ΔP, the permeate velocity will approach zero, Eq. (9), and from Eq. (11) we have:

$$1 = B \ c_{wa} \ (1 + \alpha_1 \ c_{wa} + \alpha_2 \ c_{wa}^{\ 2}) \tag{13}$$

Equation (13) is then the defining equation for c_{wa}. We will use c_{wa} as a characteristic concentration in making local concentration dimensionless. Time, distance and velocity are expressed in dimensionless forms by a proper combination of a characteristic velocity $A\Delta P$ and diffusion coefficient, D:

$$\tau = \frac{(A \ \ \Delta P)^2 t}{D}, \quad z = \frac{A \ \Delta P}{D} \ y, \quad w = \frac{|v_w|}{A \ \Delta P}, \quad \theta = c/c_{wa} \tag{14}$$

Eq. (4) may be transformed to

$$\frac{\partial\theta}{\partial\tau} \ - \ w \ \frac{\partial\theta}{\partial z} \ = \ \frac{\partial^2\theta}{\partial z^2} \tag{15}$$

where the boundary conditions of Eq. (5)-(8) become

$$- R \ w \ \theta_w \ = \ \left.\frac{\partial\theta}{\partial z}\right|_{z=0} \tag{16}$$

$$\theta(\tau,0) \ = \ \frac{c_w(t)}{c_{wa}} \ = \ \theta_w \tag{17}$$

$$\theta\ (0,z) = \theta\ (\tau,\infty) = \frac{c_o}{c_{wa}} = \theta_o \tag{18}$$

and Eq. (9) may be rewritten as

$$w = 1 - Bc_{wa}\ \theta_w\ (1 + \alpha_1 c_{wa}\ \theta_w + \alpha_2 c_{wa}^{\ 2}\ \theta_w^{\ 2}) \tag{19}$$

Introducing the similarity coordinate

$$x = z/(4\tau)^{1/2} \tag{20}$$

Equations (15)-(18) become $[\theta(\tau,z) \Rightarrow \theta(\tau,x)]$

$$4\tau\ \frac{\partial\theta}{\partial\tau} - 2\ (x + w\ \sqrt{\tau})\ \frac{\partial\theta}{\partial x} = \frac{\partial^2\theta}{\partial x^2} \tag{21}$$

$$- 2\ \sqrt{\tau}\ R\ w\ \theta_w = \frac{\partial\theta}{\partial x}\ \Big|_{x=0} \tag{22}$$

$$\theta\ (\tau,0) = \theta_w,\ \theta\ (\tau,\infty) = \theta_o \tag{23}$$

The similarity transformation, Eq. (20), used here is generally applied to obtain small time solution. However, in the
case of gel polarized ultrafiltration, Trettin and Doshi (1980 b)
have used such similarity transformation to obtain an expression
for the limiting permeate velocity. We have, therefore, used
similarity transformation to evaluate osmotic pressure limited
permeate velocity. In the case of gel polarized ultrafiltration,
$c_w = c_g$ = constant and consequently, Eq. (21) to (23) can be
solved by considering θ as a function of x only and by setting w
$\tau^{0.5}$ as a constant. However, in the osmotic pressure limiting
case considered here, c_w is a function of time. We can solve Eq.
(21) to (23) in the form of a power series in $\tau^{-0.5}$:

$$\theta = f_0(x) + \frac{f_1(x)}{\tau^{1/2}} + \frac{f_2(x)}{\tau} + \cdots \tag{24}$$

then

$$\theta_w = 1 + \frac{f_1(0)}{\tau^{1/2}} + \frac{f_2(0)}{\tau} + \ldots \qquad (25)$$

where

$$\lim_{\tau \to \infty} \theta_w = f_0(0) = 1 \qquad (26)$$

Substituting for θ_w in Eq. (19) and rearranging yields:

$$w \sqrt{\tau} = \beta_1 f_1(0) + \frac{\beta_2}{\tau^{1/2}} + \ldots \qquad (27)$$

where

$$\beta_1 = - (1 + B \alpha_1 c_{wa}^{\ 2} + 2B \alpha_2 c_{wa}^{\ 3}) \qquad (28)$$

The value of β_2 remains to be determined.

Substituting for θ and $w\sqrt{\tau}$ in Eq. (21) and considering terms of coefficient τ^0 only gives

$$-2x f_0' - 2\beta_1 f_1(0) f_0' = f_0'' \qquad (29)$$

where the boundary conditions of Eq. (22)–(23) become

$$-2R [\beta_1 f_1(0)] f_0(0) = f_0'(0) \qquad (30)$$

$$f_0(\infty) = \theta_o \qquad (31)$$

$$f_0(0) = 1 \qquad (32)$$

Equation (29) may be integrated to yield

$$\theta_o = 1 + I_1 \exp [\beta_1^2 f_1^2(0)] \int_{\beta_1 f_1(0)}^{\infty} \exp (-\xi^2) \, d\xi \qquad (33)$$

where

$$\xi = x + \beta_1 f_1(0) \qquad (34)$$

or, more simply,

$$I_1 = \frac{2(\theta_o - 1)}{\sqrt{\pi} \ \exp\left(\frac{V_w^2}{4}\right) \text{erfc}\left(\frac{V_w}{2}\right)}$$

(35)

where $\dfrac{V_w}{2} = \beta_1 \ f_1(0)$

Considering the wall boundary condition of Eq. (30), Eq. (35) becomes

$$\frac{V_w}{2} = \frac{1 - \theta_o}{R\sqrt{\pi} \ \exp\left(\frac{V_w^2}{4}\right) \text{erfc}\left(\frac{V_w}{2}\right)}$$

(36)

In a similar manner as previously, consider coefficients of $\tau^{-1/2}$ only in Eq. (21)

$$f_1'' + 2f_1' \ (x + \beta_1 \ f_1(0)] + 2f_1$$

(37)

$$= - \ 2\beta_2 \ I_1 \exp \ [-(x^2 + 2\beta_1 \ f_1(0)x)]$$

Considering the coefficients of $\tau^{-1/2}$ for the wall boundary condition of Eq. (22) yields

$$-2R \ (\beta_1 \ f_1{}^2(0) + \beta_2) = f_1'(0)$$

(38)

where

$$\beta_1 \ f_1(0) = I_1/2R \ ; \quad f_1(\infty) = 0$$

(39)

The solution for f_1 is:

$$f_1 = \left[f_1(0) + \beta_2 \ I_1 \ \sqrt{\pi} \ \int_{\frac{V_w}{2}}^{r} \exp(r^2)\text{erfc}(r)dr\right]$$

$$\exp\left[\frac{V_w{}^2}{4}\right] \exp(-r^2)$$

(40)

where $r = x + \dfrac{V_w}{2}$, and

$$\lim_{\substack{x \to \infty \\ r \to \infty}} f_1 = 0, \qquad \lim_{x \to 0} f_1 = f_1(0) \doteq -\frac{I_1}{2R\beta_1} \qquad (41)$$

Evaluating the first derivative of Eq. (40) at $x = 0$ gives

$$f'(0) = -2\beta_1 \, f_1{}^2(0) + \beta_2 \, I_1 \, \sqrt{\pi} \, \exp\left(\frac{V_w{}^2}{4}\right) \, \mathrm{erfc}\left(\frac{V_w}{2}\right) \qquad (42)$$

The wall boundary condition of Eq. (38) may be equated to Eq. (42) to yield a relationship for the value of β_2, namely

$$\beta_2 = \frac{\beta_1 \, f_1{}^2(0)(1-R)}{(R-1) + \theta_o} \qquad (43)$$

Substituting for β_2 in Eq. (27), neglecting terms smaller than $\tau^{-1/2}$ yields

$$w \sqrt{\tau} = \beta_1 \, f_1(0) \left[1 - \frac{f_1(0)(R-1)}{\sqrt{\tau}[(R-1)+\theta_o]}\right] \qquad (44)$$

The dimensionless permeate velocity will be proportional to $\tau^{-1/2}$ when

$$\sqrt{\tau} \gg \frac{f_1(0)(R-1)}{[(R-1)+\theta_o]} = \frac{I_1(1-R)}{2R \, \beta_1 \, [(R-1)+\theta_o]} \qquad (45)$$

Equation (45) is written in dimensional form as

$$t \gg \frac{D}{(A \; \Delta P)^2} \left[\frac{V_w \, (1-R)}{|\beta_1| \, [(R-1) + \theta_o]}\right] \qquad (46)$$

If the criterion suggested in Eq. (46) is met, solute concentration at the membrane surface will be approximately equal to the asymptotic value, c_{wa}. The solute concentration distribution can be described by a single independent variable, x. The problem then becomes analogous to the gel polarized ultrafiltration case solved in Trettin and Doshi (1980b). In this same paper, an integral method solution is also derived. A plot of calculated values of V_w vs. θ_0 which satisfy Eq. (36) is given in Fig. 2 for

various values of R.   An unpublished work of Vilker (1975) has
recently come to our attention where a similar concept is presented.

An analogous treatment to the unstirred batch cell may be
performed for the thin channel system where

$$u \frac{\partial c}{\partial \tilde{x}} - |v_w| \frac{\partial c}{\partial y} = D \frac{\partial^2 c}{\partial y^2} \tag{47}$$

and the boundary conditions are

at $y = 0$ $c = c_w (\tilde{x})$ \hfill (48)

$$- |v_w| c_w R = D \frac{\partial c}{\partial y} \Big|_{y = 0} \tag{49}$$

$$y \to \infty, \ c = c_o \quad \text{for all } \tilde{x} \tag{50}$$

$$\tilde{x} \to 0, \ c = c_o \ \text{for all } y \tag{51}$$

A diagram of the thin channel system is shown in Fig. 3.
Transforming Eq. (47) to dimensionless form, we find

$$\phi z \frac{\partial \theta}{\partial \lambda} - w \frac{\partial \theta}{\partial z} = \frac{\partial^2 \theta}{\partial z^2} \tag{52}$$

where

$$z = \frac{A \ \Delta P}{D} \ y, \ w = \frac{|v_w|}{A \ \Delta P} \ , \ \theta$$

$$= c/c_{wa}, \ \lambda = \frac{(A \ \Delta P)^2 \tilde{x}}{\langle u \rangle \ D}, \ \phi = \frac{3D}{h \ A \ \Delta P} \tag{53}$$

and assuming a linerarized axial velocity profile, namely,

$$u = \frac{3\langle u \rangle}{h} \ y \tag{54}$$

The boundary conditions of Eq. (48)-(51) become

$$- R w \ \theta_w = \frac{\partial \theta}{\partial z} \Big|_{z = 0} \tag{55}$$

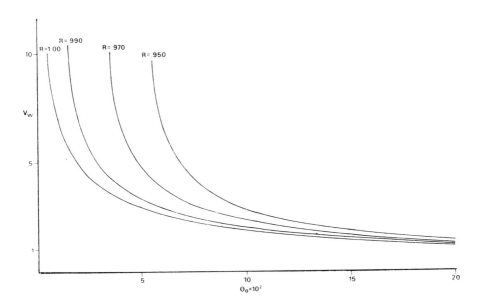

Figure 2. V_w vs. Θ_o calculated from Equation 41 for various values of R

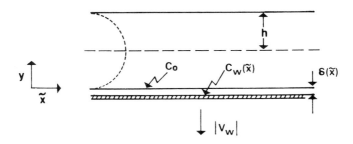

Figure 3.   Thin-channel crossflow system

$$\theta\ (\lambda,0)\ =\ \frac{c_w(\tilde{x})}{c_{wa}}\ =\ \theta_w \tag{56}$$

$$\theta\ (0,z)\ =\ \theta(\lambda,\infty)\ =\ c_o/c_{wa}\ =\ \theta_o \tag{57}$$

Equation (19) remains unchanged except that θ_w is now a function of λ instead of τ.

$$w\ =\ 1\ -\ Bc_{wa}\ \theta_w\ (1\ +\ \alpha_1 c_{wa}\ \theta_w\ +\ \alpha_2 c_{wa}{}^2\ \theta_w{}^2) \tag{19}$$

Introducing the similarity coordinate, analogous to unstirred batch cell problem, Eq. (20),

$$\eta\ =\ z\Big/\left(\frac{3\lambda}{\phi}\right)^{1/3} \tag{58}$$

Equations (52), (55)-(57) become $[\theta\ (\lambda\ z)\ \Rightarrow\ \theta\ (\lambda,\eta)]$

$$3\ \lambda\ \eta\ \frac{\partial\theta}{\partial\lambda}\ -\ \left(\eta^2\ +\ w\left(\frac{3\lambda}{\phi}\right)^{1/3}\right)\ \frac{\partial\theta}{\partial\eta}\ =\ \frac{\partial^2\theta}{\partial\eta^2} \tag{59}$$

$$-\left(\frac{3\lambda}{\theta}\right)^{1/3}\ R\ w\ \theta_w\ =\ \frac{\partial\theta}{\partial\eta}\ \Big|_{\eta\ =\ 0} \tag{60}$$

$$\theta(\lambda,0)\ =\ \theta_w \tag{61}$$

$$\theta(\lambda,\infty)\ =\ \theta_o \tag{62}$$

The corresponding gel polarized ultrafiltration problem, where $c_w\ =\ c_g\ =$ constant, is solved by Trettin and Doshi (1980a) by considering θ as a function of η only. In the osmotic pressure limited case, as we have done for the unstirred batch cell, we expand θ in the following form:

$$\theta\ =\ g_0\ (\eta)\ +\ \frac{g_1(\eta)}{\lambda^{1/3}}\ +\ \frac{g_2(\eta)}{\lambda^{2/3}}\ +\ \dots \tag{63}$$

$$\theta_w = 1 + \frac{g_1(0)}{\lambda^{1/3}} + \frac{g_2(0)}{\lambda^{2/3}} + \ldots \qquad (64)$$

where

$$\lim_{\lambda \to \infty} \theta_w = g_0(0) = 1 \qquad (65)$$

Substituting for θ_w in Eq. (19) and rearranging yields

$$w \lambda^{1/3} = \beta_1 \, g_1(0) + \frac{\beta_2}{\lambda^{1/3}} + \ldots \qquad (66)$$

Substituting for θ and $w \lambda^{1/3}$ in Eq. (59) and considering terms of coefficient λ^0 only gives

$$- \eta^2 \, g_0' - \left(\frac{3}{\phi}\right)^{1/3} \beta_1 \, g_1(0) \, g_0' = g_0'' \qquad (67)$$

where the boundary conditions of Eq. (60)–(62) become

$$-\left(\frac{3}{\phi}\right)^{1/3} \beta_1 \, g_1(0) \, g_0(0) \, R = g_0'(0) \qquad (68)$$

$$g_0^{(\infty)} = \theta_o \qquad (69)$$

$$g_0(0) = 1 \qquad (70)$$

Equation (67) may be integrated using the boundary conditions of Eq. (69)–(70) to yield

$$I_1 = \frac{\theta_o - 1}{\int_0^\infty \exp\left[- \left(\frac{1}{3}\eta^3 + W_w \eta\right)\right] d\eta} \qquad (71)$$

where

$$- W_w \, R = g_0'(0) = I_1 \qquad (72)$$

Considering the wall boundary condition of Eq. (68), Eq. (71) becomes

$$W_w = \frac{1 - \theta_o}{R \int_0^\infty \exp\left[-\left(\frac{1}{3}\eta^3 + W_w\,\eta\right)\right]\,d\eta} \tag{73}$$

Without considering coefficients of $\lambda^{-1/3}$, we may develope an <u>approximate</u> relationship defining the parameters which influence the rate at which an asymptotic wall concentration is reached. From Eq. (64)

$$\theta_w = 1 + \frac{g_1(0)}{\lambda^{1/3}} + \cdots \tag{74}$$

Therefore, for $c_w \sim c_{wa}$,

$$\lambda^{1/3} \gg g_1(0) \tag{75}$$

or simply,

$$\tilde{x} \gg \frac{D^2 \langle u \rangle}{h(A\,\Delta P)^3}\left|\frac{W_w}{\beta_1}\right|^3 \tag{76}$$

From Eq. (76) it can be seen that the membrane pure solvent flux $(A\,\Delta P)$ has a large effect in determining the required channel length to reach an asymptotic wall concentration $(c_w \sim c_{wa})$. since $\dot{\gamma}_w = \frac{3\langle u \rangle}{h}$, it may be seen that hydrodynamic shear at the membrane surface is also an important factor and Eq. (76) becomes:

$$\tilde{x} \gg \frac{D^2\,\dot{\gamma}_w}{3(A\,\Delta P)^3}\left[\frac{W_w}{\beta_1}\right]^3 \tag{77}$$

When the criterion of Eq. (46) for the unstirred batch cell, or Eq. (77) for the cross flow parallel plate system, is satisfied, it is possible to make the simplifying assumption of constant wall concentration $(c_w \sim c_{wa})$. Consequently, Eq. (36) becomes

$$\frac{c_{wa} - c_o}{c_{wa} - c_p} = \frac{\sqrt{\pi}}{2}\,V_w\,\exp\left(\frac{V_w^2}{4}\right)\,\mathrm{erfc}\left(\frac{V_w}{2}\right) \tag{78}$$

where

$$V_w = w\sqrt{\pi} = |v_w|\,(4t/D)^{1/2} \tag{79}$$

for the unstirred batch cell and Eq. (73) becomes

$$\frac{c_{wa} - c_o}{c_{wa} - c_p} = W_w \int_0^\infty \exp\left[-\left(\frac{1}{3}\eta^3 + W_w \eta\right)\right] d\eta \tag{80}$$

where

$$W_w = |v_w| \left[\frac{h \tilde{x}}{\langle u\rangle D^2}\right]^{1/3} \tag{81}$$

for the cross flow parallel plate system.

An integral method solution of Eq. (78) has been derived by Trettin and Doshi (1980b) and may be represented as

$$V_w = \left[\frac{c_{wa} - c_o}{c_{wa} - c_p}\right]\left[K_1 \frac{c_{wa} - c_p}{c_o - c_p}\right]^{1/2} \tag{82}$$

where

$$K_1 = 2n_1/(n_1 + 1) \tag{83}$$

and

$$n_1 = \frac{1}{2}\left[\left(\frac{c_{wa} - c_p}{c_o - c_p}\right) + \left(\left(\frac{c_{wa} - c_p}{c_o - c_p}\right)^2 + 8\left(\frac{c_{wa} - c_p}{c_o - c_p}\right)\right)^{1/2}\right] \tag{84}$$

Similarly, the solution of Eq. (80) for the parallel plate system has been derived by Trettin and Doshi (1980a) and is represented as

$$W_w = \left[\frac{c_{wa} - c_o}{c_{wa} - c_p}\right]\left[K_2 \frac{c_{wa} - c_p}{c_o - c_p}\right]^{1/3} \tag{85}$$

where

$$K_2 = 2n_2^2/(n_2 + 1)(n_2 + 2) \tag{86}$$

and

$$n_2 = \frac{1}{4}\left[\left(\frac{c_{wa} - c_p}{c_o - c_p}\right) + \left(\left(\frac{c_{wa} - c_p}{c_o - c_p}\right)^2 + 24\left(\frac{c_{wa} - c_p}{c_o - c_p}\right)\right)^{1/2}\right] \tag{87}$$

   In both integral method solutions the value of D and solution
density are assumed constant. Additionally, as shown in Trettin
and Doshi (1980a, b), both integral method solutions agree very
well with their corresponding exact solutions. Note that if one
wants to calculate V_w or W_w, integral method results, Equations
(82)-(87) are convenient while for the calculation of the
asymptotic wall concentration, c_{wa}, exact solution, Equations
(78)-(81) are convenient.

   In unstirred batch cell ultrafiltration, the value of $|v_w|$
is typically very small and therefore difficult to measure
instantaneously. It is possible, however, to accurately measure
eluded permeate volume (ΔV) as a function of time. Therefore,
upon integration, Eq. (79) becomes

$$\Delta V = 2A_t \, V_w \, (D/4)^{1/2} \, T^{1/2} \tag{88}$$

where

A_t = the transport surface area of membrane

T = time of permeat collection

$$\Delta V = \int_0^T A_t \, |v_w| \, dt = \text{eluded permeate volume in time T.}$$

When accumulated permeate volume is measured at three consecutive
times (T_1, T_2, T_3), it is possible to write

$$\frac{\Delta V_2 - \Delta V_1}{\Delta V_3 - \Delta V_1} = \frac{T_2^{1/2} - T_1^{1/2}}{T_3^{1/2} - T_1^{1/2}} \tag{89}$$

If sample times are selected such that $T_2 = 2T_1$, $T_3 = 4T_1$ an
accuracy of data may be checked:

$$\frac{\Delta V_2 - \Delta V_1}{\Delta V_3 - \Delta V_1} = 0.4142 \tag{90}$$

In all batch cell experiments, data acceptability limits were
established as ± 3% of the 0.4142 value. Acquired data which
were not within these limits were deleted.

   As outlined in Trettin and Doshi (1980b), a correction must
be made to the experimentally measured value of ΔV to adjust for
the permeate collected during the initial period of filtration
when $c_w < c_{wa}$ or c_g. Although the duration of this region is
small, it occurs at a time when permeate flux is greatest and is

therefore necessary to correct for.   Experimentally collected
permeate may be adjusted as follows

$$\Delta V = \Delta V_{exp} - \Delta V_{corr} \tag{91}$$

Substituting for ΔV in Eq. (88) and rearranging yields

$$\frac{\Delta V_{exp}}{T^{1/2}} = 2A_t \, V_w \, (D/4)^{1/2} + \Delta V_{corr} \, (1/T^{1/2}) \tag{92}$$

or

$$\frac{\Delta V_{exp}}{T^{1/2}} = \left[\frac{\Delta V}{T^{1/2}} \right]_{lim} + \Delta V_{corr} \, (1/T^{1/2}) \tag{93}$$

By plotting $\frac{\Delta V_{exp}}{T^{1/2}}$ vs. $1/T^{1/2}$ and extrapolating to infinite time
(T), we can minimize the effects of the initial region where c_w
is not constant, and determine the true value of $\Delta V/T^{1/2}$ [or
$(\Delta V/T^{1/2})_{lim})$ as predicted by Eq. (88).

It is important to digress momentarily to discuss in further
detail the interpretation of the $\frac{\Delta V_{exp}}{T^{1/2}}$ vs. $1/T^{1/2}$ plot.   Since
both models presented in Trettin and Doshi (1980a, 1980b) were
derived explicitly for the constant wall concentration boundary
condition, and in particular for gel polarization, the question
arises as to the difference between gel polarized behavior and
constant wall concentration (osmotic pressure equivalent) behavior.   The major similarity between the two processes of gel polarized and osmotic pressure equivalent ultrafiltration is that the
solute concentration at the membrane surface is constant with
respect to time, as in the unstirred batch cell case, or axial
position, as in the cross flow case.   Therefore, a plot of $\frac{\Delta V_{exp}}{T^{1/2}}$
vs. $1/T^{1/2}$ will be linear in the unstirred batch cell case.   The
major difference between the two processes is that in gel polarized ultrafiltration, not only is the wall concentration constant
but it is also independent of applied pressure.   This is not true
of osmotic pressure equivalent ultrafiltration where wall concen-
tion is pressure dependent.   Therefore, in a $\frac{\Delta V_{exp}}{T^{1/2}}$ vs. $1/T^{1/2}$
plot, gel polarization is indicated by an intersection of

variable ΔP lines (at constant c_o) at the same value of $\left[\dfrac{\Delta V_{exp}}{T^{1/2}}\right]_{lim}$.
A process which is osmotic pressure limited will intersect
at a different value of $\dfrac{\Delta V_{exp}}{T^{1/2}}$ for each applied pressure tested.

As can be seen, the unstirred batch cell technique represents a
unique method for characterizing macromolecular solutions as to
the pressure range in which gel polarization occurs. One must be
cautious in using the batch cell technique, however, to select
ΔP increments which are large enough to cause a discernible
change in the value of c_{wa}. This is particularly true in cases
where solution osmotic pressure is a strong function of concentration.

With the ultrafiltration of macromolecular solutions in
cross flow systems such as thin channel or tubular systems it is
usually the procedure to measure average flux rates at steady
state. Therefore, Eq. (81) may be integrated to give

$$|\bar{v}_w| = 1.5 \left[\frac{D^2 <u>}{h\ L}\right]^{1/3} W_w \tag{94}$$

$$\dot{Q}_p = 1.5 \left[\frac{D^2 <u>}{h} L^2\right]^{1/3} s\ W_w \tag{95}$$

where $|\bar{v}_w|$ = average permeate flux
and $\dot{Q}_p = s\ L\ |\bar{v}_w|$ = average volumetric permeate rate

An analogous relationship to Eq. (93) can be written to account
for initial effects where $c_w < c_{wa}$:

$$\frac{|\dot{Q}_p|_{exp}}{L^{2/3}} = \left[\frac{|\dot{Q}_p|}{L^{2/3}}\right]_{lim} + |\dot{Q}_p|_{corr} \ (1/L^{2/3}) \tag{96}$$

In all ultrafiltration systems reported in the literature, average volumetric flux rates at consecutively increasing lengths
along the conduit are not measured. As a result it is not possi-
ble to plot $\dfrac{|\dot{Q}_p|_{exp}}{L^{2/3}}$ vs. $1/L^{2/3}$ and extrapolate to infinite length
to find the true value of $\left[\dfrac{|\dot{Q}_p|}{L^{2/3}}\right]_{lim}$. Therefore, in the inter-
pretation of the available cross flow ultrafiltration data, the

correction term, to a first order approximation, is neglected. This is a reasonable assumption for the cross flow system in which the length of the initial region may be small in comparison to the total conduit length. The reason is that, ulike the batch cell system where average flux is 2 orders of magnitude less than pure solvent flux, average flux in cross flow systems is only 10 times less than pure solvent flux.

Experimental Procedure

Bovine serum albumin (BSA) (Sigma Chemicals — Cohn fraction V) was selected as a solute material to be studied in batch cell ultrafiltration. The justification of this choice was based on the fact that BSA has been used by previous investigators; their work would offer a source of comparison to our results [Blatt, et al. (1970), Kozinski and Lightfoot (1972), Shen and Probstein (1977, 1979), Probstein et al. (1978, 1979), Goldsmith (1971), and Mitra and Lundblad (1978)]. Solutions of BSA discussed in this paper were prepared in aqueous 0.15M NaCl and adjusted to pH 7.4. Sodium azide of 200 ppm concentration was added as a preservation and final solutions were filtered through a 0.8 μm Millipore filter to remove undissolved solute. All solutions were refrigerated at 10°C prior to use and solutions which had aged more than 2 weeks, or showed appreciable sedimentation, were discarded. Solute concentration was determined by ultraviolet light absorption with a spectrophotometer at the absorption peak of 280 nm.

Ultracentrifuge experiments were performed in our laboratory with BSA solutions using the optical procedure of Longsworth (1952) and Creeth (1955) as outlined by Tostevin (1966). A limitation of this method is that only low solute concentrations may be studied due to refraction fringe merging at higher concentrations (> 0.01 g/cc).

The literature contains numerous experimental determinations of the mutual diffusion coefficient of BSA in various buffer solutions [Creeth (1952), Charlwood (1953), Keller, et al. (1971), Doherty and Benedek (1974), Phillies, et al. (1976)]. The range of reported diffusion coefficient at low concentration is $D = 5.5 - 7.0 \times 10^{-7}$ cm^2/sec. However, values at higher concentrations show considerable scatter as pointed out by Shen and Probstein (1977). Phillies, et al. (1976) have studied BSA solution diffusivity in 0.15M NaCl aqueous systems over the pH range of $4.3 - 7.6$. Their data taken within the higher pH and concentration ranges have been interpreted by Probstein, et al. (1979) to yield an average value of 6.7×10^{-7} cm^2/sec. Both Creeth (1952) and Charlwood (1953) have reported the diffusivity of dilute BSA solutions to be within the range of 6.6×10^{-7} cm^2/sec to 7.1×10^{-7} cm^2/sec at 25°C. Their data also show that the effects of pH and buffer type upon the diffusion coefficient are negligible. The value of the diffusion coefficient for 0.15M NaCl BSA

solution (pH 7.4) was determined to be 6.91×10^{-7} cm^2/sec from
our ultracentrifuge experiments at 23.5°C. It has been shown by
Trettin and Doshi (1980b) that this value is reasonably constant
over a wide range of concentration in the ultrafiltration of
saline BSA solutions.

Batch cell experiments were performed in stainless steel
pressure cells manufactured by the Gelman Filter Company. The
average membrane area equalled 15.62 cm^2 and the total cell volume
was approximately 230 cm^3. The batch cells were affixed to a
support integral with the building structure to prevent extraneous
vibration. The room temperature was controlled within the range
of 21–24°C. Total permeate volume was gravimetrically measured
as a function of time for periods as long as 24 hours. Cell pressure was varied from $2.76 \times 10^5 - 17.24 \times 10^5$ N/m^2 (40 to 250
psi).

The majority of experiments were done using cellulose acetate membranes (5,000 – 10,000 MW cutoff) supplied by UOP- Fluid
Systems. Several experiments were additionally conducted using
noncellulosic (X-117) and polysulfone membranes also from UOP.
Both noncellulosic membranes performed as well as the cellulose
acetate membrane, yielding solute rejections greater than 95%.

Results and Discussion

In Trettin and Doshi (1980b), a plot of 0.15M saline BSA
solution data (pH 7.4) was presented showing that above 6.89×10^5 N/m^2 applied pressure, a gel layer may have formed upon the
membrane surface. This graph has been reproduced in Fig. 4 of
this paper with additional data taken at 2.76×10^5 N/m^2 and 4.14×10^5 N/m^2. At cell pressures of 6.89×10^5 N/m^2 or greater, the
presence of gel polarization (pressure independence) is indicated
by the intersection of $\dfrac{\Delta V_{exp}}{T^{1/2}}$ vs. $1/T^{1/2}$ plots as $T \rightarrow \infty$ for two
different pressures at constant bulk solution concentration. When
the data at lower pressures are examined, they do not intersect
at the same value of $\left[\dfrac{\Delta V}{T^{1/2}}\right]_{lim}$ as the higher pressure data. It is
interesting to note, however, that the lower pressure data plots
are linear, indicating constant wall concentration. The wall
concentration in this case corresponds approximately to the
osmotic pressure equivalent (c_{wa}) of the applied pressure.

Osmotic pressure limited ultrafiltration data were analyzed
by using Eq. (92) and the osmotic pressure data of Vilker (1975)
for 0.15M Saline BSA solutions at pH 7.4. Vilker's data are
reproduced in Fig. 5 for BSA in both 7.4 and 4.5 pH 0.15M saline
solution. The comparison between theory and experiment is quite
good as shown in Table I where the value of D was taken as 6.91×10^{-7} cm^2/sec.

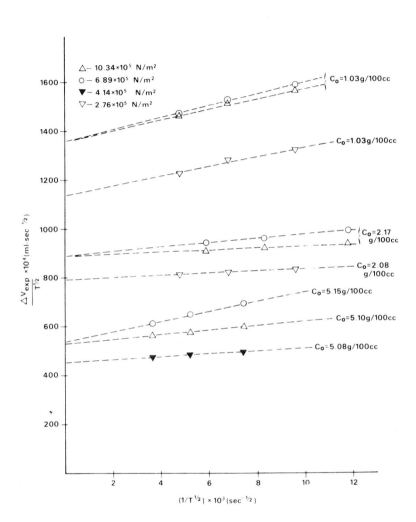

Figure 4. Unstirred batch cell UF of 0.15M NaCl BSA solution (T = 21°–24°C, pH 7.4) at various solute concentrations and applied pressures

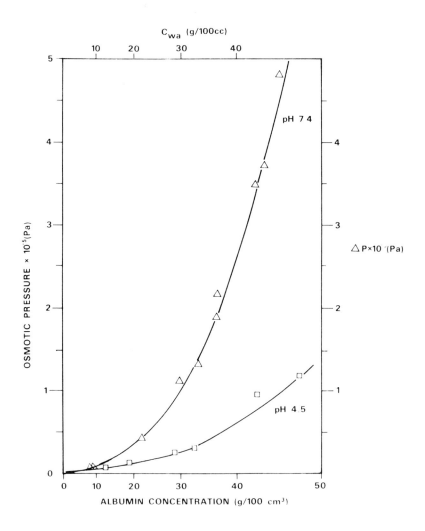

Figure 5.   Solution osmotic pressure vs. solute concentration: 0.15M NaCl BSA solution (27)

TABLE 1

0.15M SALINE BSA SOLUTION (pH 7.4) DATA–BATCH CELL

c_o [g/100cc]	c_p [g/100cc]	$\Delta P \times 10^{-5}$ [N/m^2]	c_{wa} [g/100cc]	Experimental $[\Delta V/T^{1/2}]_{lim}$ [mL-sec$^{-1/2}$]	Theoretical $[\Delta V/T^{1/2}]_{lim}$ [mL-sec$^{-1/2}$]	R_a*
1.030	0.0033	2.76	40.45	0.1137	0.1127	0.989
1.030	0.0042	4.14	44.20	0.1248	0.1164	0.931
2.080	0.0058	2.76	40.45	0.0792	0.0752	0.949
2.140	0.7090	2.76	40.45	0.0897	0.0917	1.02
2.170	0.3472	4.14	44.20	0.0880	0.0847	0.964
5.080	0.0603	4.14	44.20	0.0455	0.0461	1.01

R_a* = ratio of $\dfrac{\text{theoretical } [\Delta V/T^{1/2}]_{lim}}{\text{experimental } [\Delta V/T^{1/2}]_{lim}}$.

In order to add insight into the time required to reach an asymptotic wall concentration in the batch cell, we can calculate the value of t from Eq. (46).

$$t \gg \frac{D}{(A \ \overline{\Delta P})^2} \left[\frac{V_w (1-R)}{|\beta_1| [(R-1) + \theta_o]} \right]^2 \tag{46}$$

where we have assumed the value of R to equal 0.990. The approximate relationship of

$$\pi = 1.42 \times 10^4 \ c - 8.96 \times 10^2 \ c^2 + 17.74 \ c^3,$$
$$25 \leq c \leq 40 \ g/100 \ cc \tag{97}$$

where $\pi = [N/m^2]$, $c = [g/100 \ cc]$

is used to calculate $|\beta_1|$. Selecting the first data point in Table I, we find $\theta_0 = 2.55 \times 10^{-2}$, and from Fig. 2, $V_w = 5.55$. The calculated value of $|\beta_1|$ is found to equal 4.20, and A = $5.0 \times 10^{-9} \frac{m^2-cm}{N-sec}$ is specified. Therefore,

$$t \gg 0.264 \ seconds \tag{98}$$

which is indeed a very short time period to reach the asymptotic wall concentration at the membrane surface. Vilker's pH 7.4 data were linearly extrapolated to higher pressures where we have experienced gel polarization. At $6.89 \times 10^5 \ N/m^2$, the extrapolation indicates a value of c_{wa} equal to 54 g/100 cc. This is in reasonable agreement with our, and Kozinski and Lightfoot's (1972), determination of 58.5 g/100 cc (gel concentration) considering the accuracy of the extrapolated value and the relative insensitivity of the model to small changes in c_{wa}.

The cross flow, thin channel data of Probstein, et al., (1978) and Mitra and Lundblad (1978) were analyzed in terms of the osmotic pressure equivalent model using Vilker's osmotic pressure data for 0.15M Saline BSA solutions (pH 7.4). Although Mitra and Lundblad did not study BSA directly, but rather human serum albumin (HSA), it was felt that sufficient similarity existed between the two solutes that an approximate comparison using BSA parameters could be made [Scatchard, et al. (1944)]. Data were interpreted theoretically using the relationship of Eq. (94). In the analysis of Probstein, et al., data, the cited values of h = 0.19 cm (channel half width) and L = 43 cm (channel length) were used. Similarly, in the analysis of Mitra and Lundblad's 0.15M Saline HSA solution (pH 6.9) data, the cited values of h = 0.019 cm and L = 76 cm were used. The value of D was taken to be 6.91 x 10^{-7} cm²/sec in all calculations and solute rejection at the

membrane surface was assumed to be complete. The interpretation
of Probstein, et al. and Mitra and Lundblad's data are shown in
Tables II and III, respectively. The data of Mitra and Lundblad
which were acquired at axial velocities above 65.56 cm/sec were
not considered due to high pressure drops along the thin channel
length.

It is interesting to note in Table II that, although theoretical prediction of flux agrees well with experimental values
at applied pressures above 1.0×10^5 N/m^2, at lower pressures
experimental flux is substantially over predicted by theory.
This observation may be explained in terms of the approximate
relationship of

$$\tilde{x} \gg \left[\frac{D^2 \dot{\gamma}_w}{3(A \ \Delta P)^3} \right] \left(\frac{W_w}{|\beta_1|} \right)^3 = L^* \qquad (77)$$

At low pressures and high axial velocities, the ratio of $\dfrac{\dot{\gamma}_w}{(A \ \Delta P)^3}$

is large, and therefore longer axial distances are required to
reach an asymptotic wall concentration. When these initial distances, where $c_w < c_{wa}$, are appreciable, the osmotic pressure

equivalent model does not apply and the integral method or numerical technique employed by Leung and Probstein (1979) may have to
be used. It is shown by the 0.689×10^5 N/m^2 data in Table II
that progressively better agreement with theory is obtained as
shear rate is decreased. This observation is consistent with Eq.
(77).

In Table III, experimental flux is consistently overpredict-
ed theoretically by approximately 5%. This discrepancy may be
due to the use of BSA solution parameters (D, π) to interpret
HSA solution data.

Previous workers [Shen and Probstein (1977, 1979), Probstein, et al. (1978, 1979)] have interpreted gel polarization of
BSA solutions to occur between 2.76×10^5 and 4.14×10^5 N/m^2 applied system pressure based upon flux vs. pressure plots. Our
batch cell work has shown that gel polarization of saline BSA
solutions does not occur at pressures below 6.89×10^5 N/m^2.
This apparent discrepancy may be resolved in the following manner. In Fig. 6, we plot the value of W_w, which is directly proportional to flux, vs. ΔP, the applied pressure. The value of
W_w is calculated from Eq. (94) for the thin channel system using
the appropriate value of c_{wa} at each specific applied pressure.
The value of c_{wa} is determined from Vilker's saline BSA solution
data (pH 7.4). In Fig. 6 it can be seen that at low ΔP, the
value of $\dfrac{d W_w}{d \Delta P}$ is large and sharply decreases to a small value at

TABLE II

THIN CHANNEL UF OF 0.15M SALINE BSA SOLUTIONS
(pH 7.4) — PROBSTEIN, et al. (1978)

c_o [g/100 cc]	100 L* [cm]	$\Delta P \times 10^{-5}$ [N/m²]	c_{wa} [g/100 cc]	$\langle u \rangle$ [cm/sec]	Experimental $|\bar{v}_w| \times 10^4$ [cm/sec]	theoretical $|\bar{v}_w| \times 10^4$ [cm/sec]	R_a
1.74	0.490	2.76	40.34	34.5	6.38	5.87	0.920
1.76				23.0	4.71	5.10	1.08
1.78				17.3	4.19	4.62	1.10
1.80				11.5	3.67	4.01	1.09
1.87	0.075			5.8	3.04	3.14	1.03
1.74	2.13	2.07	37.33	34.5	6.10	5.68	0.931
1.76				23.0	4.71	4.93	1.05
1.80				11.5	3.67	3.88	1.06
1.87	0.325			5.8	3.04	3.04	1.00
1.74	6.53	1.38	32.83	34.5	5.58	5.36	0.961
1.76				23.0	4.56	4.66	1.02
1.78				17.3	4.06	4.22	1.04
1.80				11.5	3.60	3.66	1.02
1.87	1.00			5.8	2.96	2.86	0.966
1.78	6.82	1.03	30.50	17.3	3.79	4.08	1.08
1.80				11.5	3.33	3.53	1.06
1.87	2.15			5.8	3.04	2.77	0.911
1.74	60.0	0.689	26.00	34.5	3.60	4.81	1.34
1.76				23.0	3.25	4.18	1.29
1.78				17.3	3.15	3.78	1.20
1.80				11.5	2.90	3.28	1.13
1.87	9.10			5.8	2.40	2.57	1.07

TABLE III

THIN CHANNEL UF OF 0.15M SALINE HSA SOLUTIONS (pH 6.9)–MITRA AND
LUNDBLAD (1978), $\Delta P = 1.72 \times 10^5$ N/m^2, c_{wa} = 35.33 g/100 cc

c_o [g/100 cc]	$<u>$ [cm/sec]	Experimental $|\bar{v}_w| \times 10^4$ [cm/sec]	Theoretical $|\bar{v}_w| \times 10^4$ [cm/sec]	R_a
3.83	33.70	6.25	6.95	1.11
4.65	33.70	5.63	6.23	1.11
6.05	33.70	5.00	5.30	1.06
7.83	33.70	4.17	4.43	1.06
9.43	33.70	3.54	3.83	1.08
3.25	49.86	8.25	8.63	1.05
4.66	49.86	7.29	7.09	0.973
6.75	49.86	5.00	5.61	1.12
8.66	49.86	4.58	4.68	1.02
10.63	49.86	3.92	3.94	1.01
13.41	49.86	2.92	3.13	1.07
3.44	65.56	9.38	9.18	0.979
4.09	65.56	8.33	8.36	1.00
7.12	65.56	6.46	5.92	0.916
9.25	65.56	4.79	4.86	<u>1.01</u>

1.04 Av.

values of ΔP above 3.0×10^5 N/m^2. This behavior is characteristic of actual experimental plots. In fact, the difference in predicted W_w between ΔP values of 2.76×10^5 and 4.14×10^5 N/m^2 is only 5%. It is our contention that a plot of flux vs. ΔP does not necessarily indicate the presence of gel polarization at the point where flux appears to become independent of applied pressure. The small flux change behavior as a function of pressure may be due solely to the solution osmotic pressure. The pressure range of 2.76-4.14×10^5 N/m^2 is too narrow to yield an accurate interpretation of gel polarization with an average error less than 5%. Table IV gives the calculated value of $\frac{d\ W_w}{d\ \Delta P}$ as a function of ΔP for various values of c_o. The experimentally observed behavior of high concentration solutions reaching a plateau region at smaller values of ΔP as compared to low concentration solutions is explained by the fact that the value of $\frac{d\ W_w}{d\ \Delta P}$ decreases (at constant ΔP) as the solution concentration increases.

Conclusions

    It is theoretically shown for the unstirred batch cell that, in limiting cases, the assumption of constant wall (membrane) concentration with respect to time may be made even in the absence of gel formation. Although the assumption of constant wall concentration is similar in both gel and osmotic pressure limited ultrafiltration, it is important to recognize that in gel polarized ultrafiltration, wall concentration is also pressure independent since it corresponds to the solute solubility limit. This is not the case in osmotic pressure limited ultrafiltration where c_w is approximately equal to the concentration at which the developed osmotic pressure at the membrane surface equals the applied system pressure. Criteria are presented — Eq. (46) for the unstirred batch cell and Eq. (77) for the parallel plate system — to establish the validity of the constant wall concentration (osmotic pressure equivalent) assumption in osmotic pressure limited ultrafiltration.
    When the assumption of constant wall concentration is justified, data for the unstirred batch cell and thin channel systems may be interpreted using models presented in Trettin and Doshi (1980a, 1980b). Such an analysis is performed where agreement is shown to be very good between theory and osmotic pressure limited ultrafiltration experiments.
    It is further shown that the current practice of plotting permeate flux vs. ΔP in macromolecular cross-flow ultrafiltration may lead to serious misinterpretation of gel polarization. It is therefore recommended that solutions be studied in the unstirred

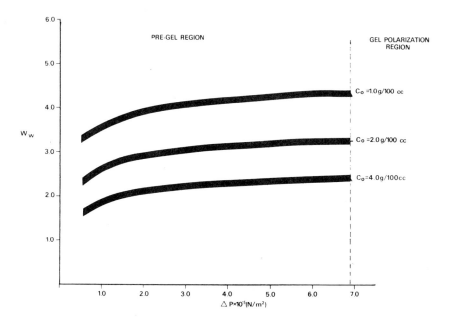

Figure 6. W_w *vs.* ΔP *thin-channel crossflow system.* *Values of* C_{wa} *calculated from Figure 5 for various applied pressures.*

TABLE IV

$$\frac{d\ W_w}{d\ \Delta P} \quad \text{VERSUS} \quad \Delta P - \text{THIN CHANNEL SYSTEM}$$

(FROM FIG. 6)

$\Delta P \times 10^{-5}$ [N/m^2]	$\dfrac{d\ W_w}{d\ \Delta P}$ (c_o = 1.0 g/100 cc)	$\dfrac{d\ W_w}{d\ \Delta P}$ (c_o = 2.0 g/100 cc)	$\dfrac{d\ W_w}{d\ \Delta P}$ (c_o = 4.0 g/100 cc)
0.58	1.15	1.00	0.90
1.00	0.62	0.55	0.45
1.65	0.37	0.31	0.26
2.60	0.22	0.18	0.16
4.45	0.10	0.09	0.08
6.89	0.07	0.06	0.05

batch cell prior to study in cross-flow systems in order to determine the pressure at which gel polarization actually occurs. In previous work, pressure independent flux is assumed to be due to the presence of gel polarization even at low pressures. Probably, the gel polarization is the exception rather than the rule in most industrial-type applications. Obviously, more care must be taken in solute and solution characterization with regard to the interpretation of ultrafiltration data.

Acknowledgments

The authors express their gratitude to the member companies of The Institute of Paper Chemistry for their support of the graduate program.
Portions of this work were used by one of the authors (DRT) as partial fulfillment of the requirements for the Ph.D. degree at The Institute of Paper Chemistry.

Nomenclature

A = membrane coefficient = $\dfrac{1}{\mu R_m}$ $\left(\dfrac{m^2-sec}{N-sec}\right)$

A_T = membrane transport surface area (cm^2)

B_0 = constant as defined by Eq. (13) (cm^3/g)

b = osmotic pressure constant as defined by Eq. (11) $\left(\dfrac{N-cm^3}{m^2-g}\right)$

b_1 = osmotic pressure constant as defined by Eq. (11) $\left(\dfrac{N}{m^2} \cdot \left(\dfrac{cm^3}{g}\right)^2\right)$

b_2 = osmotic pressure constant as defined by Eq. (11) $\left(\dfrac{N}{m^2} \cdot \left(\dfrac{cm^3}{g}\right)^3\right)$

c = solute concentration (g/cm^3) unless otherwise noted

D = solute diffusion coefficient (cm^2/sec)

d_h = hydraulic diameter (cm)

h = channel half height (cm)

I_1, I_2 = constants of integration

K_1 = dimensionless constant defined by Eq. (92)

K_2 = dimensionless constant defined by Eq. (95)

k = mass transfer coefficient (cm/sec)

$\bar{k}$ = average mass transfer coefficient (cm/sec)

L = channel length (cm)

n_1 = dimensionless constant defined by Eq. (93)

n_2 = dimensionless constant defined by Eq. (96)

$\dot{Q}_p$ $= S \ L \ |\bar{V}_w| =$ average volumetric permeate rate (cm^3/sec)

r $= x + \dfrac{W_w}{2}$

R_a $=$ ratio of $\dfrac{\text{theoretical flux}}{\text{experimental flux}}$

R_e $=$ Reynolds number $= \dfrac{<u> \ d_h \rho}{\mu}$

R $=$ solute rejection coefficient $= 1 - c_p/c_w$

Sc $=$ Schmidt number $= \mu/D\rho$

S $=$ width of membrane (cm)

$\overline{Sh}$ $=$ average Sherwood number $= \dfrac{\bar{k}d_n}{D}$

t $=$ time (sec)

T $=$ time period (sec)

u $=$ axial velocity (cm/sec)

$<u>$ $=$ average axial velocity (cm/sec)

$|\bar{v}_w|$ $=$ average permeate volumetric flux (cm/sec)

$|v_w|$ $=$ permeate volumetric flux (cm/sec)

V_w $=$ dimensionless positive flux constant for batch cell [Eq. (91)]

W_w $=$ dimensionless positive permeate flux constant for thin channel [Eq. (94)]

w $=$ dimensionless permeate flux defined by Eq. (16)

$\tilde{x}$ $=$ axial distance coordinate (cm)

x $=$ similarity coordinate defined by Eq. (22)

y $=$ transverse distance coordinate (cm)

z $=$ dimensionless transverse distance defined by Eq. (16)

Greek Letters

$\alpha_1, \ \alpha_2$ $=$ osmotic pressure constants defined by Eq. (13)

$$\frac{cc}{g}, \ \left(\frac{cc^2}{g}\right)$$

β_1 $=$ constant defined by Eq. (30)

$\Gamma_1, \ \Gamma_2$ $=$ osmotic pressure virial coefficients

$\dot{\gamma}_w$ $=$ wall shear rate (1/sec)

δ $=$ mass boundary layer thickness (cm)

ξ $=$ defined by Eq. (36)

η $=$ similarity coordinate for thin channel system defined by Eq. (65)

θ $=$ dimensionless solute concentration defined by Eq. (16)

λ = dimensionless axial distance coordinate defined by Eq. (60)

μ = solution viscosity $\dfrac{\text{N-sec}}{\text{m}^2}$

π = solution osmotic pressure (N/m^2)

ρ = solution density (g/cm^3)

τ = dimensionless time as defined by Eq. (16)

ϕ = dimensionless constant defined by Eq. (60)

ΔP = applied hydrostatic pressure (N/m^2)

ΔV = total permeate volume (cm^3)

$\Delta \pi$ = $\pi_w - \pi_p$ = solution osmotic pressure difference between wall concentration solution and permeate (N/m^2)

Subscripts

g   = of gel
m   = of membrane
o   = of bulk solution
p   = of permeate solution
w   = at wall position
wa   = of asymptotic solution
1, 2, 3   = at measurement times
exp   = experimentally measured
corr   = correction

Abstract

In macromolecular ultrafiltration, as pressure is increased, permeate flux first increases and then in a large number of cases levels out and remains more or less pressure independent. This could be due to the increase in solute concentration at the membrane surface such that either gel formation occurs or the corresponding osmotic pressure approaches the applied pressure. Limiting flux for the gel polarized case was recently analyzed for cross flow and unstirred batch cell systems by Trettin and Doshi (1980,a, b). In this paper we have analyzed the osmotic pressure limited ultrafiltration for the two systems. Our unstirred batch cell data and the literature cross flow data agree quite well with the theory. We have further shown that an unstirred batch cell system can be used to determine whether pressure independent ultrafiltration of macromolecular solution is gel or osmotic pressure limited. Other causes for the observed pressure independence may be present but are not considered in this paper.

Literature Cited

Blatt, W. F., A. Dravid, A. S. Michaels, and L. Nelsen, "Solute Polarization and Cake Formation in Membrane Ultrafiltration: Causes, Consequences, and Control Techniques", in Membrane Science and Technology, J. E. Flinn, ed. p. 47, Plenum Press, New York, N.Y. (1970).

Billmeyer, F. W., Jr., "Textbook of Polymer Science", Second Edition, Interscience, New York (1967).

Brandrup, J., and E. H. Immergut, "Polymer Handbook," Interscience, New York (1967).

Brian, P. L. T., in Desalination by Reverse Osmosis, U. Merten, editor, MIT Press, Cambridge, Mass., p. 161 (1966).

Charlwood, P. A., "Estimation of Heterogeneity from Diffusion Measurements," J. Phys. Chem., 57, 125 (1953).

Creeth, J. M., "The Use of the Gouy Diffusiometer with Dilute Protein Solutions. An Assessment of the Accuracy of the Method," Biochem. J., 51, 10 (1952).

Creeth, J. M., "Studies of Free Diffusion in Liquids with the Rayleigh Method," J. Am. Chem. Soc., 77, 6428 (1955).

Deissler, R. G., "Analysis of Turbulent Heat Transfer, Mass Transfer, and Friction in Smooth Tubes at High Prandtl and Schmidt Numbers," NACA Report No. 1210 (1955).

Doherty, P., and G. B. Benedek, "The Effect of Electric Charge on the Diffusion of Macromolecules," J. Chem. Phys., 61, 5426 (1974).

Gill, W. N., L. J. Derzansky, and M. R. Doshi, "Convective Diffusion in Laminar and Turbulent Hyperfiltration (Reverse Osmosis) Systems," in Surface and Colloid Science, Volume 4, E. Matijevic, ed., p. 261, Wiley and Sons, New York, N.Y. (1971).

Goldsmith, R. L., "Macromolecular Ultrafiltration with Microporous Membranes," Ind. Eng. Chem., Fundam., Volume 10, No. 1, p. 113 (1971).

Keller, K. H., E. R. Canales, and S. I. Yum, "Tracer and Mutual Diffusion Coefficients of Proteins, " J. Phys. Chem., 75, 379 (1971).

Kozinski, A. A., and E. N. Lightfoot, "Protein Ultrafiltration: A General Example of Boundary Layer Filtration," AIChE J., Volume 18, No. 5, p. 1030 (1972).

Leung, W. F., and R. F. Probstein, "Low Polarization in Laminar Ultrafiltration of Macromolecular Solutions," Ind. Eng. Chem., Fundam., Volume 18, No. 3, p. 274 (1979).

Longsworth, L. G., "Diffusion Measurement, at 1°, of Aqueous Solutions of Amino Acids, Peptides, and Sugars," J. Am. Chem. Soc., 74, 4155 (1952).

Michaels, A. S., "New Separation Technique for the CPI," Chem. Eng. Progress, Volume 64, No. 12, p. 31 (1968).

Mitra, F., and J. L. Lundblad, "Ultrafiltration of Immune Serum Globulin and Human Serum Albumin: Regression Analysis Studies," Separation Science and Technology, Volume 13, No. 1, p. 89 (1978).

Phillies, G. D. J., G. B. Benedek, and N. A. Mazer, "Diffusion in Protein Solutions at High Concentrations: A Study of Quasielastic Light Scattering Spectroscopy," J. Chem. Phys., 65, 1883 (1976).

Porter, M. C., "Concentration Polarization with Membrane Ultrafiltration," Ind. Eng. Chem. Prod. Res. Develop., Volume 11, No. 3, p. 234 (1972).

Probstein, R. F., J. S. Shen, and W. F. Leung, "Ultrafiltration of Macromolecular Solutions at High Polarization in Laminar Channel Flow," Desalination, Volume 24, p. 1 (1978).

Scatchard, G., A. C. Batchelder, and A. Brown, "Chemical, Clinical, and Immunological Studies on the Products of Human Plasma Fractionation. VI. The Osmotic Pressure of Plasma and of Serum Albumin," Journal of Clinical Investigation, Volume 23, p. 458 (1944).

Shen, J. S., and R. F. Probstein, "On the Prediction of Limiting Flux in Laminar Ultrafiltration of Macromolecular Solutions," Ind. Eng. Chem., Fundam., Volume 16, No. 4, p. 459 (1977).

Shen, J. S., and R. F. Probstein, "Turbulence Promotion and Hydrodynamic Optimization in and Ultrafiltration Process," Ind. Eng. Chem. Process Des. Dev., Volume 18, No. 3, p. 547 (1979).

Tostevin, J. E., "The Hydrodynamic Properties of the Alditol
    Oligosaccharides," Ph.D. Dissertation, The Institute of
    Paper Chemistry, 1966.

Trettin, D. R., and M. R. Doshi, "Limiting Flux in Ultrafiltration
    of Macromolecular Solutions," To be Published, Chemical
    Engineering Communications (1980a).

Trettin, D. R., and M. R. Doshi, "Ultrafiltration in an Unstirred
    Batch Cell," To be Published, Ind. Eng. Chem., Fundam.
    (1980b).

Vilker, V. L., Ph.D. Thesis, MIT, Dept. of Chemical Engineering,
    Cambridge, Mass. (1975).

RECEIVED December 4, 1980.

Polymer Solute Rejection by Ultrafiltration Membranes

LEOS ZEMAN and MICHAEL WALES

Abcor, Inc., 850 Main Street, Wilmington, MA 01887

Ultrafiltration membranes are used, both on industrial scale as well as in laboratories, for fractionation, purifica tion, separation and concentration of water solute or water dispersible materials.

Rejection of the solute (or dispersed colloid) is, together with permeate flux, one of the two key performance parameters of any ultrafiltration membrane. The values of rejection coefficients are of crucial importance in many applications of ultrafiltration. The objective of this contribution is to consider and analyze the individual factors affecting rejection of polymer solutes by ultrafiltration membranes. The factors that will be considered include steric rejection (sieving), solute velocity lag and solute-membrane interaction.

Our analysis exploits heavily a model concept of a spherical solute in a cylindrical capillary and we do not want to dispute the simplicity or inadequacy inherent in this model. However, we want to demonstrate that even within the framework of this idealized model, useful predictions about the membrane rejection behavior can be made.

We are not going to discuss here the effects of fouling (adsorption) or of electrostatic charge, even if we have to bear in mind that these may be overwhelmingly important in many situations. The discussion will also consider only a case of a preponderantly convective solute transport with a negligible contribution due to diffusion.

Steric Rejection

In his well known derivation of a formula for steric rejection, J. D. Ferry ($\underline{1}$) arrived in 1936 at a simple relation between the solute rejection coefficient, R_2, and the solute to pore diameter ratio, λ, where

$$\lambda = \frac{r_2}{r_3} \tag{1a}$$

0097–6156/81/0154–0411$06.00/0

$$R_2 = 1-4 \int_0^{1-\lambda} (\beta-\beta^3)d\beta = (\lambda(2-\lambda))^2; \text{ for } \lambda \leq 1 \qquad (1b)$$

and

$$R_2 = 1 \text{ for } \lambda > 1 \qquad (1c)$$

These relations can be used as rough estimates of steric rejection, if the solute and membrane pore dimensions are known. The derivation is based on a strictly model situation (see Figure 1) and a long list of necessary assumptions can be written. Apart from the simplified geometry (hard sphere in a cylindrical pore), it was also assumed that the solute travels at the same velocity as the surrounding liquid, that the solute concentration in the accessible parts of the pore is uniform and equal to the concentration in the feed, that the flow pattern is laminar, the liquid is Newtonian, diffusional contribution to solute transport is negligible (pore Peclet number is sufficiently high), concentration polarization and membrane-solute interactions are absent, etc.

Solute Velocity Lag

In general, a sphere moving through a cylindrical pore does not move with the same velocity as the surrounding fluid. Consequently, the formula (1b) has to be corrected for this effect. In 1975, Paine and Scherr (2) calculated drag coefficients k_2, k_1 which weight the contributions of the sphere and fluid velocities to the drag force F:

$$F = -6\pi\eta_1 \ (k_2 v_2 - k_1 v_1) \qquad (2)$$

The drag coefficients k_1 and k_2 are both a function of λ and β (dimensionless distance of sphere's center from the pore's axis). The dependence of k_1 and k_2 on β can be neglected without too much error (2) and the ratio of k_1/k_2 can be considered to depend only on λ.

In a steady-state situation, the drag force has to be zero and a constant solute velocity lag can be described by an equation:

$$\frac{v_2}{v_1} = \frac{k_1}{k_2} \doteq \exp \ (-0.7146\lambda^2) \qquad (3)$$

The right-hand side of Equation (3) was obtained by a least-square fit of a function (exp $(-\alpha\lambda^2)$) on the values of k_1 and k_2 reported by Paine and Scherr (2) for different values of λ. Paine and Scherr's values represent a rigorous theoretical solution for a center-line motion of a rigid sphere inside a cylindrical tube. Applying this correction, we can then write for solute rejection:

$$R_2 = 1 - (1-(\lambda(2-\lambda))^2) \exp (-0.7146\lambda^2) \qquad (4)$$

The magnitude of the solute velocity lag correction is shown in Figure 2. As seen, for a rigid sphere in a cylinder, this correction is not too large. Nevertheless, we will keep considering it in further discussions. The correction calculated from Equation (16b) of Anderson and Quinn (7), applicable for $\lambda < 0.4$, is in agreement with our results.

Polydisperse Solute

The solute hindrance coefficient, W_2, is defined as

$$W_2 = 1 - R_2 = \frac{C_{2,P}}{C_{2,F}} \qquad (5)$$

For a polydisperse polymer solute, both W_2 and R_2 are functions of the solute molecular weight, M_2. If $f(M_2)$ is the solute differential weight distributions and $W(M_2)$ the corresponding hindrance, the average rejection coefficient, $\overline{R}_2$ is defined through:

$$\overline{R}_2 = 1 - \int_0^{M_2(\lambda=1)} W_2 (M_2)\, f(M_2)\, dM_2 \qquad (6)$$

and the relation between λ and M_2 is usually of the form:

$$\lambda = \frac{a}{r_3} M_2^b \qquad (7)$$

where a, b are constants and r_3 is the membrane pore radius. The differential weight distribution function is either known from the experiment or it has to be approximated by some theoretical function. We have considered a case of polydisperse dextran solutes with the values of constants in Equation (7), $a = 0.3069$ and $b = 0.47$. For a r_3 value of $75\overset{\circ}{A}$ (close to Nuclepore $150\overset{\circ}{A}$ filter), the comparison was done between rejection coefficients calculated from M_w data alone and from the actual dextran molecular weight distribution data supplied by the producer (Pharmacia Fine Chemicals). The results are shown in Table I. It is seen that calculation of the rejection coefficient from the $M_{2,w}$ value alone leads to an overestimate of rejection.

STERIC REJECTION—J.D. FERRY, 1936

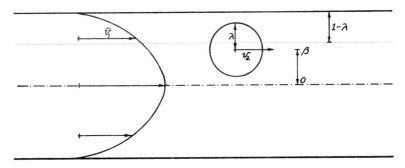

$$R_2 = 1 - \frac{c_{2,P}}{c_{2,F}} = 1 - 4\int_0^{1-\lambda} (\beta - \beta^3)\,d\beta = (\lambda(2-\lambda))^2$$

Figure 1. Schematic of a spherical solute in a cylindrical pore

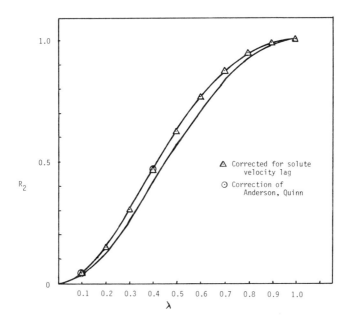

Figure 2. Effect of solute velocity lag with solute rejection as a function of λ. The line without symbols is calculated from Equation 1b, the line with triangles is from Equation 4, and the circles are calculated from Equation 16b of Anderson and Quinn (7).

Table I

Effect of Solute Polydispersity

Dextran	$M_{2,w}$	$M_{2,n}$	R_2	
			From $M_{2,w}$	From Experimental MWD
T-10	10,500	6,400	0.330	0.326
$\dfrac{M_{2,w}}{M_{2,n}} = 1.64$				
T-40	39,500	29,500	0.769	0.698
$\dfrac{M_{2,w}}{M_{2,n}} = 1.34$				
T-70	68,500	40,300	0.925	0.803
$\dfrac{M_{2,w}}{M_{2,n}} = 1.70$				

We can also assume a theoretical form of the distribution function such as the log-normal (Wesslau) distribution. In this case

$$f(M_2) = \frac{\exp\left((-\dfrac{1}{2\sigma_2^2})\ln^2(\dfrac{M_2}{M_{2,m}})\right)}{\sigma_2 M_2 \cdot \sqrt{2\pi}}, \tag{8}$$

$$\sigma_2 = (\ln\frac{M_{2,w}}{M_{2,n}})^{0.5}, \tag{9}$$

and

$$M_{2,m} = M_{2,n}\exp\left(\frac{\sigma_2^2}{2}\right) \tag{10}$$

The effect of solute polydispersity (σ_2) on rejection is shown in Figure 3. These curves were calculated again for dextrans of different $M_{2,w}$, but this time a log-normal distribution was assumed for $f(M_2)$. Equation (6) was solved numerically. It is seen again that increasing the solute polydispersity leads to a decrease in the rejection coefficient.

Membrane Pore Size Distribution

With the exception of membranes prepared by special techniques (such as track-etching), a distribution of membrane pore radii has to be assumed for ultrafiltration membranes. Equations for solute and solvent flux have then to incorporate the effect of membrane pore size distributions dN/dr_3. The solvent flux for an ensemble of pores obeying the Poiseuille equation is:

$$\bar{J}_1 = \frac{\pi \Delta P \int_0^\infty r_3^4 \, dN/dr_3 \, dr_3}{8\eta_1 \, l_3} \times 10^{-24} \tag{13}$$

and the solute flux through these pores is:

$$\bar{J}_2 = \frac{C_{2,F} \, \pi \Delta P \int_{r_2}^\infty W_2 r_3^4 \frac{dN}{dr_3} \, dr_3}{8\eta_1 \, l_3} \times 10^{-24} \tag{14}$$

The concentration of solute in the permeate, $C_{2,P}$ is given by

$$C_{2,P} = \frac{\bar{J}_2}{\bar{J}_1} \tag{15}$$

and the average steric hindrance, $\bar{W}_2$, is

$$\bar{W}_2 = \frac{C_{2,P}}{C_{2,F}} \tag{16a}$$

Then, combination of Equations (13), (14), (15) and (16a) yields:

$$\bar{W}_2 = 1 - \bar{R}_2 = \frac{\int_{r_2}^\infty W_2 r_3^4 \frac{dN}{dr_3} \, dr_3}{\int_0^\infty r_3^4 \frac{dN}{dr_3} \, dr_3} \tag{16b}$$

Equation (16b) describes the effect of membrane pore radius distribution on solute rejection. In the absence of available experimental data on wet asymmetric ultrafiltration membranes with pore radii smaller than 100Å, we have to resort to the use of an assumed theoretical distribution function.

As an example, we choose again the log-normal (Wesslau) distribution function:

$$\frac{dN}{dr_3} = \frac{\exp\left((-\frac{1}{2\sigma_3^2}) \ln^2 (\frac{r_3}{r_{3,m}})\right)}{A \cdot \sigma_3 r_3 \sqrt{2\pi}}, \tag{17}$$

where $r_{3,m}$ are the median value and σ_3 the standard deviation of $\ln r_3$, respectively. We redefine λ to become λ_m, where

$$\lambda_m = \frac{r_2}{r_{3,m}} \tag{18}$$

The steric hindrance, W_2, is defined by Equations (4) and (5) and for the purposes of numerical calculations it can be expressed as a least square-fitted polynomial

$$W_2 = \sum_{k=0}^{k=4} A_k \lambda_m^k \tag{19}$$

satisfying conditions of $W_2 = 1$ at $\lambda_m = 0$ and $W_2 = 0$ at $\lambda_m = 1$. The coefficients A_k are given in Table II.

Table II

Coefficients A_k In Equation (19)

k	A_k
0	1
1	0.04152060
2	-5.2303573
3	6.2893776
4	-2.1005409

Numerical solution of Equations (16b), (17) and (19) then allows calculation of $\bar{R}_2$ as a function of λ_m and σ_3. The results are shown in Figure 4. It is seen that membranes with pore size distributions yield rejection curves that are less steep than those calculated for membranes with uniform pore size. Passage of solute occurs even for $\lambda_m > 1.0$.

Presence of Holes

From a practical point of view, this is a very common and a very important problem. Holes may originate from defects in membrane backings, inhomogeneities in the casting solutions, airborne dust particles, etc. For simplicity, let us consider a membrane area that contains N pores of radius r_3 and N' holes of radius r_3. Water flux, J_1' through this membrane is given by:

$$J_1' = (N r_3^4 + N' r_3'^4) \frac{\pi \Delta P}{8\eta_1 l_3} \times 10^{-24} \tag{20}$$

The solute flux through this membrane is given by:

$$J_2' = ((1 - R_2) N r_3^4 + N' r_3'^4) C_{2,F} \cdot \frac{\pi \Delta P \times 10^{-24}}{8\eta_1 l_3} \tag{21}$$

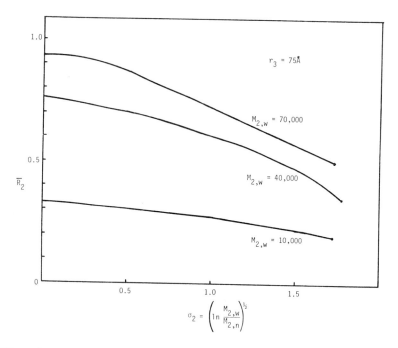

Figure 3. Effect of solute polydispersity. Curves calculated for dextrans of different $M_{2,w}$ and log-normal distribution of molecular weight.

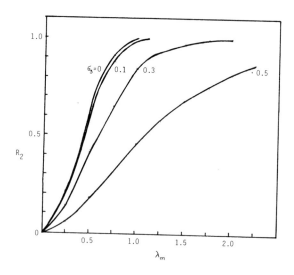

Figure 4. Effect of membrane pore-size distribution. R_2 is calculated as a function of λ_m and σ_3.

where R_2 is rejection of the hole-free membrane, and the hole is assumed to have a zero rejection coefficient for the solute. The rejection coefficient of this defective membrane, $R_{2,def}$ can be calculated as

$$R_{2,def} = 1 - \frac{J_2'}{J_1' C_{2,F}} = \frac{R_2}{1 + \alpha' \left(\frac{r_3}{r_3'}\right)^4} \tag{22}$$

where

$$\alpha = \frac{N'}{N} \tag{23}$$

To illustrate this effect, we calculate $R_{2,def}$ for $\alpha = 3 \times 10^{-7}$, $r_3 = 40\overset{\circ}{A}$ and $r_3' = 1000\overset{\circ}{A}$ (0.1μ). The calculated rejection curve (dashed line) is shown in Figure 5 and compared to that of a hole-free membrane (full line). In the solute size range of interest, the $R_2 = 1$ plateau (quantitative rejection of the solute) is never achieved. Rejection curves of this sort are very commonly encountered in practice.

Van der Waals Attractive Forces

In the derivation of J. D. Ferry's formula, Equation (1b), it was assumed that the solute concentration within the accessible part of the membrane pore is uniform and equal to $C_{2,F}$. Obviously this assumption cannot hold if we are to acknowledge the presence of interactive forces between the solute and the pore wall (membrane). Here we will concentrate only on the effect of Van der Waals forces but analogous treatments could be developed for other interactive potentials (electrostatic, etc.).

We first consider an atom within a cylindrical orifice in the membrane (component 3) of radius $r_3 = 1$ interacting with a cylindrical volume element dV_3 at a distance x (see Figure 6a). The potential energy of interaction (Van der Waals attraction) is

$$d\Phi_{atom-3} = \frac{-\rho_3 N_a}{M_3} \alpha' \frac{dV_3}{x^6} \tag{24}$$

where α' is the interaction constant.

Integration over infinite space outside of the orifice (in cylindrical coordinates yields

$$\Phi_{atom-3} (\beta') = \frac{-2\rho_3 N_a \alpha'}{M_3} \int_{y=0}^{\infty} \int_{r=1}^{\infty} \int_{\omega=0}^{\pi} \frac{r \, dr \, d\omega \, dy}{(y^2 + r^2 + \beta'^2 - 2r\beta' \cos\omega)^3}$$

$$= \frac{-2\rho_3 N_a \alpha'}{M_3} \cdot I (\beta') \tag{25}$$

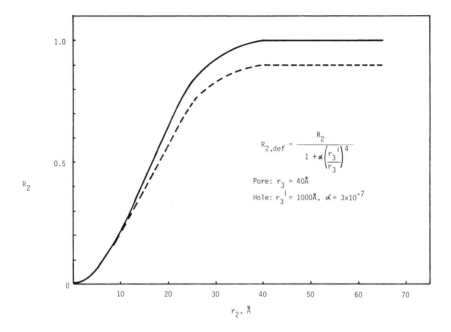

Figure 5. Effect of holes. Rejection curve calculated for a membrane with 40-Å radius pores (———) and for the same membrane containing 1000-Å holes (— — —) at a frequency of $\alpha = 3 \times 10^{-7}$ hole per pore.

the triple integral I (β') in Equation (25) can be approximated by:

$$I\ (\beta') = \exp(\exp(\exp 1.5260\beta' - 0.4637))) \qquad (26)$$

where β' denotes the dimensionless radial position of the atom.

We can now also integrate over the solute sphere with a radius λ (Figure 6b). For now, we assume that the solute is made of the same material as the membrane ($\rho_2 = \rho_3$; $M_2 = M_3$).

$$\Phi_{\text{sphere-3}}\ (\beta,\lambda) = -8\,\alpha'\ (\frac{\rho_3\ N_a}{M_3})^2 \int\limits_{\phi=0}^{\pi/2} \int\limits_{\theta=0}^{\pi} \int\limits_{s=0}^{\lambda} I\ (\beta')\ s^2\ \sin\theta\,ds\,d\theta\,d\phi$$

$$= -8\,\alpha'\ (\frac{\rho_3\ N_a}{M_3})^2 \cdot I\ (\beta,\lambda) \qquad (27)$$

and

$$\beta' = (s^2\ \sin^2\theta + \beta^2 - 2\beta s\ \sin\theta\ \sin\phi)^{1/2} \qquad (28)$$

The cluster of constants in Equation (27) can be simplified by using the Hamaker constant, H_{33}:

$$H_{33} = (\frac{\rho_3\ N_a\ \pi}{M_3})^2\ \alpha' \qquad (29)$$

and therefore

$$\Phi\ (\beta,\lambda) = \frac{-8}{\pi^2}\ H_{33}\ \cdot\ I\ (\beta,\lambda) \qquad (30)$$

The fact that the solute (component 2) and the membrane (component 3) are made from two different materials separated by the solvent (component 1) will be reflected by the use of a composite Hamaker constant.

$$H_{213} = (H_{11}^{1/2} - (H_{22}\ H_{33})^{1/4})^2 \qquad (31)$$

The energy of interaction for a spherical solute of radius λ in a solvent-filled infinite cylindrical pore with a radius $\beta=1$ and at a radial position β is therefore

$$\Phi\ (\beta,\lambda) = \frac{-8}{\pi^2}\ H_{213}\ I\ (\beta,\lambda) \qquad (32)$$

The solute concentration profile within the accessible part of the pore will be determined by the Boltzmann distribution law.

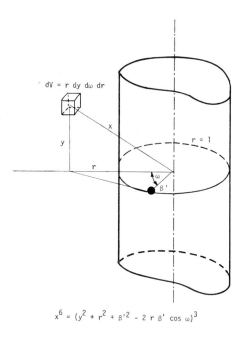

$$x^6 = (y^2 + r^2 + \beta'^2 - 2\,r\,\beta'\,\cos\,\omega)^3$$

Figure 6a.   Schematic of an atom inside an infinite cylindrical capillary

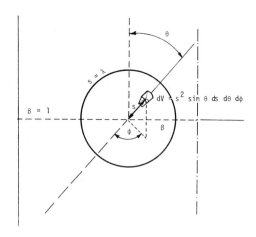

Figure 6b.   Schematic of a spherical solute within the pore

$$C_2 = \overline{C}_2 \exp(-\Phi/kT) \tag{33}$$

The value of kT considered ($25°C$) is 4.12×10^{-14} erg.

Radial distribution of solute molecules in the pore does not change the average solute concentration in the pore and therefore

$$\pi(1-\lambda)^2 C_{2,F} = \overline{C}_2 \cdot 2\pi \int_0^{1-\lambda} \exp\left(-\frac{\Phi}{kT}\right)\beta \, d\beta, \tag{34}$$

wherefrom:

$$\overline{C}_2 = \frac{C_{2,F} (1-\lambda)^2}{2} \cdot \frac{1}{\int_0^{1-\lambda} \exp\left(-\frac{\Phi}{kT}\right)\beta \, d\beta} \tag{35}$$

Equations (32), (33) and (35) allow us to calculate $C_2/C_{2,F}$ as a function of β and λ for different values of H_{213} (Hamaker constant). Due to the complexity of calculation (evaluation of two triple integrals), this is best done on a computer. Typical results of computer calculations are shown in Figure 7. The effect of Van der Waals attractive forces will lead to an accumulation of solute molecules near the walls for small values of λ but at large values of λ, the positions close to the pore axis start being preferred.

The value of H_{213} chosen in our calculation is rather large. The expected magnitude of Hamaker constants would be between 2×10^{-13}–5×10^{-15} erg depending on the "hydrophilicity" of both the solute and the membrane.

To calculate rejection coefficients, we use the formula

$$R_2 = 1 - \frac{4}{C_{2,F}} \int_0^{1-\lambda} C_2 \, (\beta-\beta^3) \, d\beta \tag{36}$$

that accounts for the presence of a concentration gradient within the accessible part of the pore. Rejection curves calculated from Equations (32), (33), (35) and (36) are shown in Figure 8. It is seen that the effect is most pronounced below $\lambda = 0.7$ and its magnitude depends on the value of the respective Hamaker constant. The rejection coefficient is increased by the attractive forces between the solute and the membrane.

It is to be expected that for large values of H, adsorption also occurs and the pore dimensions are changed correspondingly. The effects of adsorbed solute layers may be very important, but these were not considered in our analysis of the solute-membrane interaction effects.

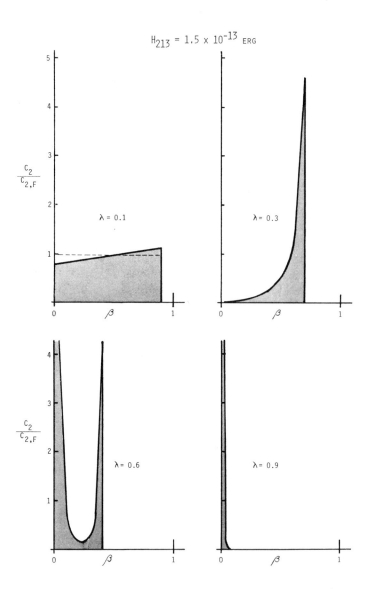

Figure 7. Example of calculated concentration profiles for the value of $\overset{\prime}{H}_{213} = 1.5$
$\times$ 10^{-13} erg and different values of λ and β

Concentration Polarization

Typical results of an ultrafiltration experiment also reflect the presence of concentration polarization. This phenomenon, i.e. accumulation of solute in front of the membrane, was
described in great detail by others (Refs. 3, 4). A consequence
of concentration polarization is a strong dependence of measured
rejection coefficients on transmembrane fluxes. An illustration
of the effect is presented in Figure 9, which shows the measured
"apparent" rejection coefficients (R_a) as a function of transmembrane flux for two water-soluble polymers (Tetronic 707 and
Carbowax 4000). It is clear from Figure 9 that if we want to
minimize the effects of concentration polarization, we have to
conduct experiments at very low values of transmembrane flux.

Theory of Steric Rejection and Experimental Results

The experimental results are going to be presented in detail
elsewhere and only a brief presentation will be given below.
The predictive power of Equation (4) was tested with defined
polymeric solutes and track-etched Nuclepore filters.
The polymers used were: linear polyethylene oxides, (Carbowaxes supplied by Union Carbide Corporation), and Dextran T
fractions, (Pharmacia Fine Chemicals). For Carbowaxes, the
solute radii used in calculations were mean radii of gyration
calculated from molecular weights via the Flory-Fox equation and
using the Mark-Houwink constants given in reference (5). For
non-linear dextrans, we used the Stokes radii calculated from
molecular weights using the correlation of data reported by
Granath and Kvist (6). Both types of polymer have very narrow
distributions of molecular weight. The solute radii are summarized in Table III.

Table III
Solute Radii

Solute	M_w (Daltons)	Radius ($\overset{o}{A}$)	
Carbowax 4000	4,010	25.4	} Mean radius
Carbowax 6000	7,000	34.6	of gyration
Dextran T10	10,500	23.8	
Dextran T40	39,500	44.4	} Stokes Radius
Dextran T70	68,500	57.5	

Nuclepore filters used have straight-through pores with
diameters specified by Nuclepore Corporation as 150, 300 and 500$\overset{o}{A}$.
These are the so-called "rated" pore diameters and they represent

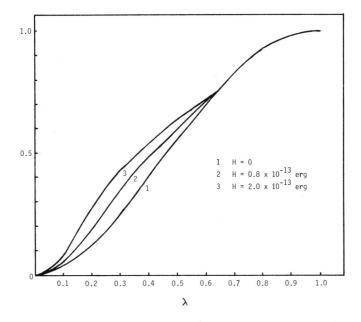

Figure 8. Effect of solute–membrane interaction on rejection. Rejection curves calculated for $H_{213} = 0$, $H_{213} = 0.8 \times 10^{-13}$ erg, and $H_{213} = 2.0 \times 10^{-13}$ erg.

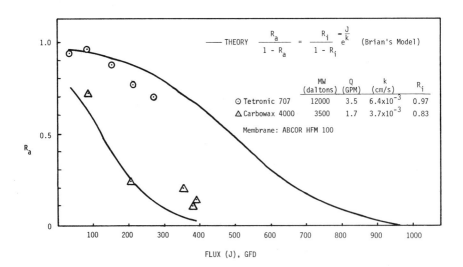

Figure 9. Effect of concentration polarization. Theoretical curves calculated for the values of R_i and k specified in the figure. Experimental data for Tetronic 707 (⊙) and Carbowax 4000 (△) ultrafiltered through the ABCOR HFM 100 membrane.

the maximum value. According to Nuclepore literature, the actual pore sizes should not vary more than +0% to -20% from the rated values.

For each filter-solute combination, λ was calculated as a ratio of the solute radius to the "rated" pore radius. The predicted value of the rejection coefficient was then calculated from Equation (4). The comparison between the predicted values and those actually measured with Carbowaxes 4000 and 600 is shown in Figure 10a and b, respectively. The measurements were carried out at several values of ΔP in order to assess the importance of contribution from concentration polarization.

Using the GPC analysis of feed and permeate solutions (Figure 11 a,b), we also calculated a part of the solute rejection curve for the given filters. The example of such a curve is a Carbowax rejection curve for Nuclepore 150Å (diameter) filter (Figure 11c). The agreement between experimental data and the prediction of Equation (4) (solid line) is very good.

A similar test was performed with Dextran T fractions and Nuclepore 150Å, 300Å, 500Å (diameter) filters. The results are summarized in Figure 12. The experimental points were obtained both from single solute measurements (+ - rejection of T10 and T70 by the 150Å filter) and from analysis of the GPC traces ($\boxed{\cdot}$ - 500Å filter, Δ-300Å filter, o-150Å filter). The agreement between the experimental data and the prediction of Equation (4) (solid line) is again surprisingly good, considering the crudeness of assumptions involved in its derivation.

Simultaneous Rejection Measurements

The GPC analysis of feed and permeate solution is ideally suited for rapid simultaneous rejection measurements. Simultaneous rejection is of great importance in ultrafiltration practice. As an example, we show here a simultaneous measurement of rejection of proteins and of lactose in whey ultrafiltration (Figure 13). The membrane used was the ABCOR HFK membrane and the feed solution had a typical composition of a partially concentrated whey stream. The feed (———) and the permeate (- - -) solutions were analyzed by GPC (Waters I-125 columns) with simultaneous monitoring of uv absorbance (A_{280}) and of refractive index difference (ΔRI). The analysis shows a quantitative rejection (R=100%) of all whey proteins and a very low rejection (R=8%) of lactose.

Conclusions

According to our analysis, the predominant effect controlling rejection of polymeric solutes by uncharged ultrafiltration membranes is the steric factor determined by the value of parameter λ.

The contributions to rejection from hydrodynamic lag, Van der Waals attraction between the solute and the membrane can be regarded as of relatively minor importance.

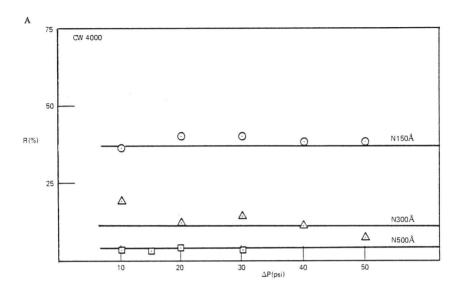

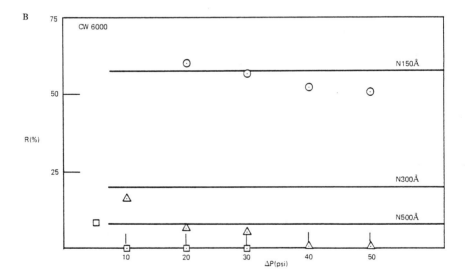

Figure 10.   R(%) as a function of ΔP for Nuclepore 150 Å (⊙), Nuclepore 300 Å (△), and Nuclepore 500 Å (⊡): (a) 0.1 Carbowax 4000; (b) 0.1 Carbowax 6000. Solid lines show theoretical predictions according to Equation 4.

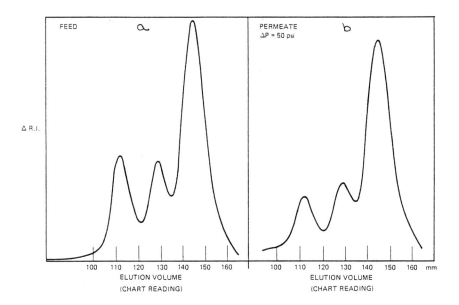

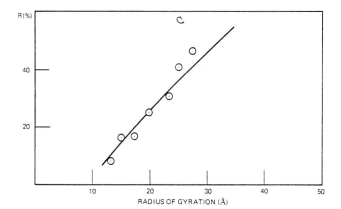

Figure 11.   Measured apparent rejection of polyethylene oxide (Carbowax) at ΔP = 50 psi: (a) GPC trace of a blend solution containing 0.02% of each Carbowax 1000, 1400, 1540, 4000, and 6000; (b) GPC trace of a permeate obtained by UF at ΔP = 50 psi through Nuclepore 150 Å membrane; (c) apparent rejection calculated from GPC traces shown in a and b, (⊙), as a function of solute radius of gyration. The solid line shows theoretical prediction according to Equation 4.

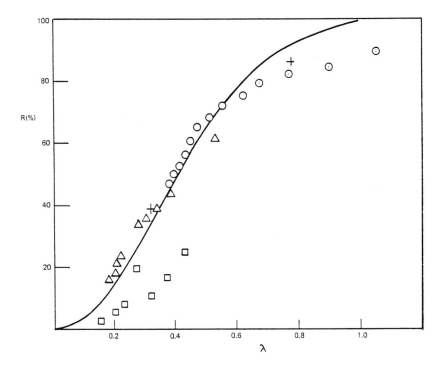

*Figure 12.   Measured apparent rejection of dextrans by Nuclepore filters calcu-
lated from GPC traces as a function of λ. Points calculated from Nuclepore 150 Å
(○), 300 Å (△), and 500 Å (□) traces. The solid line shows theoretical prediction
according to Equation 4. Rejection coefficients measured for single dextran fractions (T10 and T70) and the Nuclepore 150 Å filter are shown also (+).*

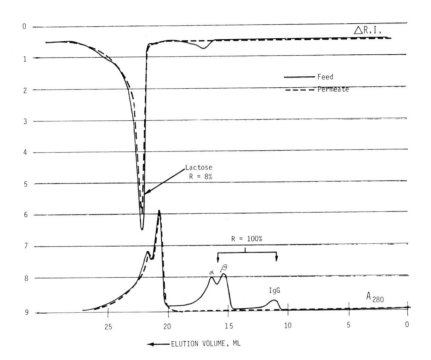

Figure 13.   Simultaneous rejection measurement by GPC. The GPC profiles: ΔRI trace (upper) and A_{280} trace (lower) for whey feed and permeate obtained by UF through the ABCOR HFK membrane. The peak labelled IgG corresponds to whey immunoglobulines; peaks labelled ∝ and β correspond to ∝-lactalbumin and β-lactoglobulin, respectively.

The typical ultrafiltration results will reflect effects of the respective size distributions of both the solute and the membrane pores, as well as of concentration polarization. All of these effects should be expected to lower the membrane rejection coefficient.

Acknowledgement

We thank Mr. Michael Morin of ABCOR, INC. for invaluable help in performing the computer calculations.

List of Symbols

A	Membrane area, cm^2
A_k	Coefficients in Equation (19), dimensionless
a	Constant in Equation (7), $\overset{o}{A}$ dalton^{-b}
b	Constant in Equation (7), dimensionless
$C_{2,F}$	Solute concentration in the feed, $g\ cm^{-3}$
$C_{2,P}$	Solute concentration in the permeate, $g\ cm^{-3}$
$f(M_2)$	Solute differential molecular weight distribution, dalton^{-1}
F	Viscous drag force, dyne
H	Hamaker constant, erg
I	Integrals
J_1	Solvent flux, $cm\ s^{-1}$
J_2	Solute flux, $g\ cm^{-2}s^{-1}$
k	Mass transfer coefficient, $cm\ s^{-1}$ (Figure 9)
k	Boltzmann constant, $erg\ {}^oK^{-1}$
k_1, k_2	Drag coefficients, dimensionless
l_3	Pore length, $\overset{o}{A}$
M_2	Solute molecular weight, dalton
$M_{2,n}$	Number average solute molecular weight, dalton

$M_{2,w}$	Weight average solute molecular weight, dalton
M_3	Membrane polymer molecular weight, dalton
N	Number of pores per unit membrane area, cm^{-2}
N'	Number of holes per unit membrane area, cm^{-2}
N_a	Arogadro number, $mole^{-1}$
r	Distance, cm
r_1	Solvent molecule radius, $\overset{o}{A}$
r_2	Solute radius, $\overset{o}{A}$
r_3	Membrane pore radius, $\overset{o}{A}$
R or R_2	Solute rejection coefficient, dimensionless
R_a	Apparent rejection coefficient, dimensionless
s	Distance, cm
T	Absolute temperature, ^{o}K
v_1	Solvent velocity, $cm\ s^{-1}$
v_2	Solute velocity, $cm\ s^{-1}$
V	Volume, cm^3
W_2	Solute hindrance coefficient, dimensionless
x	Distance, cm
y	Distance, cm
α	N'/N
α'	Van der Waals interaction constant, $erg\ cm^6$
β	Radial position of solute in the pore, dimensionless
β'	β for a single atom, dimensionless
η_1	Solvent viscosity, poise
θ	Angle, radian

λ	r_2/r_2, dimensionless
ρ_2	Solute density, g cm^{-3}
ρ_3	Membrane polymer density, g cm^{-3}
σ_2	Standard deviation of ln r_2, dimensionless
σ_3	Standard deviation of ln r_3, dimensionless
ϕ	Angle, radian
Φ	Van der Waals interaction energy, erg
ω	Angle, radian

Subscripts

1   Solvent

2   Solute

3   Membrane

Literature Cited

1. Ferry, J. D., Chem. Rev., 1936, 18, 373

2. Paine, P. L.; Scherr, P., Biophysical J., 1975, 15, 1087

3. Brian, L. T., "Desalination by Reverse Osmosis", Merten, U., Ed., The MIT Press, Cambridge, Massachusetts, 1966, 101

4. Blatt, W. F.; David, A.; Michaels, A. S.; Nelsen, L., "Membrane Science and Technology", Flinn, J. E., Ed., Plenum Publishing Corporation, New York, 1970, 47

5. Ring, W., Cantow, H. J., Holtrup, H., European Polymer J., 1966, 2, 151

6. Granath, K. A.; Kvist, B. A., J. Chromatogr., 1967, 28, 69-81

7. Anderson, J. L.; Quinn, J. A., Biophys. J., 1974, 14, 130-150

RECEIVED December 4, 1980.

Recent Applications of Dynamic Membranes

CRAIG A. BRANDON—CARRE, Inc., Seneca, SC 29678

J. LEO GADDIS—Department of Mechanical Engineering, Clemson University, Clemson, SC 29631

H. GARTH SPENCER—Department of Chemistry, Clemson University, Clemson, SC 29631

The systematic investigation of dynamically-formed membranes began with the formation of a salt rejecting membrane in 1965 at the Oak Ridge National Laboratory. (1) The dynamic hyperfiltration membrane most often used in subsequent applications has been prepared by sequential depositions of zirconium IV hydrous oxide followed by poly(acrylic acid) on a suitable porous support under pressure and cross flow conditions. Although not competitive with the conventional hyperfiltration membranes for desalination, the resulting hyperfiltration (RO) membrane possesses properties desired for some industrial applications. (2) It is suitable for applications requiring high temperature during either operation, cleaning, or sterilization and for those in which a charged membrane is advantageous.

Results from two studies involving high volume recovery of multicomponent process effluents are presented here as illustrations of recent applications of hyperfiltration membranes in a tubular configuration supported by porous stainless steel. The first is a laboratory separation of dyes from a saline dye manufacturing process effluent and the second a pilot renovation of wash water from a dye range for reuse.

The general properties of representative dynamically-formed membranes are provided in Table I.

Separation of Dye Manufacturing Process Effluent

In a typical dye synthesis the dye is salted-out of the reaction solution and captured on a filter press. The dye filtrate is normally diluted with filter washings and other water sources to as much as (100:1) (water: dye filtrate), treated, and discharged from the plant. The authentic samples of dye filtrate used in this study were highly colored, near neutral liquids with high salt concentrations (5 to 20 weight percent) and a total organic carbon (TOC) concentration of about 0.5 percent.

0097–6156/81/0154–0435$05.00/0

Table I. CARRE, Inc. Membrane Specifications

	Ultrafiltration ZOSS	Hyperfiltration ZOPA
Flow Geometry	Tubular	Tubular
Membrane Support	stainless steel (316ℓ)	stainless steel (316ℓ)
Membrane Material	zirconium oxide	zirconium oxide polyacrylate
Method of Replacement	in place chemical solution	in place chemical solution
Prefiltration Requirement	40 mesh screen	40 mesh screen
Pressure Limitation	greater than 1000 psig	greater than 1000 psig
Temperature Limitation	greater than 100°C (212°F)	greater than 100°C (212°F)
pH Range	2-13	4-11
Permeability[1] with Test Solution @ 100°F	0.1 to 0.4	0.05 - 0.07
@ 200°F	0.4 to 1.2	0.2 - 0.3
Salt Rejection[1]	5 - 20%	80 - 90%

---

[1]Test Solution 1000 mg/ℓ of $NaNO_3$ in water
Flux equals Permeability times pressure
Examples: (1) ZOSS Membrane at 1000 psig at 100°F
　　　　　　　Flux = 0.25 x 1000 = 250 gallons/day/ft^2
　　　　　(2) ZOPA Membrane at 1000 psig at 200°F
　　　　　　　Flux = 0.25 x 1000 = 250 gallons/day/ft^2
Flux with wastewater must be measured.

Four fluids were studied: filtrates from the manufacture of (a) basic yellow CI 48054, indole type; (b) acid yellow CI 13906, azo-type; (c) acid blue CI 62055, anthraquinone type; and (d) an equal mixture of the above, termed "composite". Table II identifies the structures of the product dyes. Test fluids ranging in dilution from 2:3 to 100:1 were used.

A need exists to fractionate the solutes in the dye filtrate into retained organic and passed inorganic salt fractions. The passage of simple electrolytes occurs through ultrafiltration membranes and ion-exclusion hyperfiltration membranes at a high salt concentration. Both types of dynamic membranes were tested.

The dynamic ultrafilter had been observed to retain color in spent dye solutions, but its color retention using these diluted dye filtrates (100:1) was negligible and no quantitative results are presented. A description of the experiments and preliminary results using basic yellow CI 48054 and composite filtrates has been published. (3) Results obtained with the hyperfilter using acid yellow CI 13906 and acid blue CI 62055 filtrates are described here. The properties of the dye filtrates are provided in Table III.

The effects of pertinent operating parameters on the separation process were measured. Most experiments were performed at 5.2 MPa (750 psi). Deliberate excursions in temperature were made to measure this effect and provide a means of compensating the flux data for temperature and reporting all comparison data at 45°C. The separation of solutes was anticipated to depend on concentration and pH and these effects were determined systematically.

Two experimental procedures were carried out. In the first, a 100:1 (water and dye filtrate) dilution was concentrated to one-tenth its initial volume. Rejection based on color absorbance (410 nm) and electrical conductivity, flux, pressure, temperature, and crossflow rate were measured at intervals during the concentration experiment. In the second, a slightly diluted dye filtrate (2:3) was used and the hyperfiltration at steady state was evaluated as in the first procedure. The test was repeated at dilutions reaching (100:1), with pH and temperature excursions at a dilution of 3:1.

The variation of flux with temperature for all the fluids is shown in Figure 1. Each trend is reasonably correlated by

$$J = J_o \exp[-2,500 \ (\frac{1}{T} - \frac{1}{T_o})] \qquad [1]$$

where J_o is the flux at $T_o = 318K$ (45°C). The variation of flux and rejections with pH is shown in Figures 2 and 3 for the two fluids.

Table II.   Structures of Product Dyes

Product Dye   Structure

Basic Yellow,
CI 48054

Acid Yellow,
CI 13906

Acid Blue,
CI 62055

Table III. Properties of Dye Filtrates

Property	Acid Yellow, CI 13906 (mg/L)	Acid Blue, CI 62055 (mg/L)
Cl⁻	116,000	12,600
TDS	217,000	111,000
COD	14,200	41,900
Alkalinity	6,180	21,800
Equivalent NaCl (by conductivity)	177,000	50,000
pH	9.1	9.3
Cr	0.34	0.20
Cu	0.44	760.
Ni	1.73	0.63
Zn	0.63	0.87
Hg	17.8	13.8

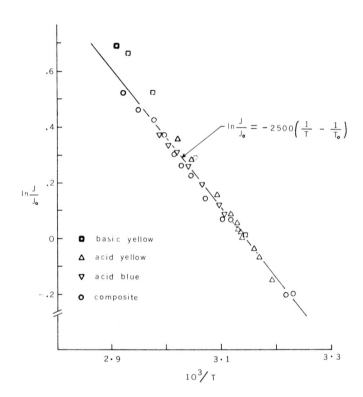

Figure 1.   Effect of temperature on membrane flux: P = 5.2 MPa (750 psi)

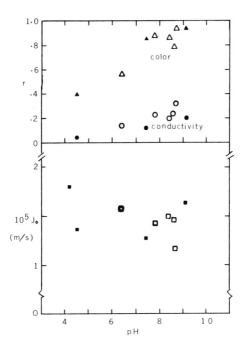

Figure 2.   Rejection (r) and flux (J$_o$) dependence on pH for the acid yellow CI 13906 filtrate: solid points at conductivity (L) = 0.026 S/cm and open points at L = 0.06 S/cm; P = 5.2 MPa (750 psi).

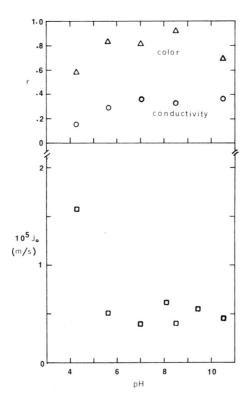

Figure 3.   Rejection (r) and flux (J$_o$) dependence on pH for the acid blue CI 62055 filtrate: conductivity (L) = 0.042 S/cm; P = 5.2 MPa (750 psi).

The dependence of the rejections on the concentration is of primary interest. The rejections and flux dependence on concentration (represented by the conductivity of the feed) is shown in Figures 4 and 5 for the two fluids. The most significant feature is the difference in rejection based on absorbance (A) and that based on conductivity (L), i.e., the difference in rejection of the colored organic dye salts and the simple salts (the major contributor to the conductivity). The membrane effectively concentrates the color with rejection, r_A, greater than 0.9 for most data while passing simple salts with rejection, r_L, less than 0.4 at high concentration. This result suggests the dependence of the separation factor, α_A^L, where

$$\alpha_A^L = \frac{1 - r_L}{1 - r_A} \qquad [2]$$

on concentration differs for the two fluids. As shown in Figure 6, α_A^L increases with concentration for the acid yellow CI 13906 filtrate but remains nearly constant for the acid blue CI 62055 filtrate. The rejection of color is coupled with that of conductivity in the latter filtrate but not in the former. These rejections are uncoupled in the basic yellow CI 48054 filtrate. (3) Increasing ionic strength decreases the ion-exclusion effectiveness of charged membranes. The results indicate that the colored components of the acid blue filtrate behave as a simple electrolyte, while the lack of a reduction in the color rejection of the other two fluids suggests the colored species are either larger or aggregated so that their rejections are independent of ionic strength. The dye filtrates contained colored species in addition to the product dye. This was determined by separating the colored species by liquid chromatography and comparing the electronic spectra of each colored elution band with the purified product dyes. Thus conclusions for the difference in behavior cannot be based on the product-dye structures.

In summary, the dynamically-formed ultrafilter did not separate colored compounds from the salt. The dynamically-formed hyperfilter effectively retained the colored compounds while providing low rejection of the salt. Because the salt rejection was low in the concentrated solutions resulting in low osmotic pressure differences, the filtration of concentrated solutions with high ionic strengths could be accomplished at the relatively low operating pressure of 5.2 MPa (750 psi).

Renovation of Dye Range Wash Water for Reuse

A project is in progress to demonstrate the closed-cycle operation of a production dye range. The cooperative agreement with LaFrance Industries involves the Environmental Protection

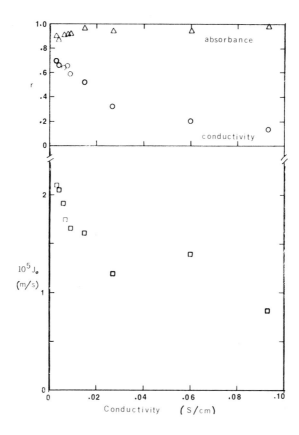

Figure 4.   Rejection (r) and flux (J$_o$) vs. conductivity for the acid yellow CI 13906 filtrate: P = 5.2 MPa (750 psi).

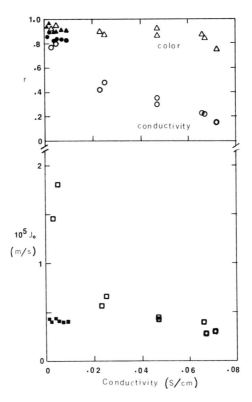

Figure 5. Rejection (r) and flux (J$_o$) vs. conductivity for the acid blue CI 62055 filtrate: filled symbols represent the concentration procedure; open symbols the dilution procedure; P = 5.2 MPa (750 psi).

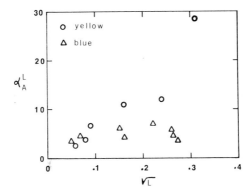

Figure 6. Dependence of the separation factor α_A^L on the conductivity (L) of the feed

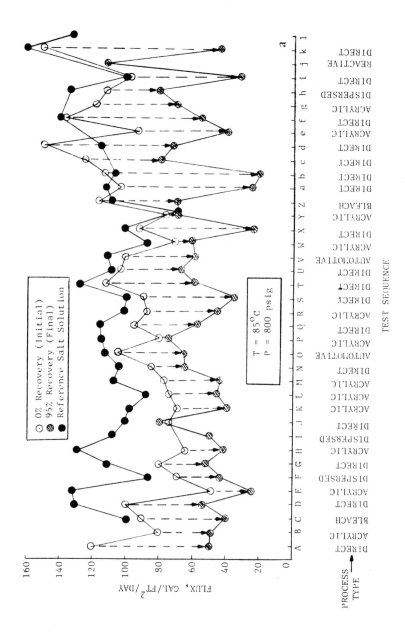

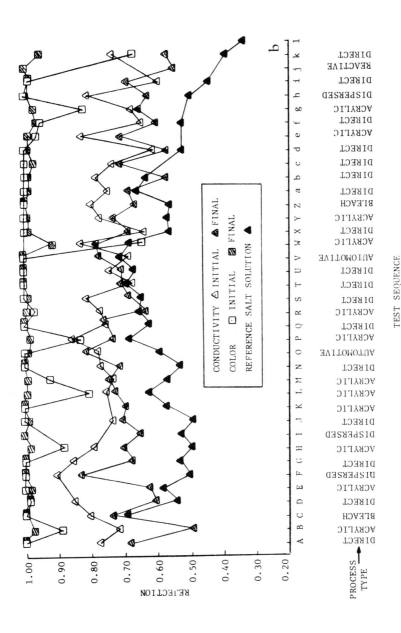

Figure 7. Membrane performance summary data for a dynamic HF membrane—Module 453

Agency, Department of Energy, and Department of Interior. The
objectives of the project are to design, install, and operate a
full-scale commercially-available hyperfiltration system at La-
France and to demonstrate its practicality. Phase I, the design
phase, has been completed. (4) The second phase, the equipment
installation, is in progress. Some data obtained in Phase I
demonstrating the performance characteristics of the dynamic
hyperfiltration membrane using this multicomponent feed up to
high (96 percent) recovery are presented and discussed here.
The objectives, process description, recovery concept, and reuse
evaluation have been reported. (2,4)

Figure 7 provides information describing the performance of
a dynamic membrane (Zr(IV)oxide - polyacrylate). The feeds are
range wash water effluents from single dye runs. Flux and rejections at initial (0) and final (0.95) recoveries are provided.
The initial flux is usually high, 50 to 120 gfd, decreasing
during the concentration to values usually in the 40 to 70 gfd
range, at 5.52 MPa (800 psi) and 85°C. The performance change
during these experiments reflects the effects of both time and
concentration. The "salt point" flux obtained using a 2g/liter
salt solution after a hot water wash was normally higher than
the initial flux obtained using the wash water feed. The color
rejection is of major concern. A suitable product for washing
is expected if the color rejection is 0.97 for the cumulative
product of a 0.95 recovery hyperfiltration. The color rejections
are generally 0.99 at 0.95 recovery, with low rejections occurring at 0.0 recovery for some dye mixtures used on acrylic fabric.
Conductivity rejections normally fall in the 0.70-0.85 range.

The major variation in performance among the various dye
types was the low initial color rejection for several acrylic
process wash effluents. Subsequently it has been found that
these rejections can be raised to acceptable levels by increasing
the pH slightly. The color rejection is normally high for direct,
acid/direct and disperse dye wash water effluents.

Although the dye formulations vary with type, shade, and hue,
they contain a thickener (gum), various surfactants, and in some
cases solvents, in addition to the dyes. Only about 15 percent
of the dye is in the wash water, while most of the auxiliary
chemicals are present.

Figure 8 shows the flux and conductivity and color rejections for a dynamic membrane at various recovery levels using
mixtures of the range wash water effluents. The temperature and
pressure effects on flux are pvovided in Figures 9 and 10.
Table IV gives the results for several analysis procedures of
the hyperfiltration concentration and permeate at three different
recovery levels. The rejections based on the analysis types are
provided in Figure 11. Concentration has little effect on the
rejections of the constituents tested.

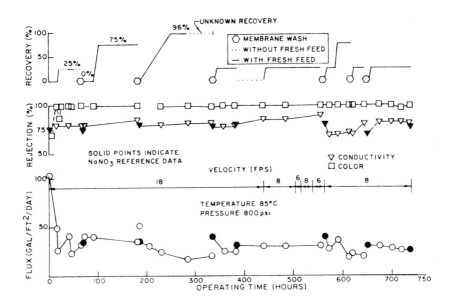

Figure 8. *Product flux, conductivity and color rejection, and recovery profile for a dynamic HF membrane—Module 452*

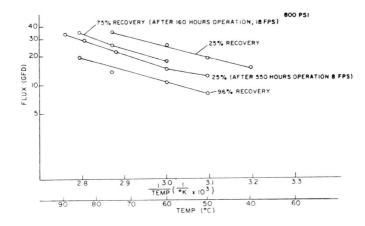

Figure 9. *Flux vs. temperature for a dynamic HF membrane—Module 452*

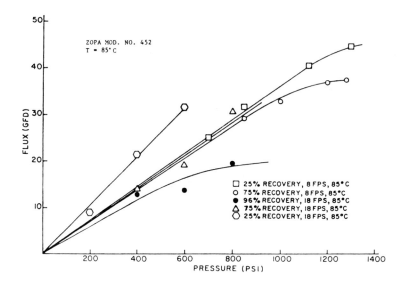

Figure 10.   Flux vs. pressure for a dynamic HF membrane—Module 452

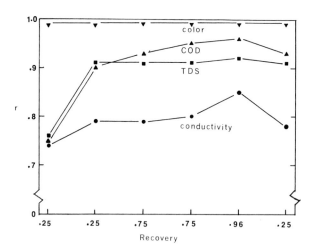

Figure 11.   Rejections in terms of analysis for dye range composite effluent

Table IV. Chemical Analyses of Concentrate and Permeate for a Dynamic Hyperfiltration Membrane; Module 452.

Recovery Level	25%		75%		96%		25%	
Sample Type	Concen.	Perm.	Concen.	Perm.	Concen.	Perm.	Concen.	Perm.
COD, mg/L	470	46	1320	69	4270	180	336	24
Conductivity μS/cm	315	67	815	162	1700	255	395	86
pH	7.0	7.4	6.9	7.2	5.1	5.6	7.7	7.4
Hardness, mg/ℓ	29	0	84	0	232	2.5	18	0
Dissolved Solids, mg/ℓ	459	42	1330	122	3280	250	487	45
Total Solids, mg/ℓ	470	51	1360	124	3330	250	494	45
Volatile Solids, mg/ℓ	288	37	791	52	2150	118	281	18
Suspended Solids, mg/ℓ	11	9	30	2	50	0	7	0
Chromium, mg/ℓ	0.020	0.003	0.340	0.004	0.010	0.027	-*	-*
Iron, mg/ℓ	0.560	0.015	1.900	0.024	1.300	0.016	-*	-*
Calcium, mg/ℓ	2.800	0.037	31.20	0.23	40.00	0.43	4.00	0.0175
Magnesium, mg/ℓ	4.780	0.240	10.60	0.29	31.40	0.76	2.87	0.030

* Not analyzed

The gum was suspected to make a major contribution to the flux decline. Experiments using a solution containing only a gum, a guar gum similar to that used in the process, confirmed this hypothesis. An additional experiment in which the guar gum was transformed into a gel by the addition of sodium tetraborate at pH 8 was performed. The flux declined further when the gel was formed and then increased when the pH was lowered to 6 to redissolve the gum.

The evidence from these experiments and long term experiments at constant recovery indicates the gum present in the dye formulation accounts for most of the flux decline. This significant, but modest, decline is cost acceptable for the system. However, work continues to understand the mechanism of this fouling and establish preventive measures.

In summary, economically acceptable fluxes and technically acceptable rejections have been obtained in pilot studies using hot dye range wash water for recoveries to at least 0.96.

Abstract

Dynamically-formed hyperfiltration membranes of the $ZrO_2 \cdot$ polyacrylate type on porous stainless steel were used in two high volumetric recovery applications. The first is the separation of dyes from a saline dye manufacturing process effluent and the second the renovation of wash water from a dye range for reuse. The dependence of the performance characteristics on recovery is described and discussed. Separation factors (dye from salt) in the first system are large and increase with concentration in two cases, but not in a third. Acceptable rejections and fluxes for reuse of the wash water were obtained to recoveries of 0.96 in the second system. The fluxes are concentration dependent.

List of Symbols

J   Flux, gallons per $(foot)^2$ per day (gfd), or m/s
J_o Flux at 318K (45°C)
T   Temperature (K)
T_o Reference temperature 318K
r_A Rejection based on absorbance at 410 nm
r_L Rejection based on conductivity
α_A^L Separation factor
L   Conductivity S/cm or µS/cm

Acknowledgements

Major contributions to this work were made by a number of people representing government agencies and industries. The authors gratefully acknowledge the cooperation and assistance of Verona Dyestuffs Division, Mobay Chemical Corporation and especially Dr. Harshad Vyas, Manager of the Ecology Department. The cooperation and assistance of the staff at LaFrance Industries is also particularly acknowledged: Perry Lockridge and Charles Smith and several maching operators and laboratory technicians.

Support for the first project was provided by USEPA under Grant 805002010; T. E. Pollack and T. M. Keinath principal investigators and S. C. Wilson project director. The second project is an interagency program No. S805182 benefiting from the guidance of Max Samfield, Sarah Allen and Robert Mournigham, USEPA; John Rossmeissel, DOE: and Frank Coley, DOI.

References

1. Marcinkowsky, A. E.; Kraus, K. A.; Phillips, H. O.; Johnson, J. S.; Shor, A. J. J. Am. Chem. Soc., 1966, 88, 5744.

2. Brandon, C. A. Closed-cycle Textile Dyeing: Full-scale Hyperfiltration Demonstration; presented at the Fifth Clemson Membrane Separation Technology Conference, Clemson University, Clemson, S.C. May 12-14, 1980.

3. Gaddis, J. L.; Spencer, H. G.; Wilson, S. C. AIChE Symp. Ser. 90, 1979, 75, 156.

4. Brandon, C. A. Closed-cycle Textile Dyeing: Full-scale Hyperfiltration Demonstration (Design); EPA-600/2-80-055, March, 1980.

RECEIVED December 4, 1980.

INDEX

INDEX

RETURN TO: CHEMISTRY LIBRARY

100 Hildebrand Hall · 510-642-3753

LOAN PERIOD 1	2 1-MONTH USE 3	
4	5	6

ALL BOOKS MAY BE RECALLED AFTER 7 DAYS

DUE AS STAMPED BELOW

FORM NO. DD 10
1M 6-09

UNIVERSITY OF CALIFORNIA, BERKELEY
Berkeley, California 94720–6000